# CHARACTERS OF FINITE GROUPS

## MATHEMATICS LECTURE NOTES

| | |
|---|---|
| Paul J. Cohen<br>Stanford University | *Set Theory and the Continuum Hypothesis* |
| Walter Feit<br>Yale University | *Characters of Finite Groups* |
| Marvin Greenberg<br>Northeastern University | *Lectures on Algebraic Topology* |
| Serge Lang<br>Columbia University | *Algebraic Functions* |
| Serge Lang<br>Columbia University | *Rapport sur la Cohomologie des Groupes* |
| Jean-Pierre Serre<br>Collège de France | *Algèbres de Lie semi-simples complexes* |
| Jean-Pierre Serre<br>Collège de France | *Lie Algebras and Lie Groups* |

# CHARACTERS OF FINITE GROUPS

*WALTER FEIT*

Yale University

W. A. BENJAMIN, INC.

New York Amsterdam 1967

CHARACTERS OF FINITE GROUPS



Library of Congress Catalog Card Number 67-20769
Manufactured in the United States of America

The manuscript was put into production on September 20, 1966;
this volume was published on October 1, 1967

W. A. Benjamin, Inc.
New York, New York 10016

# PREFACE

These notes contain the material covered in a course I gave at Yale University during the academic year 1964–1965. A knowledge of linear algebra, Galois theory, and elementary group theory is the only background required of the reader. The primary aim of this book is to familiarize the reader with some of the methods which have proved fruitful in current research in that aspect of group theory which uses the theory of characters. These notes are not meant to replace any of the textbooks on the subject but rather to supplement them. Some overlap with the many group theory books in circulation is inevitable but I have tried to keep it to a minimum.

In Chapter I representations and characters are defined and their basic properties are developed. Nowadays, this is usually done by way of the theory of algebras. However, these topics are here approached from a more classical point of view. This is done partly to illustrate the elementary nature of the material but mainly to derive the basic properties of characters as rapidly as possible.

Chapter II centers about R. Brauer's fundamental theorem concerning the character ring of a finite group and some of its generalizations. Several applications are given including some concerned with splitting fields and the Schur index.

Chapter III contains various criteria for a group to be nonsimple. Included are several classical results of Burnside and Frobenius. P. Hall's characterization of solvable groups, and J. G. Thompson's criterion for a group to have a normal p complement for an odd prime p. Many of the results in this chapter and their generalizations are of basic importance for any further study of the structure of finite groups. As is well known, most of these results can be proved by using the transfer in place of character theory.

The material in Chapter IV is mainly of recent origin. Several disconnected topics are discussed. These are meant to provide a random sample of some of the work that has recently been done in this area. Most of the proofs in this chapter utilize the concept of a trivial intersection set whose importance for character theory was first recognized by R. Brauer and M. Suzuki. Some generalizations of this concept are also treated together with the related concept of coherence.

Several people who listened to these lectures made helpful comments which were incorporated in these notes. I especially want to express my thanks to G. Seligman and F. Veldtkamp for their suggestions. I am also greatly indebted to Mr. Leonard L. Scott whose critical scutiny of the material prevented several errors from appearing in print.

Walter Feit

New Haven, Connecticut
March, 1967

# CONTENTS

# CHARACTERS OF FINITE GROUPS

# CHAPTER I

## §1. REPRESENTATIONS

Let $\mathfrak{G}$ be a group and let $\mathfrak{F}$ be a field. An $\mathfrak{F}$-representation $\mathfrak{F}$ of $\mathfrak{G}$ is a homomorphism of $\mathfrak{G}$ into the group of nonsingular linear transformations of some finite-dimensional vector space $\mathfrak{V}$ over $\mathfrak{F}$. $\mathfrak{V}$ is called the underlying vector space of $\mathfrak{F}$. The dimension of $\mathfrak{V}$ is the degree of $\mathfrak{F}$. An $\mathfrak{F}$-representation is faithful if it is an isomorphism. Two $\mathfrak{F}$-representations $\mathfrak{F}_1$, $\mathfrak{F}_2$ of $\mathfrak{G}$ are similar if they have the same underlying vector space $\mathfrak{V}$ and if there exists a nonsingular linear transformation S of $\mathfrak{V}$ such that $\mathfrak{F}_1(G) = S^{-1}\mathfrak{F}_2(G)S$ for all $G \in \mathfrak{G}$. A representation of $\mathfrak{G}$ is an $\mathfrak{F}$-representation of $\mathfrak{G}$ for some field $\mathfrak{F}$.

If $\mathfrak{G}$ is a group and $\mathfrak{F}$ is a field, then the group algebra $\mathfrak{F}(\mathfrak{G})$ of $\mathfrak{G}$ over $\mathfrak{F}$ is the ring consisting of all elements of the form $\Sigma_{\mathfrak{G}}\, a(G)G$, where $a(G) \in \mathfrak{F}$ for all $G \in \mathfrak{G}$ and where addition and multiplication are defined in a natural way as follows;

$$\sum_{\mathfrak{G}} a(G)G + \sum_{\mathfrak{G}} b(G)G = \sum_{\mathfrak{G}} \{a(G) + b(G)\}\, G$$

$$\left\{\sum_{\mathfrak{G}} a(G)G\right\}\left\{\sum_{\mathfrak{G}} b(H)H\right\} = \sum_{G,H\in\mathfrak{G}} a(G)b(H)GH$$

$$= \sum_{G\in\mathfrak{G}} \left\{ \sum_{H\in\mathfrak{G}} a(GH^{-1})b(H) \right\} G$$

If $\mathfrak{F}$ is an $\mathfrak{F}$-representation of $\mathfrak{G}$ with underlying vector space $\mathfrak{V}$, then $\mathfrak{F}$ can be extended to a ring homomorphism of $\mathfrak{F}(\mathfrak{G})$ into the ring of linear transformations of $\mathfrak{V}$ by defining $\mathfrak{F}\{\Sigma_{\mathfrak{G}} a(G)G\} = \Sigma_{\mathfrak{G}} a(G)\,\mathfrak{F}(\mathfrak{G})$. In this way $\mathfrak{V}$ has a unital $\mathfrak{F}(\mathfrak{G})$-module structure imposed on it. Conversely a finitely generated unital $\mathfrak{F}(\mathfrak{G})$-module gives rise to a uniquely determined $\mathfrak{F}$-representation of $\mathfrak{G}$. Thus the study of $\mathfrak{F}$-representations of $\mathfrak{G}$ is equivalent to the study of finitely generated unital $\mathfrak{F}(\mathfrak{G})$-modules. The module point of view has been treated extensively in the literature, see for instance the books by Curtis and Reiner or M. Hall. In these notes we will however adhere to the representation approach.

If $\mathfrak{V}$ is an n-dimensional vector space over the field $\mathfrak{F}$, then the group of nonsingular linear transformations of $\mathfrak{V}$ is isomorphic (in many ways) to the group of nonsingular $n \times n$ matrices with coefficients in $\mathfrak{F}$. Thus an $\mathfrak{F}$-representation of degree n of $\mathfrak{G}$ could equally well have been defined as a homomorphism of $\mathfrak{G}$ into the group of nonsingular $n \times n$ matrices with coefficients in $\mathfrak{F}$. It will often be convenient to consider it as such.

Let $\mathfrak{F}$ be any field. The following are some examples of $\mathfrak{F}$-representations of a group $\mathfrak{G}$.

(i) The unit $\mathfrak{F}$-representation $\mathfrak{F}$ of $\mathfrak{G}$ of degree 1 is defined by $\mathfrak{F}(G) = 1$ for all $G \in \mathfrak{G}$.

(ii) If $\mathfrak{F}$ is a homomorphism of $\mathfrak{G}$ onto a group of permutations on the n symbols 1, . . ., n, then $\mathfrak{F}$ may be interpreted as an $\mathfrak{F}$-representation in the following manner. Let $\mathfrak{V}$ be a vector space over $\mathfrak{F}$ with basis $\{v_1, \ldots, v_n\}$. Define $v_i\mathfrak{F}(G) = v_{i\mathfrak{F}(G)}$ for $G \in \mathfrak{G}$, $i = 1, \ldots, n$. Such an $\mathfrak{F}$-representation is called a permutation $\mathfrak{F}$-representation of $\mathfrak{G}$.

(iii) The (right) regular $\mathfrak{F}$-representation $\mathfrak{R}$ of $\mathfrak{G}$ is the permutation $\mathfrak{F}$-representation of $\mathfrak{G}$ arising from the (right) regular representation of $\mathfrak{G}$. More explicitly let $\mathfrak{V}$ be a vector space over $\mathfrak{F}$ with basis $\{v_H | H \in \mathfrak{G}\}$. Define $v_H\mathfrak{R}(G) = v_{HG}$ for all $G, H \in \mathfrak{G}$.

(iv) If $\mathfrak{F}_1$, $\mathfrak{F}_2$ are $\mathfrak{F}$-representations of $\mathfrak{G}$ with underlying vector spaces $\mathfrak{V}$, $\mathfrak{W}$ respectively. Then $\mathfrak{F}_1 \oplus \mathfrak{F}_2$, $\mathfrak{F}_1 \otimes \mathfrak{F}_2$ are $\mathfrak{F}$-representations of $\mathfrak{G}$ with underlying vector spaces $\mathfrak{V} \oplus \mathfrak{W}$, $\mathfrak{V} \otimes \mathfrak{W}$ respectively.

(v) If $\mathfrak{F}$ is an $\mathcal{F}$-representation of $\mathfrak{G}$ define the contragredient representation $\mathfrak{F}^*$ of $\mathfrak{F}$ by $\mathfrak{F}^*(G) = \mathfrak{F}(G^{-1})'$ for $G \in \mathfrak{G}$, where the prime denotes transpose.

Let $\mathcal{V}$ be the underlying vector space of an $\mathcal{F}$-representation $\mathfrak{F}$ of $\mathfrak{G}$. An invariant subspace of $\mathcal{V}$ is a subspace $\mathcal{W}$ such that $\mathcal{W}\,\mathfrak{F}(G) \subseteq \mathcal{W}$ for all $G \in \mathfrak{G}$. If $\mathcal{W}$ is an invariant subspace of $\mathcal{V}$ then $\mathfrak{F}$ defines $\mathcal{F}$-representations of $\mathfrak{G}$ with underlying vector spaces $\mathcal{W}$ and $\mathcal{V}/\mathcal{W}$. These representations are called constituents of $\mathfrak{F}$. An $\mathcal{F}$-representation $\mathfrak{F}$ of $\mathfrak{G}$ or its underlying vector space $\mathcal{V}$ is $\mathcal{F}$-irreducible if 0, $\mathcal{V}$ are the only invariant subspaces of $\mathcal{V}$. $\mathfrak{F}$ or $\mathcal{V}$ is $\mathcal{F}$-reducible if it is not $\mathcal{F}$-irreducible. $\mathfrak{F}$ or $\mathcal{V}$ is completely reducible if $\mathcal{V} = \mathcal{V}_1 \oplus \dots \oplus \mathcal{V}_n$, where each $\mathcal{V}_i$ is an $\mathcal{F}$-irreducible invariant subspace of $\mathcal{V}$. It is clear that $\mathcal{F}$-reducibility, $\mathcal{F}$-irreducibility and complete reducibility are all preserved if $\mathfrak{F}$ is replaced by a similar $\mathcal{F}$-representation.

In terms of matrices it is easily verified that the $\mathcal{F}$-representation $\mathfrak{F}$ of $\mathfrak{G}$ is $\mathcal{F}$-reducible if and only if there exists a nonsingular matrix S with entries in $\mathcal{F}$ such that $S^{-1}\mathfrak{F}(G)S = \begin{pmatrix} \mathfrak{A}(G) & \mathfrak{C}(G) \\ 0 & \mathfrak{B}(G) \end{pmatrix}$ for all $G \in \mathfrak{G}$, where $\mathfrak{A}$, $\mathfrak{B}$ are constituents of $\mathfrak{F}$. Furthermore $\mathfrak{F}$ is completely reducible if and only if there exists a nonsingular matrix S with coefficients in $\mathcal{F}$ such that

$$S^{-1}\mathfrak{F}(G)S = \begin{pmatrix} \mathfrak{F}_1(G) & & 0 \\ & \ddots & \\ 0 & & \mathfrak{F}_n(G) \end{pmatrix}$$

for all $G \in \mathfrak{G}$, where each $\mathfrak{F}_i$ is $\mathcal{F}$-irreducible.

(1.1) (Maschke) Let $\mathfrak{G}$ be a group and let $\mathcal{F}$ be a field such that char $\mathcal{F} \nmid |\mathfrak{G}|$. Then every $\mathcal{F}$-representation of $\mathfrak{G}$ is completely reducible.

Proof. Let $\mathfrak{F}$ be an $\mathcal{F}$-representation of $\mathfrak{G}$ of degree n. The proof is by induction on n. If $n = 1$, then $\mathfrak{F}$ is $\mathcal{F}$-irreducible. Assume now that $n > 1$. If $\mathfrak{F}$ is $\mathcal{F}$-irreducible there is nothing to prove. Thus it may be assumed that $\mathfrak{F}(G) =$

$\begin{pmatrix} \mathfrak{A}(G) & \mathfrak{C}(G) \\ 0 & \mathfrak{B}(G) \end{pmatrix}$ for all $G \in \mathfrak{G}$. Since $\mathfrak{F}(GH) = \mathfrak{F}(G)\mathfrak{F}(H)$ we see that

$$\mathfrak{C}(GH) = \mathfrak{A}(G)\,\mathfrak{C}(H) + \mathfrak{C}(G)\,\mathfrak{B}(H) \quad \text{for } G,H \in \mathfrak{G}$$

Multiply this by $\mathfrak{B}(H^{-1})$ on the right. Thus

$$\begin{aligned} &\mathfrak{C}(GH)\,\mathfrak{B}((GH)^{-1})\,\mathfrak{B}(G) \\ &\quad = \mathfrak{C}(GH)\,\mathfrak{B}(H^{-1}) \\ &\quad = \mathfrak{A}(G)\,\mathfrak{C}(H)\,\mathfrak{B}(H^{-1}) + \mathfrak{C}(G) \end{aligned}$$

Sum this over all $H \in \mathfrak{G}$, divide by $|\mathfrak{G}|$ and define

$$M = \frac{1}{|\mathfrak{G}|} \sum_{\mathfrak{G}} \mathfrak{C}(H)\,\mathfrak{B}(H^{-1})$$

Thus

$$M\mathfrak{B}(G) = \mathfrak{A}(G)M + \mathfrak{C}(G) \qquad \text{for } G \in \mathfrak{G}$$

Let $S = \begin{pmatrix} I & M \\ 0 & I \end{pmatrix}$. Then for $G \in \mathfrak{G}$

$$\mathfrak{F}(G)S = \begin{pmatrix} \mathfrak{A}(G) & \mathfrak{A}(G)M + \mathfrak{C}(G) \\ 0 & \mathfrak{B}(G) \end{pmatrix} = \begin{pmatrix} \mathfrak{A}(G) & M\mathfrak{B}(G) \\ 0 & \mathfrak{B}(G) \end{pmatrix}$$

$$= S\begin{pmatrix} \mathfrak{A}(G) & 0 \\ 0 & \mathfrak{B}(G) \end{pmatrix}$$

Therefore $S^{-1}\,\mathfrak{F}(G)S = \begin{pmatrix} \mathfrak{A}(G) & 0 \\ 0 & \mathfrak{B}(G) \end{pmatrix}$ for $G \in \mathfrak{G}$. By induction $\mathfrak{A}$ and $\mathfrak{B}$ are completely reducible and hence so is $\mathfrak{F}$.

(1.2) <u>(Schur's lemma) Let</u> $\mathfrak{F}_1$ <u>and</u> $\mathfrak{F}_2$ <u>be</u> $\mathfrak{F}$<u>-irreducible</u> $\mathfrak{F}$<u>-representations of</u> $\mathfrak{G}$ <u>for some field</u> $\mathfrak{F}$. <u>Suppose that S is</u>

a nonzero matrix with entries in $\mathfrak{F}$ such that $\mathfrak{F}_1(G)S = S\mathfrak{F}_2(G)$ for all $G \in \mathfrak{G}$. Then S is nonsingular and $\mathfrak{F}_1$ is similar to $\mathfrak{F}_2$

Proof. Let $\mathfrak{V}$, $\mathfrak{W}$ be the underlying vector space of $\mathfrak{F}_1$, $\mathfrak{F}_2$ respectively. Hence S is a linear transformation sending $\mathfrak{V}$ into $\mathfrak{W}$. Let $\mathfrak{V}_0$ be the kernel of S and let $\mathfrak{W}_0 = \mathfrak{V}S$. Since $v\mathfrak{F}_1(G)S = vS\mathfrak{F}_2(G)$ for $v \in \mathfrak{V}$, $G \in \mathfrak{G}$ it follows that $\mathfrak{V}_0$, $\mathfrak{W}_0$ is an invariant subspace of $\mathfrak{V}, \mathfrak{W}$ respectively. Since $S \neq 0$ by assumption we get that $\mathfrak{V}_0 \neq \mathfrak{V}$ and $\mathfrak{W}_0 \neq 0$. Hence $\mathfrak{V}_0 = 0$ and $\mathfrak{W}_0 = \mathfrak{W}$ by the irreducibility of $\mathfrak{V}$ and $\mathfrak{W}$. Thus S is nonsingular. Consequently $S^{-1}\mathfrak{F}_1(G)S = \mathfrak{F}_2(G)$ for $G \in \mathfrak{G}$.

If $\mathfrak{F}$ is an $\mathfrak{F}$-representation of $\mathfrak{G}$ define $\mathbf{C}_{\mathfrak{F}}(\mathfrak{F}) = \{S | S\mathfrak{F}(G) = \mathfrak{F}(G)S \text{ for } G \in \mathfrak{G}, S \text{ has coefficients in } \mathfrak{F}\}$. We remark that $\mathbf{C}_{\mathfrak{F}}(\mathfrak{F})$ is a finite-dimensional algebra over $\mathfrak{F}$ which contains all scalar matrices.

(1.3) Let $\mathfrak{F}$ be an $\mathfrak{F}$-representation of $\mathfrak{G}$ where char $\mathfrak{F} \nmid |\mathfrak{G}|$. Then $\mathfrak{F}$ is $\mathfrak{F}$-irreducible if and only if $\mathbf{C}_{\mathfrak{F}}(\mathfrak{F})$ is a division algebra.

Proof. If $\mathfrak{F}$ is $\mathfrak{F}$-irreducible then setting $\mathfrak{F} = \mathfrak{F}_1 = \mathfrak{F}_2$ in (1.2) we see that every nonzero element of $\mathbf{C}_{\mathfrak{F}}(\mathfrak{F})$ has an inverse which is then necessarily in $\mathbf{C}_{\mathfrak{F}}(\mathfrak{F})$. Thus $\mathbf{C}_{\mathfrak{F}}(\mathfrak{F})$ is a division algebra. Conversely suppose that $\mathfrak{F}$ is $\mathfrak{F}$-reducible with underlying vector space $\mathfrak{V}$. By (1.1) $\mathfrak{V} = \mathfrak{V}_1 \oplus \mathfrak{V}_2$, where $\mathfrak{V}_1$ and $\mathfrak{V}_2$ are nonzero invariant subspaces of $\mathfrak{V}$. Let S be the projection of $\mathfrak{V}$ onto $\mathfrak{V}_1$, then S is singular and it follows easily that $S \in \mathbf{C}_{\mathfrak{F}}(\mathfrak{F})$. Thus $\mathbf{C}_{\mathfrak{F}}(\mathfrak{F})$ is not a division algebra.

(1.4) Let $\mathfrak{F}$ be an algebraically closed field and let $\mathfrak{F}$ be an $\mathfrak{F}$-irreducible representation of $\mathfrak{G}$. Then $\mathbf{C}_{\mathfrak{F}}(\mathfrak{F})$ consists of scalar matrices.

Proof. Let $S \in \mathbf{C}_{\mathfrak{F}}(\mathfrak{F})$ and let x be a characteristic value of S. Then $x \in \mathfrak{F}$ since $\mathfrak{F}$ is algebraically closed. Thus

$S - xI \in \mathbf{C}_{\mathcal{F}}(\mathfrak{F})$ and $S - xI$ is singular. Hence $S - xI = 0$ by (1.2) and so $S = xI$ is a scalar matrix as required.

Let $\mathcal{K}$ be an extension field of $\mathcal{F}$. Then any $\mathcal{F}$-representation of $\mathfrak{G}$ may be considered to be a $\mathcal{K}$-representation of $\mathfrak{G}$. An $\mathcal{F}$-representation is *absolutely irreducible* if it remains irreducible in every extension field of $\mathcal{F}$.

The next two results are elementary preliminaries.

(1.5) *Suppose that char $\mathcal{F} \nmid |\mathfrak{G}|$. Let $\mathfrak{F}_1$, $\mathfrak{F}_2$ be $\mathcal{F}$-representations of $\mathfrak{G}$ and let $S$ be a matrix with coefficients in $\mathcal{F}$. Then $\mathfrak{F}_1(G)S = S\mathfrak{F}_2(G)$ for all $G \in \mathfrak{G}$ if and only if there exists a matrix $T$ with coefficients in $\mathcal{F}$ such that $S = \Sigma_{\mathfrak{G}} \mathfrak{F}_1(G^{-1})T\mathfrak{F}_2(G)$.*

*Proof*. If $\mathfrak{F}_1(G)S = S\mathfrak{F}_2(G)$ for all $G \in \mathfrak{G}$ let $T = (1/|\mathfrak{G}|)S$. Conversely

$$\mathfrak{F}_1(H) \sum_{\mathfrak{G}} \mathfrak{F}_1(G^{-1})T\mathfrak{F}_2(G)$$

$$= \sum_{G \in \mathfrak{G}} \mathfrak{F}_1(HG^{-1})T\mathfrak{F}_2(GH^{-1})\mathfrak{F}_2(H)$$

$$= \left\{\sum_{\mathfrak{G}} \mathfrak{F}_1(G^{-1})T\mathfrak{F}_2(G)\right\}\mathfrak{F}_2(H)$$

(1.6) *Assume that char $\mathcal{F} \nmid |\mathfrak{G}|$. Let $\mathcal{K}$ be an extension field of $\mathcal{F}$ and let $\mathfrak{F}$ be an $\mathcal{F}$-representation of $\mathfrak{G}$. Then $\mathbf{C}_{\mathcal{F}}(\mathfrak{F})$ consists of scalar matrices if and only if $\mathbf{C}_{\mathcal{K}}(\mathfrak{F})$ consists of scalar matrices.*

*Proof*. For any matrix $S$ with coefficients in $\mathcal{K}$ let $f(S) = \Sigma_{\mathfrak{G}} \mathfrak{F}(G^{-1})S\mathfrak{F}(G)$. For $x, y \in \mathcal{K}$ and matrices $S$ and $T$ we have that $f(xS + yT) = xf(S) + yf(T)$. Let $E_{ij}$ be the matrix whose $(i, j)$ entry is 1 and in which all other entries are 0. Thus by (1.5) every matrix in $\mathbf{C}_{\mathcal{F}}(\mathfrak{F})$, $\mathbf{C}_{\mathcal{K}}(\mathfrak{F})$ is an $\mathcal{F}$-linear, $\mathcal{K}$-linear combination respectively of the matrices $f(E_{ij})$.

Thus $\mathbf{C}_{\mathcal{F}}(\mathfrak{F})$ or $\mathbf{C}_{\mathcal{K}}(\mathfrak{F})$ consists of scalar matrices if and only if $f(E_{ij})$ is a scalar matrix for all $i, j$ .

(1.7) If $\mathfrak{F}$ is an absolutely irreducible $\mathcal{F}$-representation of $\mathfrak{G}$ then $\mathbf{C}_{\mathcal{F}}(\mathfrak{F})$ consists of scalar matrices. If char $\mathcal{F} \nmid |\mathfrak{G}|$ and $\mathbf{C}_{\mathcal{F}}(\mathfrak{F})$ consists of scalar matrices for some $\mathcal{F}$-representation $\mathfrak{F}$ of $\mathfrak{G}$ then $\mathfrak{F}$ is absolutely irreducible.

Proof. Suppose that $\mathfrak{F}$ is an absolutely irreducible $\mathcal{F}$-representation of $\mathfrak{G}$. Let $\mathcal{K}$ be the algebraic closure of $\mathcal{F}$. Then $\mathfrak{F}$ is $\mathcal{K}$-irreducible. Thus by (1.4) $\mathbf{C}_{\mathcal{K}}(\mathfrak{F})$ consists of scalar matrices. Hence also $\mathbf{C}_{\mathcal{F}}(\mathfrak{F})$ consists of scalar matrices. Conversely assume that char $\mathcal{F} \nmid |\mathfrak{G}|$ and $\mathbf{C}_{\mathcal{F}}(\mathfrak{F})$ consists of scalar matrices. Then by (1.6) $\mathbf{C}_{\mathcal{K}}(\mathfrak{F})$ consists of scalar matrices for any extension field $\mathcal{K}$ of $\mathcal{F}$. Thus $\mathbf{C}_{\mathcal{K}}(\mathfrak{F})$ is ring isomorphic to $\mathcal{K}$ and by (1.3) $\mathfrak{F}$ is $\mathcal{K}$-irreducible.

(1.8) Let $\mathfrak{G}$ be an abelian group and let $\mathfrak{F}$ be an $\mathcal{F}$-irreducible $\mathcal{F}$-representation of $\mathfrak{G}$ for some field $\mathcal{F}$. If $\mathfrak{F}$ is faithful then $\mathfrak{G}$ is cyclic. If $\mathfrak{F}$ is absolutely irreducible then $\mathfrak{F}$ has degree 1.

Proof. Since $\mathfrak{G}$ is abelian $\mathfrak{F}(G) \subseteq \mathbf{C}_{\mathcal{F}}(\mathfrak{F})$ . Thus if $\mathfrak{F}$ is faithful $\mathfrak{G}$ is isomorphic to a finite abelian subgroup of the multiplicative group consisting of nonzero elements of the division ring $\mathbf{C}_{\mathcal{F}}(\mathfrak{F})$ . Therefore $\mathfrak{G}$ is cyclic. If $\mathfrak{F}$ is absolutely irreducible then by (1.7) $\mathfrak{F}(G)$ is a scalar matrix for all $G \in \mathfrak{G}$. The irreducibility of $\mathfrak{F}$ thus implies that $\mathfrak{F}$ has degree 1.

The relations in the next theorem are called the Schur relations. They are of fundamental importance for the theory that follows.

(1.9) Let $\mathfrak{A}$, $\mathfrak{B}$ be $\mathcal{F}$-irreducible $\mathcal{F}$-representations of $\mathfrak{G}$ for some field $\mathcal{F}$ . Let $\mathfrak{A}(G) = (a_{ij}(G))$ and $\mathfrak{B}(G) = (b_{ij}(G))$ for $G \in \mathfrak{G}$ .

(i) If $\mathfrak{A}$ is not similar to $\mathfrak{B}$ then

$$\sum_{\mathfrak{G}} a_{is}(G^{-1})b_{tj}(G) = 0$$

for all i, j, s, t.

(ii) If $\mathfrak{A}$ is absolutely irreducible and char $\mathfrak{F} \nmid |\mathfrak{G}|$ then

$$\sum_{\mathfrak{G}} a_{is}(G^{-1}) a_{tj}(G) = \frac{|\mathfrak{G}|}{n} \delta_{ij} \delta_{st}$$

where n is the degree of $\mathfrak{A}$.

Proof. For any matrix S with coefficients in $\mathfrak{F}$ let $f(S) = \Sigma_{\mathfrak{G}} \mathfrak{A}(G^{-1}) S \mathfrak{B}(G)$. Then $\mathfrak{A}(H) f(S) = f(S) \mathfrak{B}(H)$ for all $H \in \mathfrak{G}$. Let $E_{st}$ be the matrix with 1 in the (s, t) entry and 0 elsewhere. The (i, j) entry of $f(E_{st})$ is $\Sigma_{\mathfrak{G}} a_{is}(G^{-1}) b_{tj}(G)$.

If $\mathfrak{A}$ and $\mathfrak{B}$ are not similar then $f(E_{st}) = 0$ by (1.2). This proves the first statement.

If $\mathfrak{A} = \mathfrak{B}$ is absolutely irreducible and char $\mathfrak{F} \nmid |\mathfrak{G}|$ then by (1.7) $f(E_{st}) = e_{st} I$. Thus

$$e_{st} \delta_{ij} = \sum_{\mathfrak{G}} a_{is}(G^{-1}) a_{tj}(G) = \sum_{\mathfrak{G}} a_{is}(G) a_{tj}(G^{-1})$$

$$= e_{ij} \delta_{st}$$

Consequently $e_{ij} = 0$ if $i \neq j$ and $e_{ii} = e$ is independent of i. Hence $e_{st} \delta_{ij} = e \delta_{st} \delta_{ij}$. Since $\mathfrak{A}(G^{-1}) \mathfrak{A}(G) = I$,

$$ne = \sum_{i=1}^{n} e = \sum_{\mathfrak{G}} \sum_{i=1}^{n} a_{si}(G^{-1}) a_{is}(G) = |\mathfrak{G}|$$

as required.

(1.10) Assume that char $\mathfrak{F} \nmid |\mathfrak{G}|$. Then there are only finitely many pairwise nonsimilar absolutely irreducible $\mathfrak{F}$-representations $\mathfrak{F}_1, \ldots, \mathfrak{F}_k$ of $\mathfrak{G}$. Let $\mathcal{K}$ be an extension field of $\mathfrak{F}$. If $\mathfrak{F}_s(G) = (a^s_{ij}(G))$ and $\mathfrak{F}_s$ has degree $n_s$ then $\{a^s_{ij}\}$ is a set of linearly independent $\mathcal{K}$-valued functions on $\mathfrak{G}$ and

$$\sum_{s=1}^{k} n_s^2 \leq |\mathfrak{G}|$$

Proof. Let $\mathfrak{F}_1, \ldots, \mathfrak{F}_k$ be a set of pairwise nonsimilar absolutely irreducible $\mathcal{K}$-representations of $\mathfrak{G}$. Let $\mathfrak{F}_s(G) = (a_{ij}^s(G))$ and let $n_s$ be the degree of $\mathfrak{F}_s$. The set of $\mathcal{K}$-valued functions on $\mathfrak{G}$ forms a $|\mathfrak{G}|$-dimensional vector space over $\mathcal{K}$. Thus it suffices to show that $\{a_{ij}^s\}$ is a set of linearly independent $\mathcal{K}$-valued functions on $\mathfrak{G}$.

Suppose that $\Sigma_{i,j,s}\, x_{ij}^s\, a_{ij}^s(G) = 0$ for all $G \in \mathfrak{G}$ and some $x_{ij}^s \in \mathcal{K}$. Then by (1.9)

$$0 = \sum_{i,j,s} \sum_{\mathfrak{G}} x_{ij}^s\, a_{ij}^s(G)\, a_{j'i'}^{s'}(G^{-1}) = \frac{|\mathfrak{G}|}{n_{s'}}\, x_{j'i'}^{s'}$$

completing the proof.

A field $\mathcal{F}$ is a splitting field of $\mathfrak{G}$ is every $\mathcal{F}$-irreducible $\mathcal{F}$-representation of $\mathfrak{G}$ is absolutely irreducible.

(1.11) Assume that char $\mathcal{F} \nmid |\mathfrak{G}|$. Then there exists a finite extension field of $\mathcal{F}$ which is a splitting field of $\mathfrak{G}$.

Proof. Let $\tilde{\mathcal{F}}$ be the algebraic closure of $\mathcal{F}$. By (1.4) and (1.7) $\tilde{\mathcal{F}}$ is a splitting field of $\mathfrak{F}$. Let $\tilde{\mathfrak{F}}_1, \ldots, \tilde{\mathfrak{F}}_k$ be a maximal set of pairwise nonsimilar absolutely irreducible $\tilde{\mathcal{F}}$-representations of $\mathfrak{G}$. Such a set exists by (1.10). Let $\tilde{\mathfrak{F}}_s(G) = (a_{ij}^s(G))$ for $G \in \mathfrak{G}$. Let $\mathcal{K}$ be the extension field of $\mathfrak{G}$ generated by all $a_{ij}^s(G)$. The finiteness of $\mathfrak{G}$ implies that $|\mathcal{K} : \mathcal{F}|$ is finite since each $a_{ij}^s(G)$ is algebraic over $\mathcal{F}$. If $\mathfrak{F}$ is a $\mathcal{K}$-irreducible $\mathcal{K}$-representation of $\mathfrak{G}$ then in $\tilde{\mathcal{F}}$, $\mathfrak{F}$ is similar to a direct sum of various $\tilde{\mathfrak{F}}_j$. Thus if $\mathfrak{F}(G) = (a_{ij}(G))$ for $G \in \mathfrak{G}$ then $a_{11}$ is an $\mathcal{F}$ linear combination of the $a_{ij}^s$. Thus by (1.9) $\mathfrak{F}$ is similar to some $\tilde{\mathfrak{F}}_s$ in $\mathcal{K}$. Hence $\mathcal{K}$ is a splitting field of $\mathfrak{G}$.

(1.12) Assume that char $\mathfrak{F} \nmid |\mathfrak{G}|$. Let $\mathfrak{F}$ be an $\mathfrak{F}$-representation of $\mathfrak{G}$. If $G \in \mathfrak{G}$ then there exists a finite extension field $\mathcal{K}$ of $\mathfrak{F}$ such that $\mathfrak{F}(G)$ is similar to a diagonal matrix in $\mathcal{K}$.

Proof. It may be assumed that $\mathfrak{G} = \langle G \rangle$. By (1.11) there exists a finite extension field $\mathcal{K}$ of $\mathfrak{F}$ which is a splitting field of $\mathfrak{G}$. Thus by (1.1) and (1.8) $\mathfrak{F}(G)$ is similar to a diagonal matrix in $\mathcal{K}$.

## §2. CHARACTERS

Let $\mathfrak{F}$ be a field of characteristic 0. Let $\mathfrak{G}$ be a group and let $\mathfrak{F}$ be an $\mathfrak{F}$-representation of $\mathfrak{G}$. For $G \in \mathfrak{G}$ let $\theta(G)$ be the trace of $\mathfrak{F}(G)$. The function $\theta$ is called the character of $\mathfrak{G}$ afforded by the $\mathfrak{F}$-representation $\mathfrak{F}$. In general a character of $\mathfrak{G}$ is a function $\theta$ which is the character afforded by some $\mathfrak{F}$-representation of $\mathfrak{G}$, where $\mathfrak{F}$ is a field of characteristic 0. An irreducible character of $\mathfrak{G}$ is a character of $\mathfrak{G}$ which is afforded by an absolutely irreducible $\mathfrak{F}$-representation of $\mathfrak{G}$, where $\mathfrak{F}$ is some field of characteristic 0.

It should be noted that this definition of a character differs from that used by some authors, for instance Curtis and Reiner. Only if $\mathfrak{F}$ has characteristic 0 does an $\mathfrak{F}$-representation of $\mathfrak{G}$ afford a character in the sense of the above definition.

(2.1) If $\theta$ is the character afforded by the representation $\mathfrak{F}$ of $\mathfrak{G}$ then $\theta(1)$ is the degree of $\mathfrak{F}$. For $G \in \mathfrak{G}$, $\theta(G)$ is a sum of complex roots of unity, and $\theta(G^{-1}) = \overline{\theta(G)}$, where the bar denotes complex conjugation. Thus $\theta$ is a complex valued function on $\mathfrak{G}$.

Proof. Clearly $\theta(1)$ is the degree of $\mathfrak{F}$. Since $\mathfrak{F}$ is an $\mathfrak{F}$-representation of $\mathfrak{G}$ where $\mathfrak{F}$ is a field of characteristic 0 it is possible to identify the algebraic closure of $\mathcal{Q}$ in the algebraic closure of $\mathfrak{F}$ as a subfield of the field of complex numbers $\mathcal{C}$. Since $\mathfrak{F}(G)^{|\mathfrak{G}|} = I$ for $G \in \mathfrak{G}$ all the characteristic roots of $\mathfrak{F}(G)$ are complex roots of unity and $\theta(G)$ is their sum. If $\epsilon$ is a complex root of unity then $\bar{\epsilon} = \epsilon^{-1}$ and so $\theta(G^{-1}) = \overline{\theta(G)}$ for $G \in \mathfrak{G}$.

(2.2) Suppose that char $\mathfrak{F} = 0$. Then

(i) Similar $\mathfrak{F}$-representations of $\mathfrak{G}$ afford the same character.

(ii) If $\theta$ is a character of $\mathfrak{G}$ then $\theta$ is a class function. That is to say $\theta(H^{-1}GH) = \theta(G)$ for $G, H \in \mathfrak{G}$.

(iii) If $\mathfrak{F} = \mathfrak{F}_1 \oplus \mathfrak{F}_2$, $\mathfrak{F}_1 \otimes \mathfrak{F}_2$ then the character afforded by $\mathfrak{F}$ is the sum, product respectively of the characters afforded by $\mathfrak{F}_1$ and $\mathfrak{F}_2$.

Proof. Statements (i) and (ii) follow from the fact that similar matrices have the same trace. The last statement is a consequence of elementary properties of traces.

The principal character $1_{\mathfrak{G}}$ of $\mathfrak{G}$ is the character afforded by the unit $\mathfrak{F}$-representations, where char $\mathfrak{F} = 0$. Thus $1_{\mathfrak{G}}(G) = 1$ for $G \in \mathfrak{G}$. The character afforded by a right regular $\mathfrak{F}$-representation of $\mathfrak{G}$ will be denoted by $\rho_{\mathfrak{G}}$.

(2.3) Suppose that $\theta$ is the character afforded by a permutation representation $\mathfrak{F}$ of $\mathfrak{G}$. Then $\theta(G)$ is equal to the number of letters fixed by the permutation $\mathfrak{F}(G)$. Thus in particular $\rho_{\mathfrak{G}}(G) = 0$ if $G \in \mathfrak{G}^{\#}$ and $\rho_{\mathfrak{G}}(1) = |\mathfrak{G}|$.

Proof. If $\mathfrak{F}(G) = (a_{ij}(G))$ then $a_{ij}(G) = 1$ if $i\mathfrak{F}(G) = j$ and $a_{ij}(G) = 0$ otherwise. Thus $\theta(G) = \Sigma a_{ii}(G)$ as required.

If $\theta$, $\eta$ are complex valued functions on $\mathfrak{G}$ let

$$(\theta, \eta)_{\mathfrak{G}} = \frac{1}{|\mathfrak{G}|} \sum_{\mathfrak{G}} \theta(G)\overline{\eta(G)}, \quad ||\theta||^2_{\mathfrak{G}} = (\theta, \theta)_{\mathfrak{G}}$$

The subscript $\mathfrak{G}$ will be omitted in case it is clear from context which group is specified. It follows immediately that the hermitian product thus defined has all the usual properties and is positive definite. If $\eta$ is a character of $\mathfrak{G}$ then by (2.1)

$$(\theta, \eta) = \frac{1}{|\mathfrak{G}|} \sum_{\mathfrak{G}} \theta(G)\eta(G^{-1})$$

(2.4) Suppose that char $\mathfrak{F} = 0$. Let $\theta, \eta$ be the characters afforded by the $\mathfrak{F}$-irreducible $\mathfrak{F}$-representations $\mathfrak{A}, \mathfrak{B}$ of $\mathfrak{G}$.

(i) If $\mathfrak{A}$ is not similar to $\mathfrak{B}$ then $(\theta, \eta) = 0$.

(ii) If $\mathfrak{A}$ is absolutely irreducible then $(\theta, \theta) = 1$.

Proof. In the notation of (1.9) $\theta(G) = \Sigma_i a_{ii}(G)$ and $\eta(G) = \Sigma_i b_{ii}(G)$ for $G \in \mathfrak{G}$. Thus

$$(\theta, \eta) = \frac{1}{|\mathfrak{G}|} \sum_{i,j} a_{ii}(G)\, b_{jj}(G^{-1})$$

Hence by (1.9) $(\theta, \eta) = 0$ if $\mathfrak{A}$ is not similar to $\mathfrak{B}$ and if $\mathfrak{A} = \mathfrak{B}$ is absolutely irreducible then

$$(\theta, \theta) = \frac{1}{\theta(1)} \sum_{i,j} \delta_{ij}\, \delta_{ij} = 1$$

(2.5) Suppose that char $\mathfrak{F} = 0$. Let $\mathfrak{F}$ be an $\mathfrak{F}$-representation of $\mathfrak{G}$ and assume that $\mathfrak{F} = \mathfrak{A}_1 \oplus \ldots \oplus \mathfrak{A}_s$, where each $\mathfrak{A}_i$ is an $\mathfrak{F}$-irreducible $\mathfrak{F}$-representation of $\mathfrak{G}$. Let $\theta, \eta$ be the character afforded by $\mathfrak{F}, \mathfrak{A}_1$ respectively. Then the number of $\mathfrak{A}_i$ similar to $\mathfrak{A}_1$ is $(\theta, \eta)/(\eta, \eta)$.

Proof. This is an immediate consequence of (2.2) and (2.4).

(2.6) Suppose that char $\mathfrak{F} = 0$. Two $\mathfrak{F}$-representations are similar if and only if they afford the same character.

Proof. This follows directly from complete reducibility and (2.5).

(2.7) If $\theta$ is a character of $\mathfrak{G}$ then $(\theta, \rho_{\mathfrak{G}}) = \theta(1)$.

Proof. Clear by (2.3).

(2.8) There exists a finite extension $\mathfrak{F}$ of $\mathbf{Q}$ depending only on $\mathfrak{G}$ such that every character of $\mathfrak{G}$ is afforded by an $\mathfrak{F}$-representation of $\mathfrak{G}$. Thus in particular $\mathfrak{F}$ is a splitting field of $\mathfrak{G}$.

Proof. By (1.11) there exists a splitting field $\mathfrak{F}$ of $\mathfrak{G}$ which is a finite extension of $\mathbf{Q}$. Let $\mathfrak{R}$ be an $\mathfrak{F}$-representation of $\mathfrak{G}$ which affords $\rho_{\mathfrak{G}}$. Every $\mathfrak{F}$-irreducible constituent of $\mathfrak{R}$ is absolutely irreducible. Thus by (2.5) and (2.7) every irreducible character of $\mathfrak{G}$ is afforded by an $\mathfrak{F}$-representation and hence every character of $\mathfrak{G}$ is afforded by an $\mathfrak{F}$-representation.

If $\theta, \eta$ are characters of $\mathfrak{G}$ then $\theta$ is a constituent of $\eta$ if either $\eta = \theta$ or $\eta = \theta + \theta_1$ for some character $\theta_1$. If $\theta$ is a constituent of $\eta$ we shall write $\theta \subseteq \eta$. If $\theta$ is irreducible then $(\theta, \eta)$ is the multiplicity of $\theta$ as a constituent of $\eta$. A character $\eta$ is multiplicity free if $(\theta, \eta) = 0$ or $1$ for every irreducible character $\theta$. The kernel of a character $\theta$ is the kernel of representation which affords $\theta$. A character $\theta$ is faithful if its kernel is $\langle 1 \rangle$.

If $\mathfrak{F}$ is a field of characteristic 0 and $\theta$ is a character of $\mathfrak{G}$ then $\mathfrak{F}(\theta)$ is the extension field of $\mathfrak{F}$ generated by the elements $\theta(G)$ for $G \in \mathfrak{G}$. Clearly $\mathfrak{F}(\theta)$ is a finite extension field of $\mathfrak{F}$. If $\mathfrak{F}(\theta) = \mathfrak{F}$ we will also write that $\theta \in \mathfrak{F}$. The field $\mathfrak{F}$ is a splitting field of the character $\theta$ if $\theta$ is afforded by an $\mathfrak{F}$-representation of $\mathfrak{G}$. If $\mathfrak{F}$ is a splitting field of $\theta$ then clearly $\theta \in \mathfrak{F}$. However it is important to note that $\mathfrak{F}(\theta)$ need not be a splitting field of $\theta$. It is an immediate consequence of this definition that $\mathfrak{F}$ is a splitting field of $\mathfrak{G}$ if and only if $\mathfrak{F}$ is a splitting field of every irreducible character of $\mathfrak{G}$.

If $\mathfrak{F}$ is a field of characteristic 0 and $\mathfrak{F}$ is an $\mathfrak{F}$-representation of $\mathfrak{G}$ which affords the character $\theta$ then for any isomorphism $\sigma$ of $\mathfrak{F}$ into its algebraic closure $\tilde{\mathfrak{F}}$, $\mathfrak{F}^{\sigma}$ is an $\tilde{\mathfrak{F}}$-representation which affords the character $\theta^{\sigma}$. Since $\theta(G)$

is a sum of roots of unity for $G \in \mathfrak{G}$, $\mathfrak{F}(\theta)$ is a normal extension of $\mathfrak{F}$ with an abelian Galois group. Thus if $\theta$ is a character of $\mathfrak{G}$ and $\sigma$ is an automorphism of $\mathbf{Q}(\theta)$, $\theta^\sigma$ is also a character of $\mathfrak{G}$. If $\theta_1 = \theta^\sigma$ for such an automorphism, $\theta$ and $\theta_1$ are said to be algebraically conjugate characters. Thus in particular $\theta$ and $\overline{\theta}$ are algebraically conjugate. It is easily seen that if $\theta$ is afforded by the representation $\mathfrak{F}$ then $\overline{\theta}$ is afforded by the contragredient representation $\mathfrak{F}^*$.

The following notation will be used in the remainder of this section.

$\chi_1 = 1_{\mathfrak{G}}, \chi_2, \ldots, \chi_k$ is the set of irreducible characters of $\mathfrak{G}$.

For $i = 1, \ldots, k$, $\mathfrak{X}_i$ is a representation which affords $\chi_i$ and $x_i = \chi_i(1)$.

$\mathfrak{K}_1 = \{1\}, \mathfrak{K}_2, \ldots$ is the set of conjugate classes of $\mathfrak{G}$, $\mathfrak{K}_{i'} = \{G^{-1} | G \in \mathfrak{K}_i\}$.

$\omega_i(\mathfrak{K}_j) = |\mathfrak{K}_j| \chi_i(G)/x_i$ for $G \in \mathfrak{K}_j$

(2.9) (i) $(\chi_i, \chi_j) = \delta_{ij}$.

(ii) $\Sigma_{\mathfrak{G}} \chi_i(G) = |\mathfrak{G}| \delta_{i1}$.

(iii) If $\theta = \Sigma a_i \chi_i$ then $(\theta, \chi_i) = a_i$ and $\|\theta\|^2 = \Sigma a_i^2$.

(iv) If $\theta$ is a character with $\|\theta\|^2 = 1$ then $\theta = \chi_i$ for some $i$.

(v) $\rho_{\mathfrak{G}} = \Sigma_i x_i \chi_i$.

(vi) $\Sigma_i x_i^2 = |\mathfrak{G}|$.

Proof. (2.4) implies (i). Let $j = 1$ in (i) to get (ii). (iii) follows from (i) and (iv) from (iii). (2.7) and (iii) imply (v). By (iii) and (v) $|\mathfrak{G}| = \|\rho_{\mathfrak{G}}\|^2 = \Sigma_i x_i^2$, proving (vi).

(2.10) Let $\mathfrak{F}$ be a field such that $\mathfrak{X}_1, \ldots, \mathfrak{X}_k$ are $\mathfrak{F}$-representations. Let $\mathfrak{X}_s(G) = (a^s_{ij}(G))$. Then any $\mathfrak{F}$-valued function on $\mathfrak{G}$ is a linear combination of the $a^s_{ij}$ with coefficients in $\mathfrak{F}$.

Proof. The set $\mathfrak{F}$-valued functions on $\mathfrak{G}$ is a $|\mathfrak{G}|$-dimensional vector space over $\mathfrak{F}$. By (1.10) and (2.9) (vi) $\{a^s_{ij}\}$ is a basis of this space.

(2.11) $$\Sigma_{\mathfrak{K}_j} \mathfrak{X}_i(G) = \omega_i(\mathfrak{K}_j)I$$

Proof. Let $S = \Sigma_{\mathfrak{K}_j} \mathfrak{X}_i(G)$. Then $\mathfrak{X}_i(H^{-1}) S \mathfrak{X}_i(H) = S$ for $H \in \mathfrak{G}$. Hence by (1.7) $S = sI$ is a scalar matrix. The trace of S is the sum of the traces of all $\mathfrak{X}_i(G)$ for $G \in \mathfrak{K}_j$. Since each such matrix has trace $\chi(G_j)$ for $G_j \in \mathfrak{K}_j$ we see that

$$x_i s = \text{trace of } S = |\mathfrak{K}_j| \chi_i(G_j)$$

Thus $s = \omega_i(\mathfrak{K}_j)$ as required.

(2.12) Let $G \in \mathfrak{K}_s$ and let $a_{ijs}$ be the number of ordered pairs $G_i$, $G_j$ with $G_i \in \mathfrak{K}_i$, $G_j \in \mathfrak{K}_j$ such that $G_i G_j = G$. Then $a_{ijs}$ is independent of the choice of G in $\mathfrak{K}_s$. Furthermore $a_{ij1} = |\mathfrak{K}_i| \delta_{ji'}$.

Proof. If $G = G_i G_j$ then $H^{-1}GH = (H^{-1}G_iH)(H^{-1}G_jH)$. The first statement follows. If $a_{ij1} \neq 0$ then there exists $G \in \mathfrak{K}_i$ such that $G^{-1} \in \mathfrak{K}_j$. Thus $i = j'$. The result follows easily.

(2.13) Let $a_{ijs}$ have the same meaning as in (2.12). Then

(i) $\omega_t(\mathfrak{K}_i)\omega_t(\mathfrak{K}_j) = \Sigma_s a_{ijs}\ \omega_t(\mathfrak{K}_s)$.

(ii) $|\mathfrak{K}_i||\mathfrak{K}_j|\chi_t(G_i)\chi_t(G_j) = x_t\ \Sigma_s a_{ijs}\ |\mathfrak{K}_s|\chi_t(G_s)$, where $G_i \in \mathfrak{K}_i$, $G_j \in \mathfrak{K}_j$, $G_s \in \mathfrak{K}_s$.

Proof. $\Sigma_{\mathfrak{K}_i} \mathfrak{X}_t(G_i)\ \Sigma_{\mathfrak{K}_j} \mathfrak{X}_t(G_j) = \Sigma_{\mathfrak{K}_i, \mathfrak{K}_j} \mathfrak{X}_t(G_iG_j) =$

$\Sigma_s a_{ijs}\ \Sigma_{\mathfrak{K}_s} \mathfrak{X}_t(G_s)$. Thus (2.11) implies (i). Multiplying (i) by $x_t^2$ and expressing $\omega_t$ in terms of $\chi_t$ yields (ii).

(2.14) If $G_i \in \mathfrak{K}_i$, $G_j \in \mathfrak{K}_j$ then

$$\sum_{t=1}^{k} \chi_t(G_i)\ \overline{\chi_t(G_j)} = \left|\frac{\mathfrak{G}}{\mathfrak{K}_j}\right| \delta_{ij}$$

Proof. Replace j by j′ in (2.13) (ii) and sum over t. By (2.9) (v) and (2.12) this yields that

$$|\mathfrak{K}_i||\mathfrak{K}_{j'}| \sum_t \chi_t(G_i)\ \overline{\chi_t(G_j)} = \sum_s a_{ij's} |\mathfrak{K}_s| \rho_{\mathfrak{G}}(G_s)$$

$$= a_{ij'1}\ |\mathfrak{G}| = |\mathfrak{K}_i|\,\delta_{ij}|\mathfrak{G}|$$

Since $|\mathfrak{K}_{j'}| = |\mathfrak{K}_j|$, the result follows.

(2.9) (i) and (2.14) are called the orthogonality relations for characters.

(2.15) Let $a_{ijm}$ be defined as in (2.12). If $G_i \in \mathfrak{K}_i$, $G_j \in \mathfrak{K}_j$, $G_m \in \mathfrak{K}_m$ then

$$a_{ijm} = \frac{|\mathfrak{K}_j|\,|\mathfrak{K}_j|}{|\mathfrak{G}|} \sum_t \frac{\chi_t(G_i)\,\chi_t(G_j)\,\overline{\chi_t(G_m)}}{x_t}$$

Proof. Multiply the expression in (2.13) (ii) by $\overline{\chi_t(G_m)}/x_t$ and sum over t. Thus by (2.14)

$$|\mathfrak{K}_i|\,|\mathfrak{K}_j| \sum_t \frac{\chi_t(G_i)\,\chi_t(G_j)\,\overline{\chi_t(G_m)}}{x_t}$$

$$= \sum_s a_{ijs} |\mathfrak{K}_s| \sum_t \chi_t(G_s)\,\overline{\chi_t(G_m)}$$

$$= |\mathfrak{K}_m|\, a_{ijm} \left|\frac{\mathfrak{G}}{\mathfrak{K}_m}\right|$$

The result follows.

(2.16) The number of irreducible characters of $\mathfrak{G}$ is equal to the number of conjugate classes of $\mathfrak{G}$. If $\mathfrak{F}$ is a field containing $\mathbb{Q}(\chi_i, \ldots, \chi_k)$ then $\{\chi_i\}$ is a basis for the space of $\mathfrak{F}$-valued class functions on $\mathfrak{G}$.

Proof. Let $k_1$ be the number of conjugate classes of $\mathfrak{G}$. By (2.9) (i) $\{\chi_i\}$ is a set of linearly independent class functions on $\mathfrak{G}$. Thus $k \leq k_1$.

Let $X = (\chi_i(G_j))$, where $G_j \in \mathfrak{K}_j$. Thus X is a $k \times k_1$ matrix. Let $X'$ be the transpose of X. By (2.14) $X'\overline{X} = ((|\mathfrak{G}|/|\mathfrak{K}_i|)\delta_{ij})$ is a nonsingular $k_1 \times k_1$ matrix. Hence the rank of X is at least $k_1$ and so $k_1 \leq k$. All statements are proved.

(2.17) Let $a_{ist}$ be defined as in (2.12). Let $A_i$ be the matrix whose (s,t) entry is $a_{ist}$. Then $\omega_t(\mathfrak{K}_i)$ for t =

$1, \ldots, k$ are characteristic roots of $A_i$. Each $\omega_t(\mathfrak{K}_i)$ is an algebraic integer.

Proof. The relation in (2.13) (i) may be rewritten as

$$\sum_{s=1}^{k} (\omega_t(\mathfrak{K}_i)\delta_{js} - a_{ijs})\,\omega_t(\mathfrak{K}_s) = 0 \quad \text{for } i,j = 1, \ldots, k$$

If $i$ is kept fixed and $j$ is allowed to range over the values $1, \ldots, k$ this yields $k$ homogeneous equations in the $k$ unknowns $\omega_t(\mathfrak{K}_1), \ldots, \omega_t(\mathfrak{K}_k)$. Since $\omega_t(\mathfrak{K}_1) = 1 \neq 0$, the determinant of the systems must vanish. Thus for each $i$ the determinant of $\omega_t(\mathfrak{K}_i)I - A_i$ is zero. Hence $\omega_t(\mathfrak{K}_i)$ is a characteristic root of $A_i$ for $t = 1, \ldots, k$. Since the entries of $A_i$ are all rational integers, $\omega_t(\mathfrak{K}_i)$ is an algebraic integer.

(2.18) $\quad x_i \,\big|\, |\mathfrak{G}|$.

Proof. Let $G_j \in \mathfrak{K}_j$. Then

$$\frac{|\mathfrak{G}|}{x_i} = \frac{|\mathfrak{G}|}{x_i}(\chi_i, \chi_i) = \sum_{j=1}^{k} \frac{|\mathfrak{K}_j|\,\chi_i(G_j)}{x_i}\,\overline{\chi_i(G_j)}$$

$$= \sum_{j=1}^{k} \omega_i(\mathfrak{K}_j)\,\overline{\chi_i(G_j)}$$

By (2.1) and (2.17) this implies that $|\mathfrak{G}|/x_i$ is an algebraic integer. Since $|\mathfrak{G}|$ and $x_i$ are rational the result follows.

## §3. COMPLEX REPRESENTATIONS

A complex representation $\mathfrak{F}$ of $\mathfrak{G}$ is unitary or orthogonal if $\mathfrak{F}(G)$ is unitary or real orthogonal respectively for all $G \in \mathfrak{G}$.

(3.1) *A complex representation of* $\mathfrak{G}$ *is similar to a unitary representation. A real representation of* $\mathfrak{G}$ *is similar to an orthogonal representation.*

*Proof.* Let $\mathfrak{F}$ be a complex representation of $\mathfrak{G}$. Let $S = \Sigma_{\mathfrak{G}} \overline{\mathfrak{F}'}(G)\, \mathfrak{F}(G)$, where the prime denotes transpose. Then $\overline{S}' = S$ and $S$ is real if $\mathfrak{F}$ is real. Each $\overline{\mathfrak{F}'(G)}\mathfrak{F}(G)$ is non-negative and $\overline{\mathfrak{F}'(1)}\mathfrak{F}(1) = I$ is positive. Thus $S$ is positive definite. The result follows since $\overline{\mathfrak{F}'(G)}S\,\mathfrak{F}(G) = S$ for $G \in \mathfrak{G}$.

The result immediately yields another proof of the complete reducibility of complex representations since the orthogonal complement of an invariant subspace of the underlying vector space of a unitary representation of $\mathfrak{G}$ is also invariant.

(3.2) *If* $\mathfrak{F}_1$, $\mathfrak{F}_2$ *are similar irreducible unitary representations of* $\mathfrak{G}$ *then there exists a unitary matrix* $U$ *such that* $U^{-1}\mathfrak{F}_1(G)U = \mathfrak{F}_2(G)$ *for* $G \in \mathfrak{G}$.

*Proof.* By assumption $S^{-1}\mathfrak{F}_1(G)S = \mathfrak{F}_2(G)$ for some complex matrix $S$. Thus $\mathfrak{F}_1(G)S = S\mathfrak{F}_2(G)$. Taking conjugate transposes this yields that

$$\overline{S}'\,\mathfrak{F}_1(G^{-1}) = \overline{S}'\,\overline{\mathfrak{F}_1'(G)} = \overline{\mathfrak{F}_2'(G)}\,\overline{S}' = \mathfrak{F}_2(G^{-1})\,\overline{S}'$$

Thus

$$\mathfrak{F}_1(G)S\overline{S}'\,\mathfrak{F}_1(G^{-1}) = S\mathfrak{F}_2(G)\,\mathfrak{F}_2(G^{-1})\overline{S}' = S\overline{S}'$$

Hence $S\overline{S}'$ commutes with $\mathfrak{F}_1(G)$ for all $G \in \mathfrak{G}$. Consequently $S\overline{S}' = cI$ is a scalar.

Therefore $c\,I$ is positive, and so $c$ is a positive real number. Hence $c = s\overline{s}$ for some complex $s$. Let $U = \frac{1}{s}S$. Then $U^{-1}\mathfrak{F}_1(G)U = \mathfrak{F}_2(G)$ for $G \in \mathfrak{G}$ and $U\overline{U}' = I$ and thus $U$ is unitary.

The results in the remainder of this section are due to Frobenius and Schur.

An irreducible complex representation $\mathfrak{F}$ is of the *first kind* if it is similar to a real representation. $\mathfrak{F}$ is of the *second kind* if $\mathfrak{F}$ is similar to $\overline{\mathfrak{F}}$ but is not of the first kind. $\mathfrak{F}$ is of the *third kind* if $\mathfrak{F}$ is not similar to $\overline{\mathfrak{F}}$.

(3.3) *Let $\mathfrak{F}$ be a complex representation of $\mathfrak{G}$ such that $\overline{\mathfrak{F}(G)} = U^{-1}\mathfrak{F}(G)U$ for some unitary matrix $U$. Then $U' = \pm U$. Furthermore $U' = U$ if and only if $\mathfrak{F}$ is of the first kind. $U' = -U$ if and only if $\mathfrak{F}$ is of the second kind.*

*Proof.* By assumption $\overline{\mathfrak{F}(G)} = U^{-1}\mathfrak{F}(G)U$. Taking complex conjugates this implies that $\mathfrak{F}(G) = U'\,\overline{\mathfrak{F}(G)}\,U'^{-1}$. Thus

$$\mathfrak{F}(G) = U'\,\overline{\mathfrak{F}(G)}\,U'^{-1} = U'U^{-1}\mathfrak{F}(G)UU'^{-1}$$

Hence $U'U^{-1} = cI$ is a scalar matrix. Thus $U' = cU$ and $U = cU' = c^2U$. Hence $c = \pm 1$. By definition $\mathfrak{F}$ is of the first or second kind. Thus it suffices to show that $\mathfrak{F}$ is of the first kind if and only if $U' = U$.

If $\mathfrak{F}$ is of the first kind then there exists a complex matrix $A$ such that $A^{-1}\mathfrak{F}(G)A$ is real for all $G \in \mathfrak{G}$. Hence for $G \in \mathfrak{G}$

$$A^{-1}\mathfrak{F}(G)A = \overline{A^{-1}}\,\overline{\mathfrak{F}(G)}\,\overline{A} = \overline{A}^{-1}U^{-1}\mathfrak{F}(G)U\overline{A}$$

Thus $U\overline{A}A^{-1} = aI$ is a scalar matrix and so $U = aA\overline{A}^{-1}$. Consequently $U' = \overline{U}^{-1} = \overline{a}^{-1}A\overline{A}^{-1}$. Thus if $U' = -U$ then $\overline{a}^{-1} = -a$ or $a\overline{a} = -1$ which is impossible. Hence $U' = U$.

Suppose that $U' = U$. Since $U$ is unitary there exists $C$ unitary and $D$ diagonal such that $C^{-1}UC = D$. Thus

$$CDC^{-1} = U = U' = C^{-1\prime}DC'$$

Hence $C'CD = DC'C$. There exists a diagonal unitary matrix $E$ such that $E^2 = D$ and $C'CE = EC'C$. Let $V = CEC^{-1}$. Then $V^2 = U$ and $V$ is unitary since $C$ is. Furthermore

$$V' = C^{-1\prime} EC' = C^{-1\prime} EC' CC^{-1} = C^{-1\prime} C' CEC^{-1}$$
$$= CEC^{-1} = V$$

Thus $V^{-1} = \overline{V}$ and

$$\overline{V^{-1} \mathfrak{F}(G)V} = VU^{-1} \mathfrak{F}(G)UV^{-1} = V^{-1} \mathfrak{F}(G)V \quad \text{for } G \in \mathfrak{G}$$

The proof is complete.

(3.4) If $\mathfrak{F}$ is a complex representation of $\mathfrak{G}$ of the second kind then $\mathfrak{F}$ has even degree.

Proof. Let n be the degree of $\mathfrak{F}$. By (3.1) and (3.2) it may be assumed that $\overline{\mathfrak{F}(G)} = U^{-1} \mathfrak{F}(G)U$ for $G \in \mathfrak{G}$ and some unitary U. By (3.3) $U' = -U$. Thus $\det U = (-1)^n \det U$. Since $\det U \neq 0$, n is even.

(3.5) For an irreducible character $\chi$ of $\mathfrak{G}$ let $\nu(\chi) = 1/|\mathfrak{G}| \sum_{\mathfrak{G}} \chi(G^2)$. Let $\chi$ be an irreducible character afforded by the complex representations $\mathfrak{F}$ of $\mathfrak{G}$ then

(i) $\nu(\chi) = 1$ if and only if $\chi$ is of the first kind.
(ii) $\nu(\chi) = -1$ if and only if $\chi$ is of the second kind.
(iii) $\nu(\chi) = 0$ if and only if $\chi$ is of the third kind.

Proof. It may be assumed that $\mathfrak{F}$ is unitary and $\mathfrak{F} = \overline{\mathfrak{F}}$ if $\mathfrak{F}$ is of the first kind. $\chi(G^2)$ is the trace of $\mathfrak{F}(G)\mathfrak{F}(G) = \mathfrak{F}(G)\overline{\mathfrak{F}(G^{-1})'}$. Thus if $\mathfrak{F}(G) = a_{ij}(G)$ then

$$\nu(\chi) = \frac{1}{|\mathfrak{G}|} \sum_{i,j} \sum_{\mathfrak{G}} a_{ij}(G)\, \overline{a_{ij}(G^{-1})}$$

If $\mathfrak{F}$ is of the third kind then $\nu(\chi) = 0$ by (1.9). If $\mathfrak{F}$ is of the first kind then by (1.9)

$$\nu(\chi) = \frac{1}{|\mathfrak{G}|} \sum_{i,j} \sum_{\mathfrak{G}} a_{i,j}(G)\, a_{ij}(G^{-1})$$

$$= \frac{1}{|\mathfrak{G}|} \sum_{i} \sum_{\mathfrak{G}} a_{ii}(G)\, a_{ii}(G^{-1}) = 1$$

Suppose that $\mathfrak{F}$ is of the second kind. By (3.2) and (3.3) there exists U unitary such that $U' = -U$ and $U^{-1}\mathfrak{F}(G)U = \overline{\mathfrak{F}(G)}$ for $G \in \mathfrak{G}$. Since $U^{-1} = \overline{U}' = -\overline{U}$ this implies that if $U = (u_{ij})$ then

$$a_{ij}(G^{-1}) = -\sum_{s,t} \overline{u}_{is}\, a_{st}(G^{-1})\, u_{tj}$$

Therefore by (1.9)

$$\nu(\chi) = -\frac{1}{|\mathfrak{G}|} \sum_{i,j,s,t} \overline{u}_{is}\, u_{tj} \sum_{\mathfrak{G}} a_{ij}(G)\, a_{st}(G^{-1})$$

$$= -\frac{1}{\chi(1)} \sum_{i,j} \overline{u_{ij}}\, u_{ij}$$

Since $\overline{U}' = U^{-1}$, $\Sigma_j\, \overline{u_{ij}}\, u_{ij} = 1$ for all $i$. Thus $\nu(\chi) = -1$ as required. All possibilities are exhausted and the proof is complete.

(3.6) *For $G \in \mathfrak{G}$ let $t(G)$ be the number of elements $H$ such that $H^2 = G$. Then*

$$t(G) = \sum_{i=1}^{k} \nu(\chi_i)\, \chi_i(G)$$

*where $\nu(\chi)$ is defined as in (3.5).*

*Proof.* Clearly $t$ is a class function on $\mathfrak{G}$. By (2.17) $t(G) = \Sigma_i\, a_i\, \chi_i(G)$ for $G \in \mathfrak{G}$. If $\mathfrak{T}(G) = \{H \mid H^2 = G\}$ then the sets $\mathfrak{T}(G)$ partition $\mathfrak{G}$. Let $G_1, G_2, \ldots$ be a system of representations for the sets $\mathfrak{T}(G)$. Then

$$a_i = \frac{1}{|\mathfrak{G}|} \sum_{\mathfrak{G}} t(G)\, \overline{\chi_i(G)} = \frac{1}{|\mathfrak{G}|} \sum_{G \in \mathfrak{G}} \sum_{\mathfrak{T}(G)} \overline{\chi_i(H^2)}$$

$$= \frac{1}{|\mathfrak{G}|} \sum_{\mathfrak{G}} \overline{\chi_i(H^2)} = \nu(\chi_i)$$

as required.

(3.7) If $\mathfrak{G}$ contains exactly t elements of order 2 then

$$t + 1 = \sum_{i=1}^{k} \nu(\chi_i)\chi_i(1) \leq \sum_{i=1}^{k} \chi_i(1)$$

where $\nu(\chi)$ is defined as in (3.5). Thus in particular $t + 1 = \Sigma_{i=1}^{k} \chi_i(1)$ if and only if every irreducible character of $\mathfrak{G}$ is afforded by a representation of the first kind.

Proof. Set $G = 1$ in (3.6).

There seems to be no analogue of (3.7) if "2" is replaced by any other integer. This striking result illustrates one of the many ways in which the prime 2 plays a special role in group theory. The symmetric groups are examples of groups in which every irreducible representation is of the first kind, in fact $\mathbb{Q}$ is a splitting field for symmetric groups see Curtis and Reiner p. 190. Thus (3.7) yields a simple method for computing the sum of the degrees of the irreducible character of the symmetric groups.

## §4. INTEGRAL REPRESENTATIONS

Let $\mathfrak{D}$ be an integral domain with quotient field $\mathfrak{F}$. An $\mathfrak{F}$-representation $\mathfrak{F}$ of $\mathfrak{G}$ is a $\mathfrak{D}$-representation of $\mathfrak{G}$ if for all $G \in \mathfrak{G}$ the entries of $\mathfrak{F}(G)$ lie in $\mathfrak{D}$. Such representations of $\mathfrak{G}$ are sometimes called integral representations.

The theory of integral representations differs markedly from the theory of $\mathfrak{F}$-representations, where $\mathfrak{F}$ is a field. We will make no attempt to study integral representations systematically, only proving some elementary results that will be needed in the sequel.

(4.1) Let $\mathfrak{D}$ be a principal ideal domain with quotient field $\mathfrak{F}$. Every $\mathfrak{F}$-representation of $\mathfrak{G}$ is similar to a $\mathfrak{D}$-representation of $\mathfrak{G}$.

Proof. Let $\mathfrak{V}$ be the underlying vector space of the $\mathfrak{F}$-representation $\mathfrak{F}$ of $\mathfrak{G}$. Let $\{v_1, \ldots, v_n\}$ be a basis of $\mathfrak{V}$. Let $\mathfrak{M}$ be the $\mathfrak{D}$-module generated by $\{v_i\,\mathfrak{F}(G) \mid i = 1, \ldots, n,\ G \in \mathfrak{G}\}$. Thus $\mathfrak{M}$ is a finitely generated torsion free $\mathfrak{D}$-module and so it has a basis $\{w_i\}$. It is easily seen that $\{w_i\}$ is also a basis of $\mathfrak{V}$ and $\mathfrak{M}\,\mathfrak{F}(G) \subseteq \mathfrak{M}$ for $G \in \mathfrak{G}$. With respect to this basis all the matrices of the representation have entries in $\mathfrak{D}$.

By (2.8) there exists a finite extension $\mathfrak{F}$ of $\mathbb{Q}$ which is a splitting field of $\mathfrak{G}$. Let p be a prime and let $\wp_0$ be a prime ideal in the ring of algebraic integers of $\mathfrak{F}$ such that $p \in \wp_0$. Define

$$\mathfrak{D} = \{a/b \mid a, b \text{ integers in } \mathfrak{F},\ b \neq 0 \pmod{\wp_0}\}$$

It is easily seen that $\mathfrak{D}$ is an integral domain with quotient field $\mathfrak{F}$. The elements of $\mathfrak{D}$ are called local integers at $\wp_0$. An element of $\mathfrak{F}$ is an algebraic integer if and only if it is local integer at every prime in the ring of integers of $\mathfrak{F}$.

Let $\pi \in \wp_0, \pi \notin \wp_0^2$. Let $\wp = (\pi)$ be the ideal of $\mathfrak{D}$ generated by $\pi$. We will show that every nonzero ideal in $\mathfrak{D}$ is of the form $\wp^i$ for some i. Hence $\mathfrak{D}$ is a principal ideal domain and $\wp$ is the unique maximal ideal in $\mathfrak{D}$. Thus $\mathfrak{D}/\wp$ is a finite field of characteristic p.

For $a/b \in \mathfrak{D}$, with a, b algebraic integers let $\nu(a/b) = \infty$ if $a = 0$ and $\nu(a/b) = i$ if $a \equiv 0 \pmod{\wp_0^i}$, $a \not\equiv 0 \pmod{\wp_0^{i+1}}$. Thus an element a of $\mathfrak{D}$ is a unit if and only if $\nu(a) = 0$. Also $\nu(\pi) = 1$. If $\mathfrak{I}$ is an ideal of $\mathfrak{D}$ choose $a \in \mathfrak{I}$ such that $\nu(a)$ is minimum. Let $\nu(a) = i$. Then

$\nu(a\pi^{-i}) = 0$ and so $\wp^i = (a) \subseteq \mathfrak{g}$. If $\nu(b) = j \geq i$ then $b\pi^{-1} \in \mathfrak{D}$ and thus $b \in \wp^i$. Hence $\mathfrak{g} = \wp^i$ as required.

Throughout this section we will adhere to the notation just introduced.

(4.1) may be used to give an alternative proof of (2.18). We will here generalize that result.

(4.2) Let $\chi$ be an irreducible character of $\mathfrak{G}$ and $\mathfrak{Z} = \mathbf{Z}(\mathfrak{G})$. Then $\chi(1) \mid |\mathfrak{G}:\mathfrak{Z}|$.

Proof. If suffices to show that $|\mathfrak{G}:\mathfrak{Z}|/\chi(1)$ is a local integer at every prime $p$. Choose a prime $p$. By (4.1) there exists a $\mathfrak{D}$-representation $\mathfrak{F}$ of $\mathfrak{G}$ which affords the character $\chi$. Let $\mathfrak{F}(G) = (a_{ij}(G))$ for $G \in \mathfrak{G}$. If $Z \in \mathfrak{Z}$ then $\mathfrak{F}(Z) = \epsilon(Z)I$, where $\epsilon(Z)$ is a root of unity. Thus for $G \in \mathfrak{G}$, $Z \in \mathfrak{Z}$

$$a_{11}(GZ)\,a_{11}(Z^{-1}G^{-1}) = a_{11}(G)\epsilon(Z)\epsilon(Z)^{-1}a_{11}(G^{-1})$$

$$= a_{11}(G)\,a_{11}(G^{-1})$$

Let $G_1, \ldots, G_m$ be a complete system of coset representatives of $\mathfrak{Z}$ in $\mathfrak{G}$. Hence for $Z \in \mathfrak{Z}$

$$\sum_{i=1}^{m} a_{11}(G_i Z)\,a_{11}(Z^{-1}G_i^{-1}) = \sum_{i=1}^{m} a_{11}(G_i)\,a_{11}(G_i^{-1})$$

Therefore by (1.9)

$$\sum_{i=1}^{m} a_{11}(G_i)\,a_{11}(G_i^{-1}) = \frac{1}{|\mathfrak{Z}|}\sum_{\mathfrak{G}} a_{11}(G)\,a_{11}(G^{-1})$$

$$= \frac{|\mathfrak{G}:\mathfrak{Z}|}{\chi(1)}$$

Since $a_{11}(G) \in \mathfrak{D}$ for $G \in \mathfrak{G}$ this implies that $|\mathfrak{G} : \mathfrak{Z}|/\chi(1) \in \mathfrak{D}$ completing the proof.

For $a \in \mathfrak{D}$ let $a^*$ denote the image of $a$ in $\mathfrak{D}/\wp = \mathfrak{D}^*$.

(4.3) Assume that $p \nmid |\mathfrak{G}|$. Let $\mathfrak{A}$, $\mathfrak{B}$ be $\mathfrak{D}$-representations of $\mathfrak{G}$ which are absolutely irreducible $\mathfrak{F}$-representations of $\mathfrak{G}$. Then $\mathfrak{A}^*$, $\mathfrak{B}^*$ are absolutely irreducible $\mathfrak{D}^*$-representations of $\mathfrak{G}$. Furthermore $\mathfrak{A}$ is similar to $\mathfrak{B}$ in $\mathfrak{F}$ if and only if $\mathfrak{A}^*$ is similar to $\mathfrak{B}^*$.

Proof. If $\mathfrak{A}^*$ is not absolutely irreducible then replacing $\mathfrak{F}$ by an extension field if necessary it may be assumed that $\mathfrak{A}^*$ is reducible. Hence there exists a matrix $T$ with coefficients in $\mathfrak{D}^*$ such that $T^{-1}\mathfrak{A}^*(G)T = \begin{pmatrix} \mathfrak{C}_1(G) & 0 \\ 0 & \mathfrak{C}_2(G) \end{pmatrix}$ for all $G \in \mathfrak{G}$. Let $S$ be any matrix with coefficients in $\mathfrak{D}$ such that $S^* = T$. Then $\det S \equiv \det T \not\equiv 0 \pmod{\wp}$. Thus $S^{-1}$ has coefficients in $\mathfrak{D}$. Hence $\{S^{-1}\mathfrak{A}(G)S\}^* = S^{*-1}\mathfrak{A}^*(G)S^*$. Thus it may be assumed that $\mathfrak{A}^*(G) = \begin{pmatrix} \mathfrak{C}_1(G) & 0 \\ 0 & \mathfrak{C}_2(G) \end{pmatrix}$ for $G \in \mathfrak{G}$. Let $\mathfrak{A}(G) = (a_{ij}(G))$ and let $n$ be the degree of $\mathfrak{A}$. By (1.9)

$$\left(\frac{|\mathfrak{G}|}{n}\right)^* = \sum_{\mathfrak{G}} a_{1n}^*(G)\, a_{n1}^*(G) = 0$$

Thus $|\mathfrak{G}|/n \equiv 0 \pmod{p}$ contrary to assumption. Hence $\mathfrak{A}^*$ and $\mathfrak{B}^*$ are absolutely irreducible.

If $\mathfrak{A}^*$ is similar to $\mathfrak{B}^*$ then, as above, it may be assumed that $\mathfrak{A}^* = \mathfrak{B}^*$. Let $\mathfrak{B}(G) = (b_{ij}(G))$ for $G \in \mathfrak{G}$. Hence by (1.9)

$$\sum_{\mathfrak{G}} a_{1n}^*(G) b_{n1}^*(G^{-1}) = \sum_{\mathfrak{G}} a_{1n}^*(G)\, a_{n1}^*(G^{-1})$$

$$= \left(\frac{|\mathfrak{G}|}{n}\right)^* \neq 0$$

and so $\mathfrak{A}$ is similar to $\mathfrak{B}$.

If $\mathfrak{A}$ and $\mathfrak{B}$ are similar in $\mathfrak{F}$ they afford the same character $\chi$. By (2.9) (i)

$$\sum_{i,j}\sum_{\mathfrak{G}} a_{ii}(G)\, b_{jj}(G^{-1}) = \sum_{\mathfrak{G}} \chi(G)\,\chi(G^{-1}) \equiv |\mathfrak{G}| \not\equiv 0 \pmod p$$

thus $\mathfrak{A}^*$ is similar to $\mathfrak{B}^*$ by (1.9).

(4.4) Assume that $p \nmid |\mathfrak{G}|$. If $\mathfrak{K}$ is any field of characteristic $p$ then a $\mathfrak{K}$-representation of $\mathfrak{G}$ is similar to a $\mathfrak{D}^*$-representation of $\mathfrak{G}$. If $\mathfrak{B}$ is a $\mathfrak{D}^*$-representation of $\mathfrak{G}$ then there exists a $\mathfrak{D}$-representation $\mathfrak{A}$ of $\mathfrak{G}$ such that $\mathfrak{A}^* = \mathfrak{B}$. Furthermore $\mathfrak{A}$ is absolutely irreducible if and only if $\mathfrak{A}^*$ is absolutely irreducible. If $\mathfrak{A}_1$, $\mathfrak{A}_2$ are $\mathfrak{D}$-representations of $\mathfrak{G}$ then $\mathfrak{A}_1$ is similar to $\mathfrak{A}_2$ in $\mathfrak{F}$ if and only if $\mathfrak{A}_1^*$ is similar to $\mathfrak{A}_2^*$.

Proof. Let $\mathfrak{X}_1, \ldots, \mathfrak{X}_k$ be a set of pairwise nonsimilar absolutely irreducible $\mathfrak{F}$-representations of $\mathfrak{G}$ such that every absolutely irreducible $\mathfrak{F}$-representation of $\mathfrak{G}$ is similar to some $\mathfrak{X}_i$. Assume further that each $\mathfrak{X}_i$ is a $\mathfrak{D}$-representation of $\mathfrak{G}$. Let $x_i$ be the degree of $\mathfrak{X}_i$. By (4.3) $\mathfrak{X}_1^*, \ldots, \mathfrak{X}_k^*$ is a set of pairwise nonsimilar absolutely irreducible $\mathfrak{D}^*$-representations of $\mathfrak{G}$. Since $\Sigma x_i^2 = |\mathfrak{G}|$ by (2.9) it follows from (1.10) that any absolutely irreducible $\mathfrak{K}$-representation of $\mathfrak{G}$ is similar to a $\mathfrak{D}^*$-representation of $\mathfrak{G}$. The first three statements now follow from complete reducibility. The last statement is a consequence of (4.3) and complete reducibility.

## §5. THE CENTER OF THE GROUP ALGEBRA

Let $\mathfrak{G}$ be a group and let $\mathfrak{F}$ be a field of characteristic 0 which is a splitting field of $\mathfrak{G}$. Let $\mathfrak{F}(\mathfrak{G})$ be the group algebra of $\mathfrak{G}$ over $\mathfrak{F}$. Let $\mathbf{Z}_{\mathfrak{F}}(\mathfrak{G})$ be the center of $\mathfrak{F}(\mathfrak{G})$. For any subset $\mathfrak{A}$ of $\mathfrak{G}$ let $\hat{\mathfrak{A}} = \Sigma_{\mathfrak{A}} G \in \mathfrak{F}(\mathfrak{G})$.

Let $\mathfrak{K}_1, \ldots, \mathfrak{K}_k$ be the conjugate classes of $\mathfrak{G}$. Let $\chi_1, \ldots, \chi_k$ be the irreducible characters of $\mathfrak{G}$. Define

$$\omega_i\left(\sum_{j=1}^{k} c_j \hat{\mathfrak{K}}_j\right) = \sum_{j=1}^{k} c_j \omega_i(\hat{\mathfrak{K}}_j)$$

where

$$\omega_i(\hat{\mathfrak{K}}_j) = \omega_i(\mathfrak{K}_j) = \frac{|\mathfrak{K}_j| \chi_i(G)}{\chi_i(1)}, \quad G \in \mathfrak{K}_j$$

Let $a_{ijs}$ have the same meaning as in (2.12).

The integers $a_{ijs}$ and the functions $\omega_i$ have a natural interpretation in terms of $\mathbf{Z}_{\mathfrak{F}}(\mathfrak{G})$ as illustrated by the next result.

(5.1) $\hat{\mathfrak{K}}_1, \ldots, \hat{\mathfrak{K}}_k$ <u>is a basis of</u> $\mathbf{Z}_{\mathfrak{F}}(\mathfrak{G})$. <u>For</u> $i,j,s = 1, \ldots, k$ $\hat{\mathfrak{K}}_i \hat{\mathfrak{K}}_j = \Sigma_s a_{ijs} \hat{\mathfrak{K}}_s$. <u>Each</u> $\omega_i$ <u>is a homomorphism of</u> $\mathbf{Z}_{\mathfrak{F}}(\mathfrak{G})$ <u>into</u> $\mathfrak{F}$. <u>Furthermore if</u> $A \in \mathbf{Z}_{\mathfrak{F}}(\mathfrak{G})$ <u>then</u> $A = 0$ <u>if and only if</u> $\omega_i(A) = 0$ <u>for</u> $i = 1, \ldots, k$.

<u>Proof</u>. For $G \in \mathfrak{G}$, $G^{-1} \hat{\mathfrak{K}}_j G = \hat{\mathfrak{K}}_j$. Thus $\hat{\mathfrak{K}}_j \in \mathbf{Z}_{\mathfrak{F}}(\mathfrak{G})$ for $j = 1, \ldots, k$. Suppose that $\Sigma_{\mathfrak{G}}\, a(G)\, G \in \mathbf{Z}_{\mathfrak{F}}(\mathfrak{G})$. Then for $H \in \mathfrak{G}$

$$\sum_{\mathfrak{G}} a(HGH^{-1})\, G = \sum_{\mathfrak{G}} a(G)\, H^{-1} G H = \sum_{\mathfrak{G}} a(G)\, G$$

Thus $\Sigma_{\mathfrak{G}}\, a(G)\, G = \Sigma_{j=1}^{k} a(G_j) \hat{\mathfrak{K}}_j$, where $G_j \in \mathfrak{K}_j$ for $j = 1, \ldots, k$. Hence $\{\hat{\mathfrak{K}}_j\}$ is a basis of $\mathbf{Z}_{\mathfrak{F}}(\mathfrak{G})$ since it is clearly a linearly independent set in $\mathfrak{F}(\mathfrak{G})$. The definition of $a_{ijs}$

yields immediately that $\hat{\mathfrak{K}}_i \hat{\mathfrak{K}}_j = \Sigma_s a_{ijs} \hat{\mathfrak{K}}_s$. By (2.13) (i) each $\omega_i$ is a homomorphism of $\mathbf{Z}_{\mathfrak{F}}(\mathfrak{G})$ into $\mathfrak{F}$. Thus clearly $\omega_i(0) = 0$ for $i = 1, \ldots, k$.

Let $A = \Sigma_{j=1}^{k} c_j \hat{K}_j$ and suppose that $\omega_i(A) = 0$ for $i = 1, \ldots, k$. Thus for $G_s \in \mathfrak{K}_s$

$$\sum_j c_j |\mathfrak{K}_j| \chi_i(G_j) \overline{\chi_i(G_s)}$$

$$= \overline{\chi_i(G_s)} \chi_i(1) \sum_j c_j \omega_i(\hat{\mathfrak{K}}_j) = 0$$

for $i = 1, \ldots, k$. Summing over i this implies by (2.14) that

$$c_s |\mathfrak{G}| = \sum_j c_j |\mathfrak{K}_j| \frac{|\mathfrak{G}|}{|\mathfrak{K}_s|} \delta_{js} = 0$$

Hence $c_s = 0$ for $s = 1, \ldots, k$ and so $A = 0$ as required.

The next result is quite general and well known.

(5.2) Let $\mathfrak{A}$ be an algebra with unit over the field $\mathfrak{F}$. Let $\omega_1, \ldots, \omega_n$ be distinct nonzero algebra homomorphisms of $\mathfrak{A}$ into $\mathfrak{F}$. Then $\{\omega_i\}$ is a set of linearly independent functions from $\mathfrak{A}$ to $\mathfrak{F}$.

Proof. Induction on n. If $n = 1$ the result is clear. Suppose that $\Sigma a_i \omega_i = 0$ with some $a_i \neq 0$. Then by induction $a_i \neq 0$ for $i = 1, \ldots, n$. Hence it may be assumed that $a_n = 1$. Thus

$$\omega_n(A) \sum_{i=1}^{n-1} a_i \omega_i(B) + \omega_n(A)\omega_n(B)$$

$$= 0 = \sum_{i=1}^{n-1} a_i \omega_i(AB) + \omega_n(AB)$$

for $A, B \in \mathfrak{A}$. Since $\omega_i(AB) = \omega_i(A)\omega_i(B)$ for $i = 1, \ldots, n$ this implies that $\sum_{i=1}^{n-1} \{\omega_n(A) - \omega_i(A)\} a_i \omega_i(B) = 0$ for $A, B \in \mathfrak{A}$. Hence by induction $\{\omega_n(A) - \omega_1(A)\} a_1 = 0$ for $A \in \mathfrak{A}$. Since $a_1 \neq 0$ this implies that $\omega_1 = \omega_n$ contrary to assumption.

(5.3) <u>In the notation introduced at the beginning of this section</u> $\omega_1, \ldots, \omega_k$ <u>are all the nonzero homomorphisms of</u> $\mathbf{Z}_{\mathfrak{F}}(\mathfrak{G})$ <u>into</u> $\mathfrak{F}$.

<u>Proof.</u> If $\omega_i = \omega_j$, then $\chi_i(G)/\chi_i(1) = \chi_j(G)/\chi_j(1)$ for $G \in \mathfrak{G}$. Hence

$$\delta_{ij} = (\chi_i, \chi_j) = \frac{\chi_j(1)}{\chi_i(1)} (\chi_i, \chi_i) = \frac{\chi_j(1)}{\chi_i(1)} \neq 0$$

Thus $i = j$. Thus $\omega_1, \ldots, \omega_k$ are k distinct nonzero algebra homomorphisms of $\mathbf{Z}_{\mathfrak{F}}(\mathfrak{G})$ into $\mathfrak{F}$. Since $\mathbf{Z}_{\mathfrak{F}}(\mathfrak{G})$ has dimension k over $\mathfrak{F}$, the space of functions from $\mathbf{Z}_{\mathfrak{F}}(\mathfrak{G})$ into $\mathfrak{F}$ is k-dimensional over $\mathfrak{F}$. The result now follows from (5.2).

The previous result can be used to characterize the irreducible characters of $\mathfrak{G}$.

(5.4) <u>Let</u> $\theta$ <u>be a function from</u> $\mathfrak{G}$ <u>to</u> $\mathfrak{F}$. <u>Then</u> $\theta = c\chi$ <u>for</u>

some irreducible character $\chi$ of $\mathfrak{G}$ and some $c \in \mathfrak{F}$ if and only if

$$(5.5) \qquad \theta(G)\theta(H) = \frac{\theta(1)}{|\mathfrak{G}|} \sum_{K \in \mathfrak{G}} \theta(GK^{-1}HK)$$

for $G, H \in \mathfrak{G}$.

Proof. If $\theta$ satisfies (5.5) then setting $G = 1$ we see that $\theta$ is a class function. Assume now that $\theta$ is any class function with $\theta(1) \neq 0$. Let $G_j \in \mathfrak{K}_j$ for $j = 1, \ldots, k$. Define a function $\omega$ on $\mathbf{Z}_{\mathfrak{F}}(\mathfrak{G})$ by $\omega(\Sigma_{j=1}^{k} c_j \hat{\mathfrak{K}}_j) = \Sigma_{j=1}^{k} c_j \omega(\hat{\mathfrak{K}}_j)$ and $\omega(\hat{\mathfrak{K}}_j) = |\mathfrak{K}_j|\theta(G_j)/\theta(1)$. Then

$$\sum_{K \in \mathfrak{G}} \theta(GK^{-1}HK) = \sum_{K \in \mathfrak{G}} \theta(L^{-1}GLL^{-1}K^{-1}HKL)$$

$$= \sum_{K \in \mathfrak{G}} \theta(L^{-1}GLK^{-1}HK)$$

Therefore

$$\sum_{K \in \mathfrak{G}} \theta(G_s K^{-1} G_t K) = \frac{1}{|\mathfrak{G}|} \sum_{K,L \in \mathfrak{G}} \theta(L^{-1}G_s LK^{-1}G_t K)$$

$$= \frac{1}{|\mathfrak{G}|}\frac{|\mathfrak{G}|}{|\mathfrak{K}_s|}\frac{|\mathfrak{G}|}{|\mathfrak{K}_t|} \sum_{H_s \in \mathfrak{K}_s} \times \sum_{H_t \in \mathfrak{K}_t} \theta(H_s H_t)$$

$$= \frac{|\mathfrak{G}|}{|\mathfrak{K}_s||\mathfrak{K}_t|} \sum_m |\mathfrak{K}_m| a_{stm}\, \theta(G_m)$$

$$= \frac{|G|\theta(1)}{|\mathfrak{K}_s||\mathfrak{K}_t|} \sum_m a_{stm}\, \omega(\mathfrak{K}_m)$$

Thus $\theta$ satisfies (5.5) if and only if

$$\omega(\mathfrak{K}_s)\,\omega(\mathfrak{K}_t) = \sum_m a_{stm}\,\omega(\mathfrak{K}_m)$$

Hence if $\theta = c\chi$ then $\theta$ satisfies (5.5).

Suppose that $\theta$ satisfies (5.5). If $\theta(1) = 0$ then $\theta = 0$ by (5.5). Assume that $\theta(1) \neq 0$. Then by (5.3) $\omega = \omega_i$ for some i. Hence $\theta(G)/\theta(1) = \chi_i(G)/\chi_i(1)$ for $G \in \mathfrak{G}$. Therefore $\theta = \theta(1)/\chi_i(1)\ \chi_i$ as required.

## §6. SOME PROPERTIES OF CHARACTERS

In this section we collect some elementary properties of characters. Several of these are useful in applications of character theory to questions concerning the structure of groups.

(6.1) Let $\chi_1, \chi_2, \ldots$ be the irreducible characters of $\mathfrak{G}$. Then for $G \in \mathfrak{G}$

$$\frac{1}{|\mathfrak{G}|}\sum_{\mathfrak{G}} \chi_s(GH^{-1})\,\chi_t(H) = \frac{\chi_s(G)}{\chi_s(1)}\,\delta_{st}$$

Proof. Let $\mathfrak{X}_s$ be a representation of $\mathfrak{G}$ which affords $\chi_s$. Let $\mathfrak{X}_s(G) = (a^s_{ij}(G))$. Then by (1.9)

$$\frac{1}{|\mathfrak{G}|}\sum_{\mathfrak{G}} \chi_s(GH^{-1})\,\chi_t(H) = \frac{1}{|\mathfrak{G}|}\sum_{i,j}\sum_{\mathfrak{G}} a^s_{ii}(GH^{-1})\,a^t_{jj}(H)$$

$$= \frac{1}{|\mathfrak{G}|}\sum_{i,j,m} a^s_{im}(G)\sum_{\mathfrak{G}} a^s_{mi}(H^{-1})$$

$$\times\, a^t_{jj}(H)$$

$$= \frac{1}{\chi_s(1)} \sum_{i,j,m} a^s_{im}(G)\, \delta_{st}\, \delta_{ij}\, \delta_{mj}$$

$$= \frac{1}{\chi_s(1)}\, \delta_{st} \sum_j a^s_{jj}(G)$$

$$= \frac{\chi_s(G)}{\chi_1(1)}\, \delta_{st}$$

(6.2) Let $\mathfrak{H}$ be a subgroup of $\mathfrak{G}$. If $\theta$ is a character of $\mathfrak{G}$ which vanishes on $\mathfrak{H}^\#$ then $|\mathfrak{H}| \mid \theta(1)$.

Proof. It may be assumed that $\mathfrak{G} = \mathfrak{H}$. Then

$$\frac{\theta(1)}{|\mathfrak{H}|} = \frac{1}{|\mathfrak{H}|} \sum_{\mathfrak{H}} \theta(H) = (\theta, 1_{\mathfrak{H}})_{\mathfrak{H}}$$

Thus $\theta(1)/|\mathfrak{H}|$ is an integer.

(6.3) If $\mathfrak{G} = \mathfrak{G}_1 \times \mathfrak{G}_2$ then a character of $\mathfrak{G}$ is irreducible if and only if it is of the form $\chi\zeta$, where $\chi$ is an irreducible character of $\mathfrak{G}/\mathfrak{G}_2$ and $\zeta$ is an irreducible character of $\mathfrak{G}/\mathfrak{G}_1$.

Proof. Let $\chi_1, \chi_2, \ldots$ be all the irreducible characters of $\mathfrak{G}/\mathfrak{G}_2$ and let $\zeta_1, \zeta_2$ be all the irreducible characters of $\mathfrak{G}/\mathfrak{G}_1$. Then

$$(\chi_i\, \zeta_j, \chi_s\, \zeta_t) = \frac{1}{|\mathfrak{G}|} \sum_{\mathfrak{G}_1} \chi_i(G)\, \overline{\chi_s(G)} \sum_{\mathfrak{G}_2} \zeta_j(G)\, \overline{\zeta_t(G)}$$

$$= \delta_{is}\, \delta_{jt}$$

Thus by (2.9) the set $\{\chi_i\, \zeta_j\}$ consists of pairwise distinct irreducible characters of $\mathfrak{G}$. Since $\Sigma_{i,j} \chi_i(1)^2 \zeta_j(1)^2 = |\mathfrak{G}|$, every irreducible character of $\mathfrak{G}$ is of this form by (2.9) (vi).

(6.4) Let p be a prime and suppose that P, G $\in \mathfrak{G}$, where P is a p-element, G is a p'-element and PG = GP. Let $\mathfrak{F}$ be an algebraic number field containing the $|\mathfrak{G}|$-th roots of unity and let $\wp$ be a prime ideal in the ring of integers of $\mathfrak{F}$ such that $p \in \wp$. If $\theta$ is a character of $\mathfrak{G}$ then

$$\theta(PG) \equiv \theta(G) (\text{mod } \wp)$$

Proof. It suffices to prove the result for every character, and hence for every irreducible character, of the abelian group $\langle P, G \rangle$. Let $\theta$ be an irreducible character of $\langle P, G \rangle$. Then $\theta(1) = 1$ and $\theta(PG) = \theta(P)\theta(G)$. Furthermore $\theta(P)$ is a $p^m$-th root of unity for some m and so $\theta(P) \equiv 1 (\text{mod } \wp)$. The result follows.

(6.5) (Solomon [2]) Let $\mathfrak{K}_1, \ldots, \mathfrak{K}_k$ be the conjugate classes of $\mathfrak{G}$. Let $G_j \in \mathfrak{K}_j$. Then $\Sigma_{j=1}^k \chi(G_j)$ is a nonnegative rational integer for any irreducible character $\chi$ of $\mathfrak{G}$.

Proof. Let $\mathfrak{A}$ be the permutation representation of $\mathfrak{G}$ on the elements of $\mathfrak{G}$ defined by $H\mathfrak{A}(G) = G^{-1}HG$ for G, H $\in \mathfrak{G}$. Let $\theta$ be the character afforded by $\mathfrak{A}$. Since $H\mathfrak{A}(G) = H$ if and only if HG = GH, the number of elements fixed by $\mathfrak{A}(G)$ is $|\mathbf{C}(G)| = |\mathfrak{G}|/|\mathfrak{K}|$, where $\mathfrak{K}$ is the conjugate class of $\mathfrak{G}$ containing G. Thus by (2.3) $\theta(G_j) = |\mathfrak{G}|/|\mathfrak{K}_j|$. Let $\theta = \Sigma_{i=1}^k a_i \chi_i$ where $\chi_1, \ldots, \chi_k$ are the irreducible characters of $\mathfrak{G}$. Then each $a_i$ is a nonnegative integer and

$$a_i = \frac{1}{|\mathfrak{G}|} \sum_j \overline{\theta(G_j)} |\mathfrak{K}_j| \chi_i(G_j) = \sum_j \chi_i(G_j)$$

L. Solomon and J. G. Thompson have pointed out the fact that in contrast to (6.5) $\Sigma_{i=1}^{k} \chi_i(G)$ need not be a nonnegative integer.

A character $\theta$ of $\mathfrak{G}$ is a linear character if $\theta(1) = 1$. A linear character is necessarily irreducible.

(6.6) Let $\chi_i$, $\chi_j$, $\chi$ be irreducible characters of $\mathfrak{G}$. The multiplicity of $\chi$ in $\chi_i \bar{\chi}_j$ is equal to the multiplicity of $\chi_i$ in $\chi\chi_j$. If furthermore $\chi$ is linear then the multiplicity of $\chi$ in $\chi_i \bar{\chi}_j$ is 0 or 1.

Proof. The multiplicity of $\chi$ in $\chi_i \bar{\chi}_j$ and the multiplicity of $\chi_i$ in $\chi\chi_j$ are both equal to $1/|\mathfrak{G}| \Sigma_{\mathfrak{G}} \overline{\chi_i(G)} \chi_j(G) \chi(G)$. If $\chi$ is linear then $\chi\chi_j$ is irreducible. Thus $\chi_i$ is a constituent of $\chi\chi_j$ if and only if $\chi_i = \chi\chi_j$ in which case the multiplicity of $\chi_i$ in $\chi\chi_j$ is 1.

(6.7) Let $\mathfrak{F}$ be a representation of $\mathfrak{G}$ which affords the character $\theta$. Let $\mathfrak{H}$ be the kernel of $\theta$. Then

(i) $|\theta(G)| \leq \theta(1)$ for $G \in \mathfrak{G}$.

(ii) $\theta(G) = \theta(1)$ if and only if $G \in \mathfrak{H}$.

(iii) If $|\theta(G)| = \theta(1)$ then $G\mathfrak{H}$ is in the center of $\mathfrak{G}/\mathfrak{H}$.

If $\theta$ is irreducible then conversely $|\theta(G)| = \theta(1)$ for $G\mathfrak{H}$ in the center of $\mathfrak{G}/\mathfrak{H}$.

Thus in particular $\{G \mid \theta(G) = \theta(1)\} \triangleleft \mathfrak{G}$ and $\{G \mid |\theta(G)| = \theta(1)\} \triangleleft \mathfrak{G}$.

Proof. Let $\theta(1) = n$. The characteristic roots $\epsilon_1, \ldots, \epsilon_n$ of $\mathfrak{F}(G)$ are complex roots of unity. Thus $|\theta(G)| = |\epsilon_1 + \cdots + \epsilon_n| \leq n$ proving (i). If $G \in \mathfrak{H}$ then $\mathfrak{F}(G) = I$ and so $\theta(G) = n = \theta(1)$. If $\theta$ is irreducible and $G\mathfrak{H}$ is in the center of $\mathfrak{G}/\mathfrak{H}$ then $\mathfrak{F}(G) = \epsilon I$ by Schur's lemma and so $|\theta(G)| = |n\epsilon| = n$. Conversely suppose that $|\theta(G)| = n$. Then $\epsilon_1 = \cdots = \epsilon_n = \epsilon$. Hence by (1.12) $\mathfrak{F}(G) = \epsilon I$. Thus

$G\mathfrak{H}$ is in the center of $\mathfrak{G}/\mathfrak{H}$. If furthermore $\theta(G) = n$ then $\epsilon = 1$ and $G \in \mathfrak{H}$.

(6.8) (Feit-Thompson [2] Lemma 4.3) Let $\mathfrak{H} \triangleleft \mathfrak{G}$ and let $\chi$ be an irreducible character of $\mathfrak{G}$ whose kernel does not contain $\mathfrak{H}$. If $G \in \mathfrak{G}$ and $\mathbf{C}(G) \cap \mathfrak{H} = \langle 1 \rangle$ then $\chi(G) = 0$.

Proof. Let $\zeta_1, \zeta_2, \ldots$ be all the irreducible characters of $\mathfrak{G}^* = \mathfrak{G}/\mathfrak{H}$. Let $\chi_1, \chi_2, \ldots$ be the remaining irreducible characters of $\mathfrak{G}$. If $\mathbf{C}(G) \cap \mathfrak{H} = \langle 1 \rangle$, then $\mathbf{C}(G)$ is mapped isomorphically into $\mathbf{C}(G^*)$, where $G^*$ is the image of $G$ in $\mathfrak{G}^*$. Thus by (2.14)

$$\sum_i |\zeta_i(G)|^2 = |\mathbf{C}(G^*)| \geq |\mathbf{C}(G)|$$

$$= \sum_i |\zeta_i(G)|^2 + \sum_i |\chi_i(G)|^2$$

Hence $\chi_i(G) = 0$ for all $i$ as required.

The next result is due to Burnside. The proof was suggested by N. Hamilton several years ago.

(6.9) If $\chi$ is a nonlinear irreducible character of $\mathfrak{G}$ then $\chi(G) = 0$ for some element $G \in \mathfrak{G}$.

Proof. If $G, H \in \mathfrak{G}$ let $G \approx H$ if $\langle G \rangle = \langle H \rangle$. It is easily seen that "$\approx$" is an equivalence relation and $G \approx H$ if and only if $G = H^i$ for some $i$ with $(i, |\mathfrak{G}|) = 1$. Let $\mathfrak{X}$ be a representation of $\mathfrak{G}$ which affords $\chi$. Let $\epsilon_1, \ldots, \epsilon_n$ be the characteristic roots of $\mathfrak{X}(H)$. If $\sigma \in \mathcal{G}_{\mathbb{Q}|\mathfrak{G}|/\mathbb{Q}}$ then there exists $i$ with $(i, |\mathfrak{G}|) = 1$ such that $\epsilon_j^{\sigma} = \epsilon_j^{i}$. Thus $\chi(H)^{\sigma} = \chi(H^i)$. Hence if $\mathfrak{A}$ is an equivalence class with respect to $\approx$ then $\mathcal{G}_{\mathbb{Q}|\mathfrak{G}|/\mathbb{Q}}$ permutes the set $\{\chi(H) \mid H \in \mathfrak{A}\}$.

Suppose that $\chi(G) \neq 0$. Let $\mathfrak{A}$ be the equivalence class with respect to $\approx$ which contains $G$. The arithmetic mean of positive real numbers is at least the geometric mean.

Since complex conjugation commutes with any element of $\mathcal{G}_{Q|\mathfrak{G}|/Q}$ this implies that

$$\frac{1}{|\mathfrak{A}|}\sum_{\mathfrak{A}}|\chi(G)|^2 \geq \left\{\prod_{\mathfrak{A}}|\chi(G)|^2\right\}^{1/|\mathfrak{A}|}$$

As $\chi(G)$ is a nonzero algebraic integer $\Pi_{\mathfrak{A}}|\chi(G))^2 \geq 1$. Therefore $\Sigma_{\mathfrak{A}}|\chi(G)|^2 \geq |\mathfrak{A}|$. Thus if $\chi(G) \neq 0$ for all $G \in \mathfrak{G}$ then by the orthogonality relations

$$|\mathfrak{G}| \geq \chi(1)^2 + \sum_{\mathfrak{G}^{\#}} |\chi(G)|^2 \geq \chi(1)^2 + |\mathfrak{G}| - 1$$

Hence $\chi(1)^2 \leq 1$ as required.

The following striking consequence of (6.9) was discovered by Brauer [4] and Wielandt. However, it is a result that seems to be difficult to use.

(6.10) $\mathfrak{G} = \mathfrak{G}'$ <u>if and only if $\Sigma_{j=1}^{k}\hat{\mathfrak{K}}_j$ is proportional to $\Pi_{j=1}^{k}\hat{\mathfrak{K}}_j$ in $\mathbf{Z}_{\mathfrak{F}}(\mathfrak{G})$, where the notation of Section 5 is used.</u>

<u>Proof.</u> Let $\chi_1 = 1_{\mathfrak{G}}$. If $\Sigma_{j=1}^{k}|\mathfrak{K}_j| = c\,\Pi_{j=1}^{k}|\mathfrak{K}_j|$ then

$$\omega_1\left(\sum_{j=1}^{k}\hat{\mathfrak{K}}_j\right) = c\omega_1\left(\prod_{j=1}^{k}\hat{\mathfrak{K}}_j\right)$$

Since

$$\omega_i\left(\sum_{j=1}^{k}\hat{\mathfrak{K}}_j\right) = \frac{1}{\chi_i(1)}\sum_{\mathfrak{G}}\chi_i(G) = \delta_{i1}|\mathfrak{G}|$$

we see by (5.1) that $\Sigma_{j=1}^{k}\hat{\mathfrak{K}}_j$ is proportional to $\Pi_{j=1}^{k}\hat{\mathfrak{K}}_j$ if and only if $\omega_i(\Pi_{j=1}^{k}\hat{\mathfrak{K}}_j) = 0$ for $i \neq 1$, or equivalently $\chi_i(G) = 0$ for some $G$ in case $i \neq 1$. Since a linear character never vanishes this statement is by (6.9) equivalent to the fact that

$\chi_1$ is the only linear character of $\mathfrak{G}$, or equivalently $\mathfrak{G} = \mathfrak{G}'$ as required.

The next result due to R. Brauer [5] generalizes a result of Burnside. A similar argument was used by Fong and Gaschütz [1] in a different context.

(6.11) Let $\theta$ be a faithful character of $\mathfrak{G}$. Suppose that $\theta$ takes on a total of r distinct values $a_1, \ldots, a_r$. Then each irreducible character $\chi$ of $\mathfrak{G}$ is a constituent of one of the characters $\theta^0 = 1_{\mathfrak{G}}, \theta, \ldots, \theta^{r-1}$.

Proof. Let $\mathfrak{A}_j = \{G | G \in \mathfrak{G}, \theta(G) = a_j\}$. Let $G_j \in \mathfrak{A}_j$. If $\chi$ is not a constituent of $\theta^s$ then

$$0 = |\mathfrak{G}|(\theta^s, \chi)_{\mathfrak{G}} = \sum_j \theta^s(G_j) \sum_{\mathfrak{A}_j} \overline{\chi(G)}$$

$$= \sum_j a_j^s \sum_{\mathfrak{A}_j} \overline{\chi(G)}$$

If this holds for $s = 0, \ldots, r-1$ then the nonvanishing of the Vandermonde determinant implies that for each j $\Sigma_{\mathfrak{A}_j} \overline{\chi(G)} = 0$. Since $\theta$ is faithful (6.7) implies that for some j, $\mathfrak{A}_j = \{1\}$. Then $\chi(1) = 0$ which is impossible.

(6.12) Let $\chi_1, \ldots \chi_k$ be all the irreducible characters of $\mathfrak{G}$. Let $\mathfrak{F}$ be a splitting field of $\mathfrak{G}$ of characteristic 0 and let $\chi_i$ be afforded by the $\mathfrak{F}$-representation $\mathfrak{X}_i$. For i, j = 1, ..., k define the matrices $S_{ij}$ by

$$\mathfrak{X}_i(G) \otimes \mathfrak{X}_j(G) = S_{ij}^{-1} \begin{bmatrix} \mathfrak{X}_{i_1}(G) & & 0 \\ & \ddots & \\ 0 & & \mathfrak{X}_{i_s}(G) \end{bmatrix} S_{ij}$$

for all $G \in \mathfrak{G}$. The set of matrices $S_{ij}$ determines the group $\mathfrak{G}$ up to isomorphism.

Proof. Let $A = (A_1, \ldots, A_k)$ be an ordered k-tuple of nonsingular matrices $A_i$ such that $A_i$ has degree $\chi_i(1)$ and

$$A_i \otimes A_j = S_{ij}^{-1} \begin{bmatrix} A_{i_1} & & 0 \\ & \ddots & \\ 0 & & A_{i_s} \end{bmatrix} S_{ij}$$

Let $\mathfrak{A}$ be the set of all such k-tuples A. If $G \in \mathfrak{G}$ let $A_G = (\mathfrak{X}_1(G), \ldots, \mathfrak{X}_k(G))$ and let $\mathfrak{A}_{\mathfrak{G}} = \{A_G\}$. For $A \in \mathfrak{A}$ let $\{a_j(A)\}$ be the various matrix entries in the set of matrices $A_1, \ldots, A_k$, where each subscript j denotes a place in one of these matrices. Thus $j = 1, \ldots, |\mathfrak{G}|$. For $G \in \mathfrak{G}$ let $a_j(A_G) = a_j(G)$. By assumption $a_i(A)\, a_j(A) = \Sigma_s\, c_{ijs}\, a_s(A)$ for $A \in \mathfrak{A}$, where $c_{ijs}$ depends only on the matrices $S_{ij}$. Thus for $A \in \mathfrak{A}$ and all i, j

$$\sum_s \{c_{ijs} - \delta_{js}\, a_i(A)\}\, a_s(A) = 0$$

By (1.10) $\{a_s\}$ is a linearly independent set of functions on $\mathfrak{A}_{\mathfrak{G}}$ and hence on $\mathfrak{A}$. Thus the determinant of the system of equations above vanishes where i is held fixed and $j = 1, \ldots, |\mathfrak{G}|$. Hence $a_i(A)$ is a characteristic root of the matrix whose (j, s) entry is $c_{ijs}$. Consequently $\mathfrak{A}$ is finite.

If $A = (A_i)$, $B = (B_i)$ are in $\mathfrak{A}$ then clearly $AB = (A_iB_i)$ and $A^{-1} = (A_i^{-1})$ are in $\mathfrak{A}$. Thus $\mathfrak{A}$ is a group and $\mathfrak{A}_{\mathfrak{G}}$ is a subgroup of $\mathfrak{A}$ isomorphic to $\mathfrak{G}$. For each i the mapping which sends A to $A_i$ is a representation of $\mathfrak{A}$ which will be denoted by $\mathfrak{Y}_i$. Since $\mathfrak{Y}_i(A_G) = \mathfrak{X}_i(G)$ for $G \in \mathfrak{G}$, $\mathfrak{Y}_i$ is absolutely irreducible. Let $\mathfrak{Y} = \mathfrak{Y}_1 \oplus \ldots \oplus \mathfrak{Y}_k$, then $\mathfrak{Y}$ is a faithful representation of $\mathfrak{A}$. By assumption every irreducible constituent in any tensor power $\mathfrak{Y}^n$ of $\mathfrak{Y}$ is similar to some $\mathfrak{Y}_i$. Thus by (6.12) every absolutely irreducible representation of $\mathfrak{A}$ is similar to some $\mathfrak{Y}_i$. Since $\mathfrak{Y}_i$ has degree $\chi_i(1)$ it follows from (2.9) (vi) that

$$|\mathfrak{A}| = \sum_{i=1}^{k} \chi_i(1)^2 = |\mathfrak{G}|$$

Thus $\mathfrak{G}$ is isomorphic to $\mathfrak{A}$. As $\mathfrak{A}$ is determined by the matrices $S_{ij}$ the result follows.

An algebraic number a is said to <u>require the m-th roots of unity</u> if $\mathcal{Q}(a) \subseteq \mathcal{Q}_m$, and m is the smallest integer with this property. Note that if m here is even then $4|m$.

The next result is due to Blichfeldt and Burnside. The proof given here was first published by R. Brauer [5].

(6.13) <u>Let $\chi$ be an irreducible character of $\mathfrak{G}$. Let $p_1, \ldots, p_n$ be distinct primes. Assume that there exist elements $G_1, \ldots, G_n \in \mathfrak{G}$ such that $\chi(G_i)$ requires the $p_i^{a_i}$-th roots of unity for some $a_i > 0$, $i = 1, \ldots, n$. Then $\mathfrak{G}$ contains an element G of order $p_1^{a_1} \ldots p_n^{a_n}$.</u>

<u>Proof</u>. Let $p_i^{b_i} \| |\mathfrak{G}|$ and $p_i^{b_i+1} \nmid |\mathfrak{G}|$. Then $a_i \leq b_i$. Let $\mathcal{F}_i$ be the field of $|\mathfrak{G}|/p_i^{b_i-a_i+1}$-th roots of unity over $\mathcal{Q}$. Since $\chi(G_i) \notin \mathcal{F}_i$ there exists an element $\delta_i \in \mathcal{G}_{\mathcal{Q}|\mathfrak{G}|/\mathcal{F}_i}$ such that $\delta_i(\chi(G_i)) \neq \chi(G_i)$. On the other hand $\delta_i(\chi(G_j)) = \chi(G_j)$ for $j \neq i$. If the result is false then for $G \in \mathfrak{G}$, $\delta_i(\chi(G)) = \chi(G)$ for some i depending on G, $1 \leq i \leq n$. Therefore $\Pi_{i=1}^{n} (1 - \delta_i)(\chi(G)) = 0$ for all $G \in \mathfrak{G}$. Hence $\Pi_{i=1}^{n} (1 - \delta_i)(\chi) = 0$. Expanding this product we get that

$$\chi + \sum_{i<j} \delta_i \delta_j(\chi) + \cdots$$
$$= \sum_i \delta_i(\chi) + \sum_{i<j<k} \delta_i \delta_j \delta_k(\chi) + \cdots$$

Hence there exist $i_1, \ldots, i_j$ for some $j \geq 1$ such that $\chi = \delta_{i_1} \cdots \delta_{i_j}(\chi)$. Thus

$$\chi(G_{i_1}) = \delta_{i_1} \cdots \delta_{i_j}(\chi(G_{i_1})) = \delta_{i_1}(\chi(G_{i_1}))$$

contrary to what was shown above.

It is an open question, raised by J. Thompson, whether it is possible to find G in (6.13) such that $G = H_1 \ldots H_n$, where $H_i H_j = H_j H_i$ for $i, j = 1, \ldots, n$ and where $H_i$ is conjugate to $G_i$ for $i = 1, \ldots, n$.

Another open question related to (6.13) is the following: Let $\chi$ be an irreducible character of $\mathfrak{G}$ and let m be the smallest integer such that $\mathbb{Q}(\chi) \subseteq \mathbb{Q}_m$. Is it true that $\mathfrak{G}$ contains an element of order m?

See Brauer [6] problem 41 for comments related to this question.

## §7. CHARACTER TABLES

Let $\chi_1, \ldots, \chi_k$ be the irreducible characters of $\mathfrak{G}$ and let $\mathfrak{K}_1, \ldots, \mathfrak{K}_k$ be the conjugate classes of $\mathfrak{G}$. Let $G_j \in \mathfrak{K}_j$ for $j = 1, \ldots, k$. The matrix $X = (\chi_i(G_j))$ is a character table of $\mathfrak{G}$. Any character table of $\mathfrak{G}$ can be transformed into any other by permuting characters and conjugate classes.

If $\mathfrak{H} \triangleleft \mathfrak{G}$ then $\mathfrak{H}$ is the kernel of $\rho_{\mathfrak{G}/\mathfrak{H}}$. Thus $\mathfrak{H}$ is the intersection of the kernels of some characters. Hence if X is given it is possible to find the lattice of normal subgroups of $\mathfrak{G}$ by using (6.7) and to determine which classes lie in a given normal subgroup. Thus in particular it is possible to determine whether $\mathfrak{K}_j = \{1\}$. Hence $\chi_i(1)$ can be read off from X. By (2.9) X determines $|\mathfrak{G}|$. Then by (2.14) X determines $|\mathfrak{K}_j|$ for each j. Thus $|\mathbf{Z}(\mathfrak{G})|$ is determined by X. Since $\mathfrak{G}'$ is the intersection of the kernels of all the linear characters $|\mathfrak{G}'|$ can also be determined.

There exist two nonisomorphic nonabelian groups of order 8. We will show that they have the same character table. Let $\mathfrak{G}$ be any nonabelian group of order 8. Then $\mathfrak{G}' = \mathbf{Z}(\mathfrak{G})$ and $|\mathfrak{G}'| = 2$. Thus $\mathfrak{G}$ has exactly 4 linear characters $\chi_i$, $i = 1, \ldots, 4$. Since $\Sigma_{i=1}^{k} \chi_i(1)^2 = 8$ it follows that $\mathfrak{G}$ has exactly one other irreducible character $\chi_5$ with $\chi_5(1) = 2$. If $Z \in \mathbf{Z}(\mathfrak{G})^\#$ then by (6.7) $|\chi_5(Z)| = 2$. Thus $\chi_5(Z) = \pm 2$ since $Z^2 = 1$. Since Z is in the kernel of $\chi_i$ for $i = 1, \ldots, 4$ it cannot be in the kernel of $\chi_5$. Thus by (6.7) $\chi_5(Z) = -2$. Hence $\chi_5(1)^2 + \chi_5(Z)^2 = 8$ and so $\chi_5(G) = 0$ for $G \notin \mathbf{Z}(\mathfrak{G})$. It is now easy to show that a character table of $\mathfrak{G}$ is

$$\begin{pmatrix} 1 & 1 & 1 & 1 & 1 \\ 1 & -1 & 1 & -1 & 1 \\ 1 & 1 & -1 & -1 & 1 \\ 1 & -1 & -1 & 1 & 1 \\ 2 & 0 & 0 & 0 & -2 \end{pmatrix}$$

Dade [1] has shown that if in addition to X it is known when a conjugate class consists of m-th powers of the elements in another conjugate class, for all integers m, then this information is still not sufficient to determine $\mathfrak{G}$ up to isomorphism. It is an open problem to find reasonable conditions which together with a character table will characterize a group $\mathfrak{G}$. For a discussion of this question see Brauer [6, §4].

(7.1) <u>Let</u> $a_{ijs}$ <u>have the same meaning as in</u> (2.12). <u>A knowledge of all the</u> $a_{ijs}$ <u>is equivalent to a knowledge of</u> X.

Proof. Given X then as remarked above, $|\mathfrak{G}|$, $|\mathfrak{K}_j|$ and $\chi_i(1)$ can be determined. Thus by (2.15) $a_{ijs}$ is determined for all i,j,s.

Suppose that all $a_{ijs}$ are given. By (5.1) and (5.3) the matrix $(\omega_i(\mathfrak{K}_j))$ is determined. $\mathfrak{K}_j = \{1\}$ if and only if for all i $a_{jji} = \delta_{ij}$. Thus by (2.12) $|\mathfrak{K}_j|$ is determined for all j. Hence also $|\mathfrak{G}| = \Sigma_j |\mathfrak{K}_j|$ can be found. Since $\omega_i(\mathfrak{K}_j) = |\mathfrak{K}_j| \chi_i(G_j)/\chi_i(1)$ we see that $\chi_i(G_j)/\chi_i(1)$ is determined. Thus by (2.9) it is possible to determine

$$\sum_j \frac{\overline{\chi_i(G_j)}}{\chi_i(1)} \omega_i(\mathfrak{K}_j) = \frac{1}{\chi_i(1)^2} \sum_j |\mathfrak{K}_j| |\chi_i(G_j)|^2$$

$$= \frac{|\mathfrak{G}|}{\chi_i(1)^2}$$

Hence $\chi_i(1)$ can be computed and thus also $\chi_i(G_j)$.

## §8. INDUCED REPRESENTATIONS

Let $\mathfrak{H}$ be a subgroup of $\mathfrak{G}$. Let $\mathfrak{H}G_1, \ldots, \mathfrak{H}G_m$ be all the distinct right cosets of $\mathfrak{H}$ in $\mathfrak{G}$. If $\mathfrak{F}$ is an $\mathcal{F}$-representation of $\mathfrak{H}$ of degree n let $\mathfrak{F}(G)$ be the zero matrix of degree n in case $G \in \mathfrak{G} - \mathfrak{H}$. Define $\mathfrak{F}^*(G) = (\mathfrak{F}(G_i G G_j^{-1}))$ for $G \in \mathfrak{G}$, where each pair of indices denotes a submatrix of degree n.

(8.1) <u>If $\mathfrak{F}$ is an $\mathcal{F}$-representation of $\mathfrak{H}$ of degree</u> n <u>then</u> F* <u>is an $\mathcal{F}$-representation of $\mathfrak{G}$ of degree</u> $|\mathfrak{G}:\mathfrak{H}|$ n.

Proof. For $G, H \in \mathfrak{G}$ let $B_{ij} = (\Sigma_s \mathfrak{F}(G_i G G_s^{-1}) \mathfrak{F}(G_s H G_j^{-1}))$. Then $\mathfrak{F}^*(G) \mathfrak{F}^*(H) = (B_{ij})$. Given i there exists a unique t such that $G_iG \in \mathfrak{H}G_t$ or $G_iGG_t^{-1} \in \mathfrak{H}$. Thus $B_{ij} = \mathfrak{F}(G_iGG_t^{-1})$ $\mathfrak{F}(G_tHG_j^{-1})$. $G_iGHG_j^{-1} \in \mathfrak{H}$ if and only if $G_iGG_t^{-1} \in \mathfrak{H}G_jH^{-1}G_t^{-1}$ and this is the case if and only if $G_tHG_j^{-1} \in \mathfrak{H}$. Thus $B_{ij} = 0$ if $G_iGHG_j^{-1} \notin \mathfrak{H}$ and

$$B_{ij} = \mathfrak{F}(G_iGG_t^{-1})\,\mathfrak{F}(G_tHG_j^{-1}) = \mathfrak{F}(G_iGHG_j^{-1})$$

if $G_iGHG_j^{-1} \in \mathfrak{H}$. Hence $\mathfrak{F}^*(G)\,\mathfrak{F}^*(H) = \mathfrak{F}^*(GH)$. $\mathfrak{F}^*(1) = I$ and thus $\mathfrak{F}^*(G)$ is nonsingular for $G \in \mathfrak{G}$.

The representation $\mathfrak{F}^*$ defined above is said to be induced by $\mathfrak{F}$.

An $\mathfrak{F}$-representation $\mathfrak{F}$ of $\mathfrak{G}$ is monomial if there exists a permutation $\mathfrak{F}$-representation $\mathfrak{F}_0$ of $\mathfrak{G}$ such that the underlying vector space $\mathfrak{V}$ of $\mathfrak{F}$ has a basis $\{v_i\}$ with the property that $v_i\mathfrak{F}(G) = \lambda_i(G)\, v_i\mathfrak{F}_0(G)$ for $G \in \mathfrak{G}$, where $\lambda_i(G) \in \mathfrak{F}$. $\mathfrak{F}_0$ is called the associated permutation representation of $\mathfrak{F}$. If $\mathfrak{F}_0$ is transitive then $\mathfrak{F}$ is transitive.

A character of $\mathfrak{G}$ is a monomial character or a permutation character if it is afforded by a monomial representation or a permutation representation respectively.

(8.2) The tensor product of monomial $\mathfrak{F}$-representations or permutation $\mathfrak{F}$-representations of $\mathfrak{G}$ is a monomial $\mathfrak{F}$-representation or a permutation $\mathfrak{F}$-representation respectively.

Proof. This follows directly from the definition.

(8.3) Let $\mathfrak{H}$ be a subgroup of $\mathfrak{G}$. Let $\mathfrak{F}$ be a representation of $\mathfrak{H}$ of degree 1 and let $\mathfrak{F}_0$ be the unit representation of $\mathfrak{H}$. Then $\mathfrak{F}^*$ is a transitive monomial representation of $\mathfrak{G}$ and $\mathfrak{F}_0^*$ is its associated permutation representation. Conversely if $\mathfrak{A}$ is a transitive monomial representation of

$\mathfrak{G}$ with associated permutation representation $\mathfrak{A}_0$ and if $\mathfrak{H}$ is a subgroup of $\mathfrak{G}$ consisting of all elements G such that $\mathfrak{A}_0(G)$ leaves a given object fixed then $\mathfrak{A}$ is similar to $\mathfrak{F}^*$ and $\mathfrak{A}_0 = \mathfrak{F}_0^*$, where $\mathfrak{F}$ is a representation of degree 1 of $\mathfrak{H}$ and $\mathfrak{F}_0$ is the unit representation of $\mathfrak{H}$.

Proof. Let $\mathfrak{H} = \mathfrak{H}G_1, \ldots, \mathfrak{H}G_m$ be all the right cosets of $\mathfrak{H}$ in $\mathfrak{G}$. Let $\mathfrak{V}$ be a vector space with basis $v_1, \ldots, v_m$. The definition of $\mathfrak{F}^*$ implies that $v_i\mathfrak{F}^*(G) = \mathfrak{F}(G_iGG_t^{-1})v_t$, where $G_iGG_t^{-1} \in \mathfrak{H}$. This proves the first statement and also shows that $\mathfrak{A}_0 = \mathfrak{F}_0^*$. Let $\mathfrak{A}(G) = (a_{ij}(G))$ for $G \in \mathfrak{G}$. Since $\mathfrak{A}_0$ is the associated permutation representation we see that $a_{ij}(G) = 0$ if $G_iGG_j^{-1} \notin \mathfrak{H}$. Let $G_1 = 1$. Let $a_{1i}(G_i) = c_i$, let $\mathfrak{B}(G) = (c_i\delta_{ij})\mathfrak{A}(G)(c_i^{-1}\delta_{ij})$ and let $\mathfrak{B}(G) = (b_{ij}(G))$. Then $b_{1i}(G_i) = 1 = b_{i1}(G_i^{-1})$. Thus if $G_iGG_j^{-1} \in \mathfrak{H}$ then

$$b_{ij}(G) = b_{i1}(G_i^{-1})\,b_{11}(G_iGG_j^{-1})\,b_{1j}(G_j) = b_{11}(G_iGG_j^{-1})$$

Since $\mathfrak{B}$ is a representation of $\mathfrak{G}$ it follows that $\mathfrak{F} = b_{11}$ is a representation of $\mathfrak{H}$ of degree 1. Thus $\mathfrak{B} = \mathfrak{F}^*$ as required.

It is not true in (8.3) that $\mathfrak{A} = \mathfrak{F}^*$ for some representation of degree 1 of $\mathfrak{H}$. For example let $\mathfrak{G} = \langle G\rangle$ be the group of order 2. Let $\mathfrak{A}(G) = \begin{pmatrix} 0 & -1 \\ -1 & 0 \end{pmatrix}$. Then $\mathfrak{A} \neq \mathfrak{F}_0^*$ in any field of characteristic $\neq 2$ and $\mathfrak{F}_0$ is the unique representation of degree 1 of $\mathfrak{H} = \langle 1\rangle$.

## §9. INDUCED CHARACTERS

Let $\mathfrak{H}$ be a subgroup of $\mathfrak{G}$ and let $\theta$ be a complex valued class function on $\mathfrak{H}$. Define $\theta(G) = 0$ for $G \in \mathfrak{G} - \mathfrak{H}$ and

$$\theta^*(G) = \frac{1}{|\mathfrak{H}|}\sum_{\mathfrak{G}} \theta(HGH^{-1})$$

for $G \in \mathfrak{G}$. The function $\theta^*$ is said to be induced by $\theta$. Clearly $\theta^*$ is a complex valued class function on $\mathfrak{G}$ and $(\theta_1 + \theta_2)^* = \theta_1{}^* + \theta_2{}^*$.

(9.1) Let $\mathfrak{H}$ be a subgroup of $\mathfrak{G}$ and let $\theta$ be the character afforded by the representation $\mathfrak{F}$ of $\mathfrak{H}$. Then $\theta^*$ is the character afforded by $\mathfrak{F}^*$. Any two representations induced by $\mathfrak{F}$ are similar.

Proof. Let $\eta$ be the character afforded by $\mathfrak{F}^*$. By definition $\eta(G) = \Sigma_i(G_iGG_i^{-1})$, where $\{G_i\}$ is a complete system of right coset representations of $\mathfrak{H}$ in $\mathfrak{G}$. Since $\theta$ is a class function on $\mathfrak{H}$, $\theta(HG_iGG_i^{-1}H^{-1}) = \theta(G_iGG_i^{-1})$ for $H \in \mathfrak{H}$. Thus

$$|\mathfrak{H}|\eta(G) = \sum_{H \in \mathfrak{H}} \sum_i \theta(HG_iGG_i^{-1}H^{-1})$$

$$= \sum_{M \in \mathfrak{G}} \theta(MGM^{-1})$$

$$= |\mathfrak{H}|\,\theta^*(G)$$

The last statement now follows from (2.6).

An important consequence of (9.1) is the fact that the class function induced by a character of a subgroup is again a character. This is probably the most important method for constructing characters of groups.

Frequently we will be considering various subgroups of a given group $\mathfrak{G}$. In such situations $\theta^*$ will always denote the class function of $\mathfrak{G}$ induced by the class function $\theta$ on any subgroup of $\mathfrak{G}$.

(9.2) Let $\mathfrak{H} \subseteq \mathfrak{K} \subseteq \mathfrak{G}$ where $\mathfrak{H}$ and $\mathfrak{K}$ are subgroups of $\mathfrak{G}$. Let $\theta$ be a complex valued class function on $\mathfrak{H}$ and let $\tilde{\theta}$ be the class function of $\mathfrak{K}$ induced by $\theta$. Then $\theta^* = \tilde{\theta}^*$.

Proof. Let $\theta(G) = 0$ for $G \in \mathfrak{G} - \mathfrak{H}$. For $M \in \mathfrak{K}$ $\tilde{\theta}(M) =$

$(1/|\mathfrak{H}|)\Sigma_{\mathfrak{L}}\,\theta(LML^{-1})$. Let $\tilde{\theta}(G) = 0$ for $G \in \mathfrak{G} - \mathfrak{L}$. Therefore $\tilde{\theta}(M) = (1/|\mathfrak{H}|)\Sigma_{\mathfrak{G}}\,\theta(LML^{-1})$ for $M \in \mathfrak{G}$. Hence by definition

$$\tilde{\theta}^{*}(M) = \frac{1}{|\mathfrak{L}|}\frac{1}{|\mathfrak{H}|}\sum_{G \in \mathfrak{G}}\sum_{L \in \mathfrak{L}} \theta(GLML^{-1}G^{-1})$$

$$= \frac{1}{|\mathfrak{H}|}\sum_{\mathfrak{G}} \theta(GMG^{-1}) = \theta^{*}(M)$$

for $M \in \mathfrak{G}$.

If $\mathfrak{H}$ is a subgroup of $\mathfrak{G}$ and $\theta$ is a complex valued class function on $\mathfrak{G}$ then the restriction of $\theta$ to $\mathfrak{H}$, denoted by $\theta_{|\mathfrak{H}}$, is clearly a complex valued class function of $\mathfrak{H}$.

(9.3) Let $\mathfrak{H}$ be a subgroup of $\mathfrak{G}$. Let $\theta, \eta$ be complex valued class functions of $\mathfrak{H}, \mathfrak{G}$ respectively. Then $\theta^{*}\eta = (\theta\eta_{|\mathfrak{H}})^{*}$

Proof. Let $\theta(G) = 0$ for $G \in \mathfrak{G} - \mathfrak{H}$. For $M \in \mathfrak{G}$

$$(\theta\eta_{|\mathfrak{H}})^{*}(M) = \frac{1}{|\mathfrak{H}|}\sum_{\mathfrak{G}} \theta(GMG^{-1})\,\eta(GMG^{-1})$$

$$= \eta(M)\frac{1}{|\mathfrak{H}|}\sum_{\mathfrak{G}} \theta(GMG^{-1})$$

$$= \eta\theta^{*}(M)$$

(9.4) (Frobenius reciprocity theorem) Let $\mathfrak{H}$ be a subgroup of $\mathfrak{G}$. Let $\theta, \eta$ be complex valued class functions of $\mathfrak{H}, \mathfrak{G}$ respectively. Then

$$(\eta, \theta^{*})_{\mathfrak{G}} = (\eta_{|\mathfrak{H}}, \theta)_{\mathfrak{H}}$$

Proof. By definition

$$(\eta,\theta^*)_{\mathfrak{G}} = \frac{1}{|\mathfrak{G}|}\frac{1}{|\mathfrak{H}|}\sum_{G,H\in\mathfrak{G}} \overline{\eta(G)}\,\theta(HGH^{-1})$$

$$= \frac{1}{|\mathfrak{G}|}\frac{1}{|\mathfrak{H}|}\sum_{G,H\in\mathfrak{G}} \overline{\eta(HGH^{-1})}\,\theta(HGH^{-1})$$

$$= \frac{1}{|\mathfrak{G}|}\frac{1}{|\mathfrak{H}|}\sum_{G,H\in\mathfrak{G}} \overline{\eta(G)}\,\theta(G)$$

$$= \frac{1}{|\mathfrak{H}|}\sum_{\mathfrak{G}} \overline{\eta(G)}\,\theta(G)$$

Since $\theta(G) = 0$ for $G \in \mathfrak{G} - \mathfrak{H}$ this implies that

$$(\eta,\theta^*)_{\mathfrak{G}} = \frac{1}{|\mathfrak{H}|}\sum_{\mathfrak{H}} \overline{\eta(G)}\,\theta(G) = (\eta_{|\mathfrak{H}},\theta)_{\mathfrak{H}}$$

(9.5) Let $\mathfrak{H}$ be a subgroup of $\mathfrak{G}$. Let $\chi_1,\ldots,\chi_k$ be all the irreducible characters of $\mathfrak{G}$ and let $\zeta_1,\ldots,\zeta_m$ be all the irreducible characters of $\mathfrak{H}$. Let $\chi_{i|\mathfrak{H}} = \Sigma_j\, a_{ij}\zeta_j$ and let $\zeta_j^* = \Sigma_i\, b_{ij}\chi_i$. Then $a_{ij} = b_{ij}$ for all i and j.

Proof. By (9.4)

$$a_{ij} = (\chi_{i_{|\mathfrak{H}}},\zeta_j)_{\mathfrak{H}} = (\chi_i,\zeta_j^*)_{\mathfrak{G}} = b_{ij}$$

(9.6) Let $\theta$ be a permutation character afforded by the permutation representation $\mathfrak{F}$ of $\mathfrak{G}$. The number of domains of transitivity of $\mathfrak{F}$ is equal to $(\theta,1_{\mathfrak{G}})_{\mathfrak{G}}$.

Proof. If $\mathfrak{F}$ has m domains of transitivity then by (8.3) $\theta = 1_{\mathfrak{H}_1}^* + \ldots + 1_{\mathfrak{H}_m}^*$, where $\mathfrak{H}_1,\ldots,\mathfrak{H}_m$ are subgroups of $\mathfrak{G}$. By (9.5) $(1_{\mathfrak{H}}^*,1_{\mathfrak{G}})_{\mathfrak{G}} = 1$ for any subgroup $\mathfrak{H}$ of $\mathfrak{G}$. The result follows.

If $\mathfrak{H}$ is a subgroup of $\mathfrak{G}$, $G \in \mathfrak{G}$ and $\theta$ is a complex valued class function on $\mathfrak{H}$ define the complex valued class function $\theta^G$ on $\mathfrak{H}^G$ by $\theta^G(M) = \theta(GMG^{-1})$ for $M \in \mathfrak{H}^G$. Thus $\{\theta^G\}^H = \theta^{GH}$. If $\theta$ is a character of $\mathfrak{H}$ then $\theta^G$ is a character of $\mathfrak{H}^G$.

The following elegant result was discovered by Gallagher [1]. However it is a result that seems to be difficult to apply.

(9.7) The following conditions are equivalent.

(i) If $G_1, G_2, \ldots$ are elements of $\mathfrak{G}$ whose orders are pairwise relatively prime then $\Pi_i G_i = 1$ if and only if $G_i = 1$ for each i.

(ii) If $\chi$ is a nonprincipal irreducible character of $\mathfrak{G}$ then there exists a prime p and a $S_p$-group $\mathfrak{P}$ such that $(\chi_{|\mathfrak{P}}, 1_{\mathfrak{P}}) = 0$.

Proof. Let $p_1, \ldots, p_n$ be the set of all distinct primes dividing $|\mathfrak{G}|$. Let $\mathfrak{P}_i$ be a $S_{p_i}$-group and let $\theta_i = 1^*_{\mathfrak{P}_i} = \Sigma_j c_{ij} \chi_j$, where $\chi_1 = 1_{\mathfrak{G}}, \chi_2, \ldots$ are the irreducible characters of $\mathfrak{G}$. Let

$$s = \frac{1}{|\mathfrak{G}|^{n-1}} \sum_{\substack{G_1, \ldots, G_n \\ G_1 G_2 \ldots G_n = 1}} \theta_1(G_1) \ldots \theta_n(G_n)$$

Observe that $s \geq 1$ and $s = 1$ if and only if $\Pi_i \theta_i(G_i) = 0$ for $(G_1, \ldots, G_n) \neq (1, \ldots, 1)$. Since $\theta_i$ vanishes on $p_i'$-elements it may be assumed that in the definition of s, $G_i$ ranges over the $p_i$-elements of $\mathfrak{G}$. Since $\theta_i(G) > 0$ for any $p_i$-element $G_i$ it follows easily that $s = 1$ if and only if condition (i) is satisfied.

For any n-tuple $(G_1, \ldots, G_n)$ define $H_i = G_1 \ldots G_i$ for $i = 1, \ldots, n-1$. Thus

$$s = \frac{1}{|\mathfrak{G}|^{n-1}} \sum_{H_1, \ldots, H_{n-1}} \theta_1(H_1)\theta_2(H_1^{-1}H_2) \cdots \theta_n(H_{n-1}^{-1})$$

$$= \frac{1}{|\mathfrak{G}|^{n-1}}$$

$$\times \sum_{H_1,\ldots,H_{n-1}} \left\{\sum_{j_1} c_{1j_1}\chi_{j_1}(H_1)\right\} \cdots \left\{\sum_{j_n} c_{nj_n}\chi_{j_n}(H_{n-1}^{-1})\right\}$$

$$= \sum_{j_1,\ldots,j_n} c_{1j_1}\cdots c_{nj_n} \frac{1}{|\mathfrak{G}|^{n-1}}$$

$$\times \sum_{H_1,\ldots,H_{n-1}} \chi_{j_1}(H_1)\cdots\chi_{j_n}(H_{n-1}^{-1})$$

Applying (6.1) $n - 1$ times this yields that

$$s = \sum_j \left(\prod_{i=1}^{n} c_{ij}\right) \frac{1}{\chi_j(1)^{n-2}}$$

$$= \prod_{i=1}^{n} c_{i1} + \sum_{j\neq 1} \left(\prod_{i=1}^{n} c_{ij}\right) \frac{1}{\chi_j(1)^{n-2}}$$

By the Frobenius reciprocity theorem $\Pi_{i=1}^{n} c_{i1} = 1$. Thus $s = 1$ if and only if for $j \neq 1$ there exists $i$ such that $c_{ij} = 0$. In other words $s = 1$ if and only if condition (ii) is satisfied. Thus the statement that $s = 1$ is equivalent to both statements (i) and (ii).

It was first pointed out by P. Hall that condition (i) of (9.7) is satisfied in case $\mathfrak{G}$ is solvable. This can be proved by induction in a straightforward manner. He also conjectured that the converse is true. The proof of this conjecture has recently been given by J. Thompson. However, it is far beyond the scope of these notes.

(9.8) <u>(Mackey) Let $\mathfrak{H}, \mathfrak{L}$ be subgroups of $\mathfrak{G}$. Let $\theta, \eta$ be complex valued class functions on $\mathfrak{H}, \mathfrak{L}$ respectively. Let $\mathfrak{H}G_1\mathfrak{L}; \ldots, \mathfrak{H}G_m\mathfrak{L}$ be all the $(\mathfrak{H}, \mathfrak{L})$ double cosets in $\mathfrak{G}$ and let $\mathfrak{G}_i = \mathfrak{H}^{G_i} \cap \mathfrak{L}$ for $i = 1, \ldots, m$. Then</u>

$$(\theta^*, \eta^*)_{\mathfrak{G}} = \sum_{i=1}^{m} \left( \theta^{G_i}{}_{|\mathfrak{G}_i}, \eta_{|\mathfrak{G}_i} \right)_{\mathfrak{G}_i}$$

<u>Proof.</u> By definition

$$(\theta^*, \eta^*)_{\mathfrak{G}} = \frac{1}{|\mathfrak{H}|}\frac{1}{|\mathfrak{L}|}\frac{1}{|\mathfrak{G}|} \sum_{N \in \mathfrak{G}} \sum_{M, G \in \mathfrak{G}} \theta^M(G)\overline{\eta^N(G)}$$

$$= \frac{1}{|\mathfrak{H}|}\frac{1}{|\mathfrak{L}|}\frac{1}{|\mathfrak{G}|} \sum_{M, N, G \in \mathfrak{G}} \theta^{MN^{-1}}(G)\overline{\eta(G)}$$

If $MN^{-1} = HG_iL$ for $H \in \mathfrak{H}$, $L \in \mathfrak{L}$ then $\theta^{HG_iL} = \theta^{G_iL}$ and

$$\sum_{G \in \mathfrak{G}} \theta^{MN^{-1}}(G)\overline{\eta(G)} = \sum_{G \in \mathfrak{G}} \theta^{G_iL}(G)\overline{\eta(G)}$$

$$= \sum_{G \in \mathfrak{G}} \theta^{G_i}(G)\overline{\eta^{L^{-1}}(G)}$$

$$= \sum_{G \in \mathfrak{G}} \theta^{G_i}(G)\overline{\eta(G)}$$

$$= \sum_{G \in \mathfrak{G}_i} \theta^{G_i}(G)\overline{\eta(G)}$$

Thus

$(\theta^*, \eta^*)$

$$= \frac{1}{|\mathfrak{H}|}\frac{1}{|\mathfrak{L}|}\frac{1}{|G|}\sum_{i=1}^{m}\sum_{M\in\mathfrak{G}}\sum_{\substack{N\in\mathfrak{G}\\ MN^{-1}\in\mathfrak{H}G_i\mathfrak{L}}}\sum_{G\in\mathfrak{G}_i}\theta^{G_i}(G)\overline{\eta(G)}$$

$$= \frac{1}{|\mathfrak{H}|}\frac{1}{|\mathfrak{L}|}\frac{1}{|\mathfrak{G}|}\sum_{i=1}^{m}\sum_{M\in\mathfrak{G}}|\mathfrak{H}G_i\mathfrak{L}|\,|\mathfrak{G}_i|\left(\theta^{G_i}{}_{|\mathfrak{G}_i}, \eta_{|\mathfrak{G}_i}\right)_{\mathfrak{G}_i}$$

$$= \sum_{i=1}^{m}\frac{|\mathfrak{H}G_i\mathfrak{L}|\;|\mathfrak{G}_i|}{|\mathfrak{H}|\;|\mathfrak{L}|}\left(\theta^{G_i}{}_{|\mathfrak{G}_i}, \eta_{|\mathfrak{G}_i}\right)_{\mathfrak{G}_i}$$

The result now follows since $|\mathfrak{H}|\,|\mathfrak{L}| = |\mathfrak{H}G_i\mathfrak{L}|\,|\mathfrak{G}_i|$.

(9.9) Let $\theta$ be the character afforded by a transitive permutation representation $\mathfrak{F}$ of $\mathfrak{G}$. Let $\mathfrak{H}$ be the subgroup of $\mathfrak{G}$ consisting of all elements G such that $\mathfrak{F}(G)$ leaves a given object fixed. Then $||\theta||^2_{\mathfrak{G}}$ is equal to the number of domains of transitivity of $\mathfrak{H}$. Thus in particular $\mathfrak{F}$ is doubly transitive if and only if $||\theta||^2_{\mathfrak{G}} = 2$.

Proof. By (8.3) $\theta = 1^*_{\mathfrak{H}}$. Let $\mathfrak{H} = \mathfrak{L}$ and $\theta = \eta = 1_{\mathfrak{H}}$ in (9.8). Then in the notation of (9.8)

$$||\theta||^2_{\mathfrak{G}} = \sum_{i=1}^{m} ||1_{\mathfrak{G}_i}||^2_{\mathfrak{G}_i} = m$$

Thus $||\theta||^2_{\mathfrak{G}}$ is the number of double cosets of $\mathfrak{H}$ in $\mathfrak{G}$ which implies the result.

Suppose that $\mathfrak{H} \triangleleft \mathfrak{G}$ Let $\theta$ be a complex valued class function on $\mathfrak{H}$. Then $\theta^G$ is also a class function on $\mathfrak{H}$ for $G \in \mathfrak{G}$. Define the inertial group $\mathfrak{J}(\theta)$ of $\theta$ by

$$\mathfrak{J}(\theta) = \{G \mid G \in \mathfrak{G}, \theta^G = \theta\}$$

Clearly $\mathfrak{H} \subseteq \mathfrak{J}(\theta)$ and $\theta^G = \theta^H$ if and only if $GH^{-1} \in \mathfrak{J}(\theta)$.

(9.10) Let $\mathfrak{H} \lhd \mathfrak{G}$ and let $\theta$ be a character of $\mathfrak{H}$. Let $\{G_i\}$ be a complete system of right coset representatives of $\mathfrak{J}(\theta)$ in $\mathfrak{G}$. Then $\theta^*{}_{|\mathfrak{H}} = |\mathfrak{J}(\theta):\mathfrak{H}|\ \Sigma_i\, \theta^{G_i}$. If $\chi$ is an irreducible character of $\mathfrak{G}$ then there exists an irreducible character $\theta$ of $\mathfrak{H}$ and a positive integer $e = e_{\mathfrak{H}}(\chi)$ such that $\chi_{|\mathfrak{H}} = e\ \Sigma_i\, \theta^{G_i}$ where $\{G_i\}$ is a complete system of coset representatives of $\mathfrak{J}(\theta)$ in $\mathfrak{G}$.

Proof. The first statement follows directly from the definition of $\theta^*$. Let $\chi$ be an irreducible character of $\mathfrak{G}$ and let $\theta$ be an irreducible constituent of $\chi_{|\mathfrak{H}}$. Then $\chi \subseteq \theta^*$ by the Frobenius reciprocity theorem. Since $(\chi_{|\mathfrak{H}}, \theta)_{\mathfrak{H}} = (\chi_{|\mathfrak{H}}, \theta^G)_{\mathfrak{H}}$ for $G \in \mathfrak{G}$ $\chi_{|\mathfrak{H}}$ has the required form.

The integer $e_{\mathfrak{H}}(\chi)$ appearing in (9.10) is the index of ramification of $\chi$ with respect to $\mathfrak{H}$.

(9.11) Let $\chi$ be an irreducible character of $\mathfrak{G}$. Let $\mathfrak{H} \lhd \mathfrak{G}$ and let $\theta$ be an irreducible constituent of $\chi_{|\mathfrak{H}}$. Let $\zeta$ be an irreducible constituent of $\chi_{|\mathfrak{J}(\theta)}$ such that $\theta \subseteq \zeta_{|\mathfrak{H}}$. Then $\chi = \zeta^*$ and $e_{\mathfrak{H}}(\chi) = e_{\mathfrak{H}}(\zeta)$.

Proof. By the Frobenius reciprocity theorem $\chi \subseteq \zeta^*$. Hence it suffices to show that $\zeta^*$ is irreducible. Let $\{G_i\}$ be a complete system of right coset representatives of $\mathfrak{J}(\theta)$ in $\mathfrak{G}$. As $\mathfrak{H} \lhd \mathfrak{G}$, $\mathfrak{H} \subseteq \mathfrak{J}(\theta) \cap \mathfrak{J}(\theta)^{G_i}$. As $\zeta_{|\mathfrak{H}} = e_{\mathfrak{H}}(\zeta)\, \theta$,

$\zeta^{G_i}_{|\mathfrak{H}} = e_{\mathfrak{H}}(\zeta)\,\theta^{G_i}$ and $(\theta, \theta^{G_i})_{\mathfrak{H}} = 0$ for $G_i \notin \mathfrak{Z}(\theta)$ we see that $(\zeta^{G_i}_{|\mathfrak{G}_i}, \zeta_{|\mathfrak{G}_i})_{\mathfrak{G}_i} = 0$ for $G_i \notin \mathfrak{Z}(\theta)$, where $\mathfrak{G}_i = \mathfrak{Z}(\theta) \cap \mathfrak{Z}(\theta)^{G_i}$. Thus by (9.8)

$$||\zeta^*||^2_{\mathfrak{G}} = ||\zeta||^2_{\mathfrak{Z}(\theta)} = 1$$

which shows that $\zeta^*$ is irreducible. Furthermore

$$\chi_{|\mathfrak{H}} = \zeta^*_{|\mathfrak{H}} = e_{\mathfrak{H}}(\zeta) \sum_i \theta^{G_i}$$

which implies that $e_{\mathfrak{H}}(\zeta) = e_{\mathfrak{H}}(\chi)$.

(9.12) Let $\chi$ be an irreducible character of $\mathfrak{G}$. Let $\mathfrak{H} \triangleleft \mathfrak{G}$ and let $\theta$ be an irreducible constituent of $\chi_{|\mathfrak{H}}$. If $\mathfrak{Z}(\theta)/\mathfrak{H}$ is cyclic then $e_{\mathfrak{H}}(\chi) = 1$. If $\mathfrak{Z}(\theta)/\mathfrak{H}$ is solvable then

$$e_{\mathfrak{H}}(\chi) \mid |\mathfrak{Z}(\theta) : \mathfrak{H}|$$

Proof. Assume that $\mathfrak{Z}(\theta)/\mathfrak{H} = \langle G\mathfrak{H}\rangle$ is cyclic. In showing that $e = e_{\mathfrak{H}}(\chi) = 1$ it may be assumed by (9.11) that $\mathfrak{G} = \mathfrak{Z}(\theta)$. Let $\mathfrak{F}$ be a complex representation of $\mathfrak{H}$ which affords the character $\theta$. Define $\mathfrak{F}^G(H) = \mathfrak{F}(GHG^{-1})$. Since $\theta^G = \theta$ there exists a matrix C such that $C^i\mathfrak{F}(H)C^{-i} = \mathfrak{F}^{G^i}(H)$ for $H \in \mathfrak{H}$. Thus if $n = |\mathfrak{G}:\mathfrak{H}|$, $C^{-n}\mathfrak{F}(G^n)$ is a scalar matrix by Schur's lemma. Hence there exists a scalar matrix S so that $S^n = C^{-n}\mathfrak{F}(G^n)$. Define $\mathfrak{F}(G^iH) = S^iC^i\mathfrak{F}(H)$ for $H \in \mathfrak{H}$, $i = 0, \ldots, n-1$. Thus $\mathfrak{F}(G^iH) = S^iC^i\mathfrak{F}(H)$ for all i, $H \in \mathfrak{H}$ and if $H_1, H_2 \in \mathfrak{H}$ then

$$\mathfrak{F}(G^i H_1)\, \mathfrak{F}(G^j H_2) = S^i C^i\, \mathfrak{F}(H_1)\, S^j C^j\, \mathfrak{F}(H_2)$$

$$= S^{i+j} C^{i+j}\, \mathfrak{F}(G^{-j} H_1\, G^j)\, \mathfrak{F}(H_2)$$

$$= S^{i+j} C^{i+j}\, \mathfrak{F}(G^{-j} H_1\, G^j H_2)$$

$$= \mathfrak{F}(G^i H_1 G^j H_2)$$

Thus $\mathfrak{F}$ is in this way extended to a representation of $\mathfrak{G}$. Let $\chi_1$ be the character afforded by this representation. Then $\theta^* = \chi_1 \rho_{\mathfrak{G}/\mathfrak{H}}$. Since $\mathfrak{G}/\mathfrak{H}$ is cyclic $\rho_{\mathfrak{G}/\mathfrak{H}} = \Sigma_i \lambda_i$, where $\lambda_i$ ranges over all the distinct linear characters of $\mathfrak{G}/\mathfrak{H}$. Thus $\theta^* = \Sigma_i \chi_1 \lambda_i$. As $\lambda_i$ is linear $\chi_1 \lambda_i$ is irreducible and $\chi_1 \lambda_i(1) = \chi_1(1) = \theta(1)$. Since $\chi$ is an irreducible constituent of $\theta^*$, $\chi = \chi_1 \lambda_i$ for some i. Thus $\chi(1) = \theta(1)$ and so $e_{\mathfrak{H}}(\chi) = 1$.

Suppose now that $\Im(\theta)/\mathfrak{H}$ is solvable. It remains to show that $e_{\mathfrak{H}}(\chi) \mid |\Im(\theta):\mathfrak{H}|$. The proof is by induction on $|\mathfrak{G}:\mathfrak{H}|$. It may be assumed by (9.11) that $\mathfrak{G} = \Im(\theta)$. Thus $\chi_{|\mathfrak{H}} = e\theta$ where $e = e_{\mathfrak{H}}(\chi)$. If $\mathfrak{G} = \mathfrak{H}$ the result is trivial. Suppose that $\mathfrak{G} \neq \mathfrak{H}$. Since $\mathfrak{G}/\mathfrak{H}$ is solvable there exists $\mathfrak{G}_1 \lhd \mathfrak{G}$ such that $|\mathfrak{G}:\mathfrak{G}_1| = p$ is a prime. The first part of the theorem implies that $\chi_{|\mathfrak{G}_1} = \Sigma_{i=1}^n \zeta_i$, where n = 1 or p and $\zeta_1, \ldots, \zeta_n$ are distinct irreducible characters of $\mathfrak{G}_1$ with $e_{\mathfrak{H}}(\zeta_i) = e_{\mathfrak{H}}(\zeta_j)$. By induction $e_{\mathfrak{H}}(\zeta_i) \mid |\mathfrak{G}_1:\mathfrak{H}|$. Since $e_{\mathfrak{H}}(\chi) = n e_{\mathfrak{H}}(\zeta_1)$ and $n|p$ this implies that $e_{\mathfrak{H}}(\chi)|p e_{\mathfrak{H}}(\zeta_1)$ and so $e_{\mathfrak{H}}(\chi) \mid |\mathfrak{G}:\mathfrak{H}|$ as required.

It can be shown that if $\mathfrak{H} \lhd \mathfrak{G}$, $\chi$ is an irreducible character of $\mathfrak{G}$ and $\theta$ is an irreducible constituent of $\chi_{|\mathfrak{H}}$ then in general $e_{\mathfrak{H}}(\chi) \mid |\mathfrak{Z}(\theta):\mathfrak{H}|$. However a proof of this result involves the theory of projective representations. See Curtis and Reiner p. 364. We will content ourselves with another special case.

(9.13) (Ito [1]) Let $\chi$ be an irreducible character of $\mathfrak{G}$. Let $\mathfrak{H} \triangleleft \mathfrak{G}$ and let $\theta$ be an irreducible constituent of $\chi_{|\mathfrak{H}}$. Assume that $\mathfrak{H}$ is abelian. Then $e_{\mathfrak{H}}(\chi) \mid |\mathfrak{Z}(\theta):\mathfrak{H}|$. Thus in particular $\chi(1) \mid |\mathfrak{G}:\mathfrak{H}|$.

Proof. By (9.11) it may be assumed that $\mathfrak{Z}(\theta) = \mathfrak{G}$ and $\chi$ is faithful. Thus $\chi_{|\mathfrak{H}} = e\theta$, where $e = e_{\mathfrak{H}}(\chi)$ and $\theta$ is a faithful character of $\mathfrak{H}$. Since $\mathfrak{H}$ is abelian $\theta(1) = 1$ and so $\mathfrak{H}$ is cyclic. As $\theta^G = \theta$ for $G \in \mathfrak{G}$ it follows that $\mathfrak{H} \subseteq \mathbf{Z}(\mathfrak{G})$. Thus $|\mathfrak{G}:\mathbf{Z}(\mathfrak{G})| \mid |\mathfrak{G}:\mathfrak{H}|$. Hence by (4.2) $\chi(1) \mid |\mathfrak{G}:\mathfrak{H}|$. The result follows since $\chi(1) = e\theta(1) = e$.

There is no known general criterion which ensures that $e_{\mathfrak{H}}(\chi) = 1$. The next result gives a sufficient condition for this to happen and is a slight generalization of part of Lemma 4.5 in Feit-Thompson [2].

We will here and elsewhere make use of the following theorem due to Schur and Zassenhaus. See for instance Scott p. 224 and p. 227 or Zassenhaus p. 162.

If $\mathfrak{H} \triangleleft \mathfrak{G}$ and $\mathfrak{H}$ is an S-subgroup of $\mathfrak{G}$ then there exists a subgroup $\mathfrak{L}$ of $\mathfrak{G}$ such that $\mathfrak{H}\mathfrak{L} = \mathfrak{G}$ and $\mathfrak{H} \cap \mathfrak{L} = 1$. If furthermore either $\mathfrak{H}$ or $\mathfrak{G}/\mathfrak{H}$ is solvable and $\mathfrak{L}_1$ is another subgroup of $\mathfrak{G}$ such that $\mathfrak{H}\mathfrak{L}_1 = \mathfrak{G}$ and $\mathfrak{H} \cap \mathfrak{L}_1 = 1$ then $\mathfrak{L}$ is conjugate to $\mathfrak{L}_1$ in $\mathfrak{G}$.

The group $\mathfrak{L}$ in the theorem above is said to be a complement of $\mathfrak{H}$ in $\mathfrak{G}$. It is clear that $\mathfrak{L}$ is isomorphic to $\mathfrak{G}/\mathfrak{H}$.

(9.14) Assume that $\mathfrak{H} \triangleleft \mathfrak{G}$. Let $\theta$ be an irreducible character of $\mathfrak{H}$. Assume that $\mathfrak{H}$ is a S-subgroup of $\mathfrak{Z}(\theta)$ and $\mathfrak{Z}(\theta)/\mathfrak{H}$ is abelian. Let $\tilde{\theta}$ be the character of $\mathfrak{Z}(\theta)$ induced by $\theta$. Then there exists an irreducible character $\zeta$ of $\mathfrak{Z}(\theta)$ such that $\zeta_{|\mathfrak{H}} = \theta$. Furthermore $\tilde{\theta} = \Sigma\, \zeta\lambda_i$ where $\lambda_i$ ranges over the irreducible characters of $\mathfrak{Z}(\theta)/\mathfrak{H}$, each $\zeta\lambda_i$ is irreducible and $\zeta\lambda_i = \zeta\lambda_j$ if and only if $i = j$. If furthermore $\chi$ is an irreducible constituent of $\theta^*$ then $\chi_{|\mathfrak{H}} = \Sigma_j \theta^{G_j}$ where $\{G_j\}$ is a complete system of coset representatives of $\mathfrak{Z}(\theta)$ in $\mathfrak{G}$.

Proof. By the Schur Zassenhaus theorem there exists an abelian complement $\mathfrak{A}$ of $\mathfrak{H}$ in $\mathfrak{Z}(\theta)$. Let $\mathfrak{L}$ be a maximal subgroup of $\mathfrak{Z}(\theta)$ such that $\mathfrak{L}$ has a character $\zeta$ with $\zeta_{|\mathfrak{H}} = \theta$. If $\mathfrak{L} \neq \mathfrak{Z}(\theta)$ then there exists $\mathfrak{L}_1 \subseteq \mathfrak{Z}(\theta)$ such that $|\mathfrak{L}_1 : \mathfrak{L}| = p$ is a prime and $\mathfrak{L} \lhd \mathfrak{L}_1$ since $\mathfrak{Z}(\theta)/\mathfrak{H}$ is abelian. Let $\mathfrak{B} = \mathfrak{L} \cap \mathfrak{A}$, $\mathfrak{B}_1 = \mathfrak{L}_1 \cap \mathfrak{A}$. Let $\hat{\theta}$ be the character of $\mathfrak{L}$ induced by $\theta$. Then $\hat{\theta} = \zeta\rho_{\mathfrak{L}/\mathfrak{H}}$. Thus $\hat{\theta} = \Sigma_i \zeta\lambda_i$, where $\lambda_i$ ranges over the irreducible characters of $\mathfrak{L}/\mathfrak{H}$. If $B \in \mathfrak{B}_1$ then $\hat{\theta}^B = \theta$. Thus $\zeta^B = \zeta\lambda_i$ for some i. Let q be a prime, $q \mid |\mathfrak{B}:\mathfrak{H}|$ and let Q be a q-element, $Q \in \mathfrak{B}$. Since $\zeta(1) = \theta(1)$ and $\theta(1) \mid |\mathfrak{H}|$ we get that $\zeta(1) \not\equiv 0 \pmod{q}$ as $\mathfrak{H}$ is a S-subgroup of $\mathfrak{Z}(\theta)$. Thus by (6.4) $\zeta(Q) \neq 0$. Since $\mathfrak{B}_1$ is abelian

$$\zeta(Q) = \zeta^B(Q) = \zeta(Q)\lambda_i(Q)$$

Therefore $\lambda_i(Q) = 1$. Thus the kernel of $\lambda_{i|\mathfrak{B}}$ contains every element of prime power order and so $\mathfrak{B}$ is in the kernel of $\lambda_i$. Thus $\zeta^B = \zeta$. Since $\mathfrak{L}_1/\mathfrak{L}$ is cyclic it now follows from (9.12) that there exists a character $\zeta_1$ of $\mathfrak{L}_1$ such that $\zeta_{1|\mathfrak{L}} = \zeta$ and so $\zeta_{1|\mathfrak{H}} = \theta$ contrary to the maximality of $\mathfrak{L}$. We have shown the existence of a character $\zeta$ of $\mathfrak{Z}(\theta)$ such that $\zeta_{|\mathfrak{H}} = \theta$. Therefore $\tilde{\theta} = \zeta\rho_{\mathfrak{Z}(\theta)/\mathfrak{H}} = \Sigma\, \zeta\lambda_i$, where $\lambda_i$ ranges over the irreducible characters of $\mathfrak{Z}(\theta)/\mathfrak{H}$. Each $\zeta\lambda_i$ is irreducible as $\lambda_i$ is linear. By the Frobenius reciprocity theorem

$$(\tilde{\theta}, \zeta\lambda_i)_{\mathfrak{J}(\theta)} = (\theta, \zeta\lambda_{i|\mathfrak{H}})_{\mathfrak{H}} = ||\theta||^2_{\mathfrak{H}} = 1$$

Thus $\zeta\lambda_i \neq \zeta\lambda_j$ if $i \neq j$.

If $\chi$ is an irreducible constituent of $\theta^* = \Sigma_i (\zeta\lambda_i)^*$ then $\chi$ is an irreducible constituent of some $(\zeta\lambda_i)^*$. Since $(\zeta\lambda_i)^*_{|\mathfrak{H}} = \Sigma_j \theta^{G_j}$, where $\{G_j\}$ is a complete system of coset representatives of $\mathfrak{J}(\theta)$ in $\mathfrak{G}$ the result follows.

## §10. M-GROUPS

An M-group is a group $\mathfrak{G}$ all of whose irreducible characters are monomial. A complete classification of M-groups has not been given. However there exist large classes of groups which are M-groups. First a result which restricts the nature of M-groups.

(10.1) (Taketa) Every M-group is solvable.

Proof. Let $\mathfrak{G}^{(0)} = \mathfrak{G}$ and $\mathfrak{G}^{(i+1)} = [\mathfrak{G}^{(i)}, \mathfrak{G}^{(i)}]$. Let $\mathfrak{G}$ be an M-group. If $\mathfrak{G}$ is not solvable then $\mathfrak{G}^{(i)} = \mathfrak{G}^{(i+1)} \neq \langle 1 \rangle$, for some i. Let $\chi$ be an irreducible character of $\mathfrak{G}$ of minimum degree which does not contain $\mathfrak{G}^{(i)}$ in its kernel. By assumption $\chi = \lambda^*$ where $\lambda$ is a linear character of some subgroup $\mathfrak{H}$ of $\mathfrak{G}$. Let $\mu = 1_{\mathfrak{H}}$. By the Frobenius reciprocity theorem $1_{\mathfrak{G}} \subseteq \mu^*$. Thus if $\zeta$ is an irreducible constituent of $\mu^*$ then $\zeta(1) < \chi(1)$ and so $\mathfrak{G}^{(i)}$ is in the kernel of $\zeta$. Hence $\mathfrak{G}^{(i)}$ is in the kernel of $\mu$. This implies that $\mathfrak{G}^{(i)} \subseteq \mathfrak{H}$. Consequently $\mathfrak{G}^{(i)} = \mathfrak{G}^{(i+1)} \subset \mathfrak{H}'$ and thus $\mathfrak{G}^{(i)}$ is in the kernel of $\lambda$. Since $\mathfrak{G}^{(i)} \triangleleft \mathfrak{G}$ this yields that $\mathfrak{G}^{(i)}$ is in the kernel of $\lambda^* = \chi$ contrary to hypothesis.

The following result is essentially due to Blichfeldt. The proof is due to Brauer.

(10.2) Assume that $\mathfrak{H} \lhd \mathfrak{G}$, $\mathfrak{H}$ is abelian and $\mathfrak{G}/\mathfrak{H}$ is a p-group for some prime p. Then $\mathfrak{G}$ is an M-group.

Proof. The proof is by induction on $|\mathfrak{G}|$. Let $\chi$ be an irreducible character of $\mathfrak{G}$. If $\chi(1) = 1$ then $\chi$ is monomial. Suppose that $\chi(1) > 1$. Let $\mathfrak{L} = \{\lambda_j\}$ be the group of all linear characters of $\mathfrak{G}$ such that $\chi\lambda_j = \chi$. By (6.6) $\chi\overline{\chi} = \Sigma_{\mathfrak{L}}\lambda_j + \theta$, where $\theta$ is a sum of nonlinear irreducible characters of $\mathfrak{G}$. By (9.13) the degree of every irreducible character of $\mathfrak{G}$ is a power of p. Since $\chi\overline{\chi}(1) = |\mathfrak{L}| + \theta(1)$ this implies that $p \mid |\mathfrak{L}|$. Hence there exists $\lambda \in \mathfrak{L}^{\#}$ such that $\lambda^p = 1_{\mathfrak{G}}$. Let $\mathfrak{G}_0$ be the kernel of $\lambda$. Thus $|\mathfrak{G}:\mathfrak{G}_0| = p$ and $(\chi\overline{\chi}_{|\mathfrak{G}_0}, 1_{\mathfrak{G}_0}) \geq 2$. Hence $\chi_{|\mathfrak{G}_0}$ is reducible. Let $\zeta$ be an irreducible constituent of $\chi_{|\mathfrak{G}_0}$. Then $\zeta(1) < \chi(1)$ and so $p\zeta(1) \leq \chi(1)$ since $\zeta(1)$ and $\chi(1)$ are powers of p. By the Frobenius reciprocity theorem $\chi \subset \zeta^*$ and so $\chi(1) \leq \zeta^*(1) = p\zeta(1)$. Consequently $\chi(1) = p\zeta(1)$ and therefore $\chi = \zeta^*$. By induction $\zeta$ is monomial and so $\chi$ is monomial.

(10.3) The direct product of M-groups is an M-group. Every nilpotent group is an M-group.

Proof. Let $\mathfrak{G} = \mathfrak{H}_1 \times \ldots \times \mathfrak{H}_n$ where each $\mathfrak{H}_i$ is an M-group. Let $\chi$ be an irreducible character of $\mathfrak{G}$. By (6.3) $\chi = \chi_1 \cdots \chi_n$, where $\chi_i$ is an irreducible character of $\mathfrak{H}_i$ for $i = 1, \ldots, n$. By assumption each $\chi_i$ is monomial. The first statement follows from (8.2). The second statement follows from the first and (10.2).

For generalizations of (10.2) and (10.3) see references in Curtis and Reiner p. 357.

# CHAPTER II

## §11. THE SCHUR INDEX

(11.1) Let $\mathcal{F}$ be a field of characteristic 0 and let $\mathcal{K}$ be a finite extension field of $\mathcal{F}$. If $\theta$ is a character of $\mathfrak{G}$ which is afforded by a $\mathcal{K}$-representation $\mathfrak{F}$ of $\mathfrak{G}$ then $Tr_{\mathcal{K}/\mathcal{F}}(\theta)$ is a character of $\mathfrak{G}$ which is afforded by an $\mathcal{F}$-representation of $\mathfrak{G}$.

Proof. Let $\mathfrak{F}(G) = (a_{ij}(G))$ for $G \in \mathfrak{G}$. Let $\mathfrak{R}$ be the regular representation of $\mathcal{K}$ over $\mathcal{F}$. Define $\mathfrak{A}(G) = (\mathfrak{R}(a_{ij}(G)))$ for $G \in \mathfrak{G}$, where each $\mathfrak{R}(a_{ij}(G))$ is a submatrix of degree $[\mathcal{K}:\mathcal{F}]$. Then $\mathfrak{A}$ is an $\mathcal{F}$-representation of $\mathfrak{G}$ and $Tr_{\mathcal{K}/\mathcal{F}}(\theta)$ is the character afforded by $\mathfrak{A}$.

(11.2) Let $\chi$ be an irreducible character of $\mathfrak{G}$ and let $\mathcal{F}$ be a field of characteristic 0. Then there exists a positive integer m such that $m\chi$ is afforded by an $\mathcal{F}(\chi)$-representation of $\mathfrak{G}$.

Proof. By (1.11) there exists a finite extension field $\mathcal{K}$ of $\mathcal{F}(\chi)$ which is a splitting field of $\chi$. Since $Tr_{\mathcal{K}/\mathcal{F}(\chi)}(\chi) = [\mathcal{K}:\mathcal{F}]\chi$ the result follows from (11.1).

Let $\chi$ be an irreducible character of $\mathfrak{G}$ and let $\mathcal{F}$ be a field of characteristic 0. The Schur index $m_{\mathcal{F}}(\chi)$ is defined to be the smallest positive integer such that $m_{\mathcal{F}}(\chi)\chi$ is the character afforded by an $\mathcal{F}(\chi)$-representation of $\mathfrak{G}$.

(11.3) Let $\chi$ be an irreducible character of $\mathfrak{G}$ and let $\mathcal{F}$ be a field of characteristic 0.

(i) *If* $m\chi$ *is the character afforded by some* $\mathfrak{F}(\chi)$*-representation of* $\mathfrak{G}$ *then* $m_{\mathfrak{F}}(\chi) \mid m$.

(ii) *If* $\mathfrak{K}$ *is a finite extension field of* $\mathfrak{F}$ *which is a splitting field of* $\chi$ *then* $m_{\mathfrak{F}}(\chi) \mid [\mathfrak{K}:\mathfrak{F}(\chi)]$.

*Proof*. (i) It may be assumed that $m\chi$ is afforded by an $\mathfrak{F}(\chi)$-irreducible $\mathfrak{F}(\chi)$-representation $\mathfrak{F}$ of $\mathfrak{G}$. The minimality of $m_{\mathfrak{F}}(\chi)$ implies that $m_{\mathfrak{F}}(\chi)\chi$ is afforded by an $\mathfrak{F}(\chi)$-irreducible $\mathfrak{F}(\chi)$-representation $\mathfrak{A}$ of $\mathfrak{G}$. By (1.9) and (2.9) $\mathfrak{A}$ and $\mathfrak{F}$ are similar. Thus $m = m_{\mathfrak{F}}(\chi)$.

(ii) By (11.1) $[\mathfrak{K}:\mathfrak{F}(\chi)]\chi$ is afforded by an $\mathfrak{F}(\chi)$-representation of $\mathfrak{G}$. The result follows from (i).

It can be shown by using the theory of algebras that an irreducible character $\chi$ always has a splitting field $\mathfrak{K}$ such that $m_{\mathfrak{F}}(\chi) = [\mathfrak{K}:\mathfrak{F}(\chi)]$. See Curtis and Reiner § 70.

(11.4) *Let* $\mathfrak{F}$ *be a field of characteristic* 0. *Let* $\theta$ *be the character afforded by some* $\mathfrak{F}$*-irreducible* $\mathfrak{F}$*-representation of* $\mathfrak{G}$. *Then there exists an irreducible character* $\chi$ *of* $\mathfrak{G}$ *such that* $\theta = m_{\mathfrak{F}}(\chi) \Sigma \chi^{\sigma}$ *where* $\sigma$ *ranges over* $\mathcal{G}_{\mathfrak{F}(\chi)/\mathfrak{F}}$ *and* $\theta$ *is the unique character afforded by an* $\mathfrak{F}$*-irreducible* $\mathfrak{F}$*-representation of* $\mathfrak{G}$ *which has* $\chi$ *as a constituent. Thus if* $\eta$ *is the character afforded by some* $\mathfrak{F}$*-representation of* $\mathfrak{G}$ *and* $\chi$ *is a constituent of* $\eta$ *then* $m_{\mathfrak{F}}(\chi) \mid (\chi, \eta)$.

*Proof.* Let $\mathcal{G} = \mathcal{G}_{\mathfrak{F}(\chi)/\mathfrak{F}}$. Let $\chi$ be an irreducible character of $\mathfrak{G}$ such that $(\theta, \chi) = m \neq 0$. Since $\mathfrak{F}(\theta) = \mathfrak{F}$, $(\theta, \chi^{\sigma}) = (\theta, \chi)$ for $\sigma \in \mathcal{G}$. Thus $\theta = m \Sigma_{\mathcal{G}} \chi^{\sigma} + \theta_0$, where $(\theta_0, \chi^{\sigma}) = 0$ for all $\sigma \in \mathcal{G}$. By (11.1) $m_{\mathfrak{F}}(\chi) \Sigma_{\mathcal{G}} \chi^{\sigma}$ is afforded by some $\mathfrak{F}$-representation of $\mathfrak{G}$. Thus by (1.9) and (2.9) $m_{\mathfrak{F}}(\chi) \Sigma_{\mathcal{G}} \chi^{\sigma} = \theta + \theta_1$, where $\theta_1 = 0$ or $\theta_1$ is a character. Consequently $\theta = m \Sigma_{\mathcal{G}} \chi^{\sigma}$ and $m \leq m_{\mathfrak{F}}(\chi)$. Since $\theta$ and $m_{\mathfrak{F}}(\chi)\chi$ are both afforded by $\mathfrak{F}(\chi)$-representations of $\mathfrak{G}$ we see that $\theta = m_{\mathfrak{F}}(\chi)\chi + \theta_2$, where $\theta_2 = 0$ or $\theta_2$ is a character. Hence $m_{\mathfrak{F}}(\chi) \leq m$ as required. The uniqueness of $\theta$ follows directly from (1.9) and (2.9).

(11.5) Let $\chi$ be an irreducible character of $\mathfrak{G}$. Then $m_{\mathfrak{F}}(\chi) \mid \chi(1)$ where $\mathfrak{F}$ is any field of characteristic 0.

Proof. $\rho_{(\mathfrak{G})}$ is afforded by an $\mathfrak{F}$-representation $\mathfrak{R}$ of $\mathfrak{G}$. Let $\mathfrak{F}$ be an $\mathfrak{F}$-irreducible constituent of $\mathfrak{R}$ which affords a character $\theta$ with $(\theta, \chi) \neq 0$. By (11.4) $(\theta, \chi) = m_{\mathfrak{F}}(\chi)$ and $\rho_{(\mathfrak{G})} = a\theta + \eta$ where $(\eta, \chi) = 0$ and a is a positive integer. Consequently

$$\chi(1) = (\chi, \rho_{(\mathfrak{G})}) = a\, m_{\mathfrak{F}}(\chi)$$

as required.

Let n be an integer, $n \geq 1$. Define the dihedral group $\mathfrak{D}_n$ by

$$\mathfrak{D}_n = \langle A, B \mid A^{2^n} = 1,\ B^2 = 1,\ B^{-1}AB = A^{-1} \rangle$$

For $n \geq 2$ define the (generalized) quaternion group $\mathfrak{Q}_n$ by

$$\mathfrak{Q}_n = \langle A, B \mid A^{2^n} = 1,\ B^2 = A^{2^{n-1}},\ B^{-1}AB = A^{-1} \rangle .$$

It follows directly from the definition that $|\mathfrak{D}_n| = |\mathfrak{Q}_n| = 2^{n+1}$ and each of $\mathfrak{D}_n$ and $\mathfrak{G}_n$ has a normal cyclic subgroup of index 2. If n = 1 then $\mathfrak{D}_n$ is the noncyclic group of order 4. It is easily verified that $A^{2^{n-1}} = B^2$ is the unique involution in $\mathfrak{Q}_n$ while $\mathfrak{D}_n$ has $2^n + 1$ involutions. Furthermore every proper homomorphic image of $\mathfrak{D}_n$ or $\mathfrak{Q}_n$ of order at least 4 is a dihedral group.

(11.6) Let $\mathfrak{G}$ be a 2-group such that $\langle A \rangle \lhd \mathfrak{G}$ and $|\mathfrak{G} : \langle A \rangle| = 2$. The degree of an irreducible character of $\mathfrak{G}$ is either 1 or 2. If $\mathfrak{G}$ is nonabelian and $\chi$ is a faithful irreducible character of $\mathfrak{G}$ then $\chi = \lambda^*$ for some faithful linear character $\lambda$ of $\langle A \rangle$. If furthermore $\mathfrak{G} = \mathfrak{D}_n$ or $\mathfrak{Q}_n$ then $\chi(A^i) = \epsilon^i + \epsilon^{-i}$, where $\lambda(A) = \epsilon$.

Proof. By (9.10) $\chi(1) \leq 2$. If $\mathfrak{G}$ is nonabelian and $\chi$ is faithful then $\chi(1) = 2$. Let $B \in \mathfrak{G} - \langle A \rangle$. Hence $\chi_{|\langle A \rangle} = \lambda + \lambda^B$ and $\chi = \lambda^*$ by the Frobenius reciprocity theorem. If $\mathfrak{G} = \mathfrak{D}_n$ or $\mathfrak{Q}_n$ then $B^{-1}AB = A^{-1}$ and so

$$\lambda^B(A^i) = \lambda(A^{-i}) = \overline{\lambda(A^i)}$$

Thus $\chi(A^i) = \epsilon^i + \epsilon^{-i}$ as required.

In Section 7 it was observed that $\mathfrak{D}_2$ and $\mathfrak{Q}_2$ have the same character tables. By making use of (11.6) it can be shown that for $n \geq 2$ $\mathfrak{D}_n$ and $\mathfrak{Q}_n$ have the same character tables. However the next two results show that $\mathfrak{D}_n$ and $\mathfrak{Q}_n$ differ in properties concerning the Schur index.

(11.7) Let $\mathfrak{F}$ be a field of characteristic 0. Let $\mathfrak{G}$ be a 2-group such that $\langle A \rangle \lhd \mathfrak{G}$, $|\mathfrak{G}:\langle A \rangle| = 2$ and there exists $B \in \mathfrak{G} - \langle A \rangle$ such that $B^2 = 1$. Then $m_{\mathfrak{F}}(\chi) = 1$ for every irreducible character $\chi$ of $\mathfrak{G}$. Thus in particular $m_{\mathfrak{F}}(\chi) = 1$ for every irreducible character $\chi$ of $\mathfrak{D}_n$.

Proof. It may be assumed that $\chi$ is faithful. If $\chi(1) = 1$ the result is clear. If $\chi(1) \neq 1$ then by (11.6) $\chi(1) = 2$ and $\chi(G) = 0$ for $G \in \mathfrak{G} - \langle A \rangle$. Hence

$$\left(1^*_{\langle B \rangle}, \chi\right)_{\mathfrak{G}} = \frac{1}{|\mathfrak{G}|} 1^*_{\langle B \rangle}(1)\,\chi(1) = 1$$

Since $1^*_{\langle B \rangle}$ is afforded by a $\mathbb{Q}$-representation of $\mathfrak{G}$ (11.4) implies that $m_{\mathfrak{F}}(\chi) = 1$.

(11.8) Let $\chi$ be a faithful irreducible character of $\mathfrak{Q}_n$ and let $\mathfrak{F}$ be a subfield of the field of real numbers. Then $m_{\mathfrak{F}}(\chi) = 2$.

Proof. By (11.5) and (11.6) $m_{\mathfrak{F}}(\chi) = 1$ or 2. Hence it suffices to show that $m_{\mathfrak{F}}(\chi) = 2$ for $\mathfrak{F}$ equal to the field of real numbers. By (11.6) $\chi \in \mathfrak{F}$. Every element in $\mathfrak{Q}_n$ is of the form $A^i$ or $BA^i$. Furthermore $(A^i)^2 = A^{2i}$ and

$$(BA^i)^2 = B^2B^{-1}A^iBA^i = B^2A^{-i}A^i = B^2$$

Therefore by (11.6)

$$\sum_{\mathfrak{G}} \chi(G^2) = \sum_{i=1}^{2^n} \chi(A^{2i}) + 2^n \chi(B^2)$$

$$= \sum_{i=1}^{2^n} (\epsilon^{2i} + \epsilon^{-2i}) - 2^{n+1}$$

$$= -2^{n+1}$$

Thus by (3.5) $m_{\mathfrak{F}}(\chi) \neq 1$ and so $m_{\mathfrak{F}}(\chi) = 2$ as required.

Let $\chi$ be a faithful irreducible character of $\mathfrak{Q}_n$. By using the theory of algebras it is quite easy to describe all the splitting fields of $\chi$ over $\mathbb{Q}$. We will only need the following result.

(11.9) Let $\chi$ be an irreducible character of $\mathfrak{Q}_n$. Then $\mathbb{Q}(\sqrt{-1}, \chi)$ and $\mathbb{Q}(\sqrt{-3}, \chi)$ are both splitting fields of $\chi$.

Proof. If $\chi$ is not faithful then $\chi$ is a character of a dihedral group and the result follows from (11.7). Suppose that $\chi$ is faithful. By (11.6) $\mathbb{Q}(\chi) = \mathbb{Q}(\epsilon + \epsilon^{-1})$ is the maximal real subfield of $\mathbb{Q}_{2^n}$. Since $\sqrt{-1} \in \mathbb{Q}_{2^n}$ we get that $\mathbb{Q}(\chi, \sqrt{-1}) = \mathbb{Q}_{2^n}$. Since $\chi = \lambda^*$ where $\lambda$ is a linear character of a subgroup and $\lambda \in \mathbb{Q}_{2^n}$ it follows immediately that $\mathbb{Q}(\chi, \sqrt{-1})$ is a splitting field for $\chi$.

Let $\mathfrak{F} = \mathbb{Q}(\sqrt{-3}, \chi)$. We will prove that $\mathfrak{F}$ is a splitting field of $\chi$ by exhibiting a group of nonsingular matrices with coefficients in $\mathfrak{F}$ which is isomorphic to $\mathfrak{Q}_n$ and whose trace function coincides with $\chi$. Let $\omega = (-1 + \sqrt{-3})/2 \in \mathfrak{F}$. Then $\omega$ is a primitive cube root of unity and $\omega^2 + \omega + 1 = 0$.

Let $J = \begin{pmatrix} \omega & \omega^2 \\ \omega^2 & -\omega \end{pmatrix}$. It is easily verified that the characteristic roots of J are $\sqrt{-1}$ and $-\sqrt{-1}$. Thus J is diagonable in some extension field of $\mathfrak{F}$. Let $\epsilon = a + b\sqrt{-1}$ where a, b are real. Thus a, b $\in \mathfrak{F}$. Define

$$A_0 = \begin{pmatrix} a & 0 \\ 0 & a \end{pmatrix} + bJ \qquad B_0 = \begin{pmatrix} 0 & 1 \\ -1 & 0 \end{pmatrix}$$

Thus $A_0$ has the characteristic values $\epsilon$ and $\bar{\epsilon} = \epsilon^{-1}$. Since J is diagonable in some extension field so is $A_0^i$ for every i. Hence $A_0^{2^n} = I$ and $A_0^{2^{n-1}} = \begin{pmatrix} -1 & 0 \\ 0 & -1 \end{pmatrix} = B_0^2$. Furthermore

$$B_0^{-1} A_0 B_0 = \begin{pmatrix} a & 0 \\ 0 & a \end{pmatrix} - bJ = A_0^{-1}$$

Hence the mapping sending $B^i A^j$ to $B_0^i A_0^j$ is a homomorphism of $\mathfrak{Q}_n$ onto $\langle A_0, B_0\rangle$. Since $|\mathfrak{Q}_n| = 2^{n+1} = |\langle A_0, B_0\rangle|$, this mapping is an isomorphism. For $G \in \langle A_0, B_0\rangle$ let $\chi_0(G)$ denote the trace of G. Then $\chi_0$ is a faithful character of $\mathfrak{G}_n$. Since $\mathfrak{Q}_n$ is nonabelian $\chi_0$ is irreducible. By (11.6) $\chi_0 \subseteq \mathfrak{F}$ and any two faithful irreducible characters of $\mathfrak{Q}_n$ are algebraically conjugate. Since $\chi_0(A) = \epsilon + \epsilon^{-1} = \chi(A)$ this implies that $\chi = \chi_0$. Thus $\mathfrak{F}$ is a splitting field of $\chi$ as required.

## §12. A COMBINATORIAL RESULT AND SOME CONSEQUENCES

The following result due to Brauer [1, Lemma 1] is very useful.

(12.1) Let $A = (a_{ij})$ be a nonsingular matrix of degree k with complex entries. If $\sigma$ is a permutation of the $k^2$ ordered pairs (i,j) i, j = 1, . . . , k define $A^\sigma = (a_{\sigma(i,j)})$. Suppose that $\mathfrak{M}$ is a group of permutations on the $k^2$ ordered pairs (i, j) such that for $\sigma \in \mathfrak{M}$ $A^\sigma$ can be derived from A by permuting the rows of A and $A^\sigma$ can also be derived from A by permuting the columns of A. Then the number of orbits under the action of $\mathfrak{M}$ consisting of rows is equal to the number of orbits under the action $\mathfrak{M}$ consisting of columns. If furthermore $\mathfrak{M}$ is cyclic then the number of rows left fixed by $\mathfrak{M}$ is equal to the number of columns left fixed by $\mathfrak{M}$.

Proof. If $\sigma \in \mathfrak{M}$ then by assumption there exist permutation matrices $\mathfrak{A}(\sigma)$, $\mathfrak{B}(\sigma)$ such that $\mathfrak{A}(\sigma)A = A^\sigma = A\mathfrak{B}(\sigma)$.

$\mathfrak{A}(\sigma)$ and $\mathfrak{B}(\sigma)$ are uniquely determined since A is nonsingular. Then $\mathfrak{A}(\sigma)\,\mathfrak{A}(\tau) = \mathfrak{A}(\tau\sigma)$ and $\mathfrak{B}(\sigma)\,\mathfrak{B}(\tau) = \mathfrak{B}(\sigma\tau)$. Thus $\mathfrak{A}'$ and $\mathfrak{B}$ are both permutation representations of $\mathfrak{M}$, where $'$ denotes transpose. Since A is nonsingular $A^{-1}\,\mathfrak{A}(\sigma)\,A = \mathfrak{B}(\sigma)$ and so $\mathfrak{A}'(\sigma)$ and $\mathfrak{B}(\sigma)$ have the same trace. Thus $\mathfrak{A}'$ and $\mathfrak{B}$ afford the same character $\theta$. The first statement now follows from (9.6). If $\mathfrak{M} = \langle\sigma\rangle$ is cyclic then the number of rows or columns left fixed by $\mathfrak{M}$ is $\theta(\sigma)$ by (2.3).

In applications of (12.1) A will generally be the character table of some group $\mathfrak{G}$. We will first introduce some terminology.

Let $\mathfrak{F}$ be a field of characteristic 0. Let $\epsilon$ be a primitive $|\mathfrak{G}|^{\text{th}}$ root of unity and let $\mathcal{G} = \mathcal{G}_{\mathfrak{F}(\epsilon)/\mathfrak{F}}$. Every element in $\mathcal{G}$ is of the form $\sigma_s$ for some integer s with $(s, |\mathfrak{G}|) = 1$ and $0 < s < |\mathfrak{G}|$, where $\epsilon^{\sigma_s} = \epsilon^s$. Two elements $G, H \in \mathfrak{G}$ are <u>$\mathfrak{F}$-conjugate</u> if G is conjugate to $H^s$ for some s with $\sigma_s \in \mathcal{G}$. It is clear that $\mathfrak{F}$-conjugation is an equivalence relation. The equivalence classes are the <u>$\mathfrak{F}$-conjugate classes of</u> $\mathfrak{G}$. If $\epsilon \in \mathfrak{F}$ then G and H are $\mathfrak{F}$-conjugate if and only if they are conjugate. At the other extreme G is $\mathbb{Q}$-conjugate to H if and only if $\langle G\rangle$ is conjugate to $\langle H\rangle$.

(12.2) <u>Let $\theta$ be a character of $\mathfrak{G}$ and let $\mathfrak{F}$ be a field of characteristic 0. Then $\theta \in \mathfrak{F}$ if and only if $\theta$ is constant on $\mathfrak{F}$-conjugate classes of $\mathfrak{G}$.</u>

<u>Proof.</u> Let $\epsilon$ be a primitive $|\mathfrak{G}|^{\text{th}}$ root of unity. Thus $\theta \in \mathfrak{F}(\epsilon)$. If $\sigma_s \in \mathcal{G}_{\mathfrak{F}(\epsilon)/\mathfrak{F}}$ then $\theta^{\sigma_s}(G) = \theta(G^s)$ for $G \in \mathfrak{G}$. The result follows.

The next result was probably known to Schur.

(12.3) <u>Let $\mathfrak{F}$ be a field of characteristic 0. The maximal number of pairwise nonsimilar $\mathfrak{F}$-representations of $\mathfrak{G}$ is equal to the number of $\mathfrak{F}$-conjugate classes of $\mathfrak{G}$. If furthermore $\mathcal{G}_{\mathfrak{F}(\epsilon)/\mathfrak{F}}$ is cyclic, where $\epsilon$ is a primitive $|\mathfrak{G}|$ th root of unity the number of irreducible characters of $\mathfrak{G}$ whose values lie in $\mathfrak{F}$ is equal to the number of conjugate classes of $\mathfrak{G}$ which are $\mathfrak{F}$-conjugate classes.</u>

Proof. Let $X = (\chi_i(G_j))$ be a character table of $\mathfrak{G}$. Let $\mathcal{G} = \mathcal{G}_{\mathfrak{F}(\epsilon)/\mathfrak{F}}$. If $\sigma_s \in \mathcal{G}$ then the mapping sending $\chi_i$ to $\chi_i^{\sigma_s}$ permutes the irreducible character of $\mathfrak{G}$. The number of orbits under the action of $\mathcal{G}$ equals the number of characters of the form $\Sigma_\sigma \chi_i^\sigma$, where $\sigma$ ranges over $\mathfrak{G}_{\mathfrak{F}(\chi_i)/\mathfrak{F}}$. By (11.4) this is the maximal number of pairwise nonsimilar $\mathfrak{F}$-representations of $\mathfrak{G}$. The number of irreducible characters fixed by all the elements of $\mathcal{G}$ is the number of irreducible characters whose values all lie in $\mathfrak{F}$. The mapping sending G into $G^s$ for $\sigma_s \in \mathcal{G}$ permutes the conjugate classes of $\mathfrak{G}$. The number of orbits being the number of $\mathfrak{F}$-conjugate classes of $\mathfrak{G}$. A conjugate class is fixed under the action of $\mathcal{G}$ if and only if it is an $\mathfrak{F}$-conjugate class. Since $\chi_i^{\sigma_s}(G_j) = \chi_i(G_j^s)$ and X is nonsingular the result follows from (12.1).

A conjugate class of $\mathfrak{G}$ is a real conjugate class if it is an $\mathfrak{F}$-conjugate class where $\mathfrak{F}$ is the field of real numbers. An element G is a real element if it is contained in a real conjugate class.

The next result is of fundamental importance for many applications.

(12.4) (Burnside) An element G is real if and only if G is conjugate to $G^{-1}$. The number of real valued irreducible characters of $\mathfrak{G}$ is equal to the number of real conjugate classes of $\mathfrak{G}$. If $|\mathfrak{G}|$ is odd then $\{1\}$ is the only real conjugate class and $1_{\mathfrak{G}}$ is the only real valued irreducible character of $\mathfrak{G}$.

Proof. The first two statements follow immediately from (12.3).

Suppose that $|\mathfrak{G}|$ is odd and G is real. Then there exists $H \in \mathfrak{G}$ such that $H^{-1}GH = G^{-1}$. Taking inverses we get that $H^{-1}G^{-1}H = G$. Thus $H^{-2}GH^2 = G$ and so $H^2 \in \mathbf{C}(G)$. Since $|\mathfrak{G}|$ is odd H is a power of $H^2$ and so $H \in \mathbf{C}(G)$. Thus $G = G^{-1}$ or $G^2 = 1$. Hence $G = 1$. Therefore $\{1\}$ is the only real conjugate class in $\mathfrak{G}$. Consequently by the first part of the theorem $\mathfrak{G}$ has only one real valued irreducible character which must necessarily be $1_{\mathfrak{G}}$.

## §13. RATIONAL VALUED CHARACTERS

The results in this section have applications in number theory.

(13.1) Let $\mathfrak{A}$ be a cyclic group. For $A \in \mathfrak{A}$ define

$$\alpha_{\mathfrak{A}}(A) = |\mathfrak{A}| \quad \text{if } \mathfrak{A} = \langle A \rangle$$

$$= 0 \quad \text{if } \mathfrak{A} \neq \langle A \rangle$$

Then $\alpha_{\mathfrak{A}}$ is a rational integral combination of permutation characters of $\mathfrak{A}$.

Proof. The proof is by induction on $|\mathfrak{A}|$. If $|\mathfrak{A}| = 1$ then $\alpha_{\mathfrak{A}} = 1_{\mathfrak{A}}$. Suppose that $|\mathfrak{A}| > 1$. Let $\mathfrak{B}$ be a subgroup of $\mathfrak{A}$ with $\mathfrak{B} \neq \mathfrak{A}$. If $\mathfrak{B} = \langle B \rangle$ then $\alpha^*_{\mathfrak{B}}(B) = |\mathfrak{A}|$ and if $\mathfrak{B} \neq \langle B \rangle$ then $\alpha^*_{\mathfrak{B}}(B) = 0$. Thus if $\beta = \Sigma\, \alpha^*_{\mathfrak{B}}$ where $\mathfrak{B}$ ranges over all subgroups of $\mathfrak{A}$ with $\mathfrak{B} \neq \mathfrak{A}$, then $\beta(A) = |\mathfrak{A}|$ if $\langle A \rangle \neq \mathfrak{A}$ and $\beta(A) = 0$ if $\langle A \rangle = \mathfrak{A}$. Hence $\alpha_{\mathfrak{A}} = |\mathfrak{A}|\, 1_{\mathfrak{A}} - \beta$ and the result follows by induction.

(13.2) (Artin) Every rational valued character of $\mathfrak{G}$ is a rational linear combination of characters of the form $1^*_{\mathfrak{A}}$, where $\mathfrak{A}$ ranges over the cyclic subgroups of $\mathfrak{G}$.

Proof. Let $\mathfrak{V}$ be the vector space over $\mathbb{Q}$ consisting of all rational linear combinations of rational valued characters of $\mathfrak{G}$ and let n be the dimension of $\mathfrak{V}$. By (12.3) there exist n pairwise nonconjugate cyclic subgroups $\mathfrak{A}_1, \ldots, \mathfrak{A}_n$ of $\mathfrak{G}$. Let $\alpha_i = \alpha_{\mathfrak{A}_i}$ be defined as in (13.1). Then $\alpha^*_i$ vanishes outside the $\mathbb{Q}$-conjugate class of $\mathfrak{G}$ which contains a generator of $\mathfrak{A}_i$. Thus $\alpha^*_1, \ldots, \alpha^*_n$ is a basis of $\mathfrak{V}$ as required.

(13.3) (R. Brauer) There exist cyclic subgroups $\mathfrak{A}_j$ of $\mathfrak{G}$ and nonprincipal linear characters $\zeta_j$ of $\mathfrak{A}_j$ such that $\rho_{\mathfrak{G}} = 1_{\mathfrak{G}} + \Sigma\, a_j\, \zeta^*_j$, where each $a_j$ is a positive rational number.

Proof. For a cyclic group $\mathfrak{A}$ let $\alpha_{\mathfrak{A}}$ be defined as in (13.1). Let $\beta_{\mathfrak{A}} = \varphi(|\mathfrak{A}|)\rho_{\mathfrak{A}} - \alpha_{\mathfrak{A}}$, where $\varphi$ is the Euler function. If $\zeta$ is an irreducible character of $\mathfrak{A} = \langle A \rangle$ then $\zeta(A^i) = \epsilon^i$, where $\epsilon$ is an $|\mathfrak{A}|^{\text{th}}$ root of unity. Therefore $\Sigma_i \zeta(A^i)\alpha_{\mathfrak{A}}(A^i) = |\mathfrak{A}| \operatorname{Tr}_{Q_{|\mathfrak{A}|}/Q}(\epsilon)$. Thus $|(\zeta, \alpha_{\mathfrak{A}})_{\mathfrak{A}}| \leq \varphi(|\mathfrak{A}|)$. This implies that

$$(\zeta, \beta_{\mathfrak{A}})_{\mathfrak{A}} = \varphi(|\mathfrak{A}|) - (\zeta, \alpha_{\mathfrak{A}})_{\mathfrak{A}} \geq 0$$

Since $(\rho_{\mathfrak{G}}, 1_{\mathfrak{G}}) = 1$ it now suffices to show that $\rho_{(\mathfrak{G})} - 1_{(\mathfrak{G})} = (1/|\mathfrak{G}|)\Sigma \beta^*_{\mathfrak{A}}$, where $\mathfrak{A}$ ranges over all cyclic subgroups $\mathfrak{A}$ of $\mathfrak{G}$.

Let $\chi$ be an irreducible character of $\mathfrak{G}$. Then $(\chi, \rho_{\mathfrak{G}} - 1_{\mathfrak{G}})$ $\chi(1) - (\chi, 1_{\mathfrak{G}})$. On the other hand the Frobenius reciprocity theorem implies that

$$\left(\chi, \frac{1}{|\mathfrak{G}|} \Sigma \beta^*_{\mathfrak{A}}\right) = \frac{1}{|\mathfrak{G}|} \Sigma \left(\chi, \beta^*_{\mathfrak{A}}\right)_{\mathfrak{G}}$$

$$= \frac{1}{|\mathfrak{G}|} \Sigma \left(\chi_{|\mathfrak{A}|}, \beta_{\mathfrak{A}}\right)_{\mathfrak{A}}$$

$$= \frac{1}{|\mathfrak{G}|} \Sigma \varphi(|\mathfrak{A}|)\, \chi(1)$$

$$- \frac{1}{|\mathfrak{G}|} \Sigma \frac{1}{|\mathfrak{A}|} \sum_{\langle A \rangle = \mathfrak{A}} |\mathfrak{A}|\, \chi(A)$$

$$= \chi(1) - (\chi, 1_{\mathfrak{G}})$$

Since $\chi$ was an arbitrary irreducible character $\rho_{\mathfrak{G}} - 1_{\mathfrak{G}} = (1/|\mathfrak{G}|)\Sigma \beta^*_{\mathfrak{A}}$ as required.

## §14. $\mathfrak{F}$-ELEMENTARY GROUPS

Let $\mathfrak{F}$ be a field of characteristic 0. A group $\mathfrak{H}$ is $\mathfrak{F}$-elementary with respect to the prime p if

(i) $\mathfrak{H} = \mathfrak{A}\mathfrak{P}$, where $\mathfrak{A} \lhd \mathfrak{H}$, $\mathfrak{A}$ is a cyclic $p'$-group and $\mathfrak{P}$ is a p-group.

(ii) If two elements of $\mathfrak{A}$ are conjugate in $\mathfrak{H}$ then they are $\mathfrak{F}$-conjugate in $\mathfrak{A}$.

Let $\epsilon$ be a primitive $|\mathfrak{A}|^{th}$ root of unity. The second condition is equivalent to

(ii)′ Let $\mathfrak{A} = \langle A \rangle$. If $A^i$ is conjugated to $A^j$ in $\mathfrak{H}$ then there exists $\sigma \in \mathcal{G}_{\mathfrak{F}(\epsilon)/\mathfrak{F}}$ such that $(\epsilon^i)\sigma = \epsilon^j$

The group $\mathfrak{H}$ is said to be $\mathfrak{F}$-elementary if it is $\mathfrak{F}$-elementary with respect to some prime p. $\mathfrak{H}$ is elementary if it is $\mathfrak{F}$-elementary, where $\mathfrak{F}$ is a field containing a primitive $|\mathfrak{A}|^{th}$ root of unity. It is easily seen that an $\mathfrak{F}$-elementary group $\mathfrak{H}$ is elementary if and only if $\mathfrak{H} = \mathfrak{A} \times \mathfrak{P}$. A group $\mathfrak{H}$ is $\mathbb{Q}$-elementary if and only if $\mathfrak{H} = \mathfrak{A}\mathfrak{P}$, where $\mathfrak{A} \lhd \mathfrak{H}$, $\mathfrak{A}$ is cyclic and $\mathfrak{P}$ is a p-group.

It will be shown later that questions concerning Schur indices of characters of an arbitrary group $\mathfrak{G}$ can be reduced to the corresponding questions for $\mathfrak{F}$-elementary subgroups of $\mathfrak{G}$. These questions are however far from being answered for $\mathfrak{F}$-elementary groups. The results in this section will be needed later.

Fong [1] first proved (14.1) by making use of the theory of modular characters. The remaining results in this section may be found in Solomon [1], though (14.3) is a slight generalization of the corresponding result there and the proof of (14.2) is here simplified. Some of the results in this section have also been obtained by Berman and Witt by different methods (see Curtis and Reiner for references). Roquette [2] first published a proof of (14.5). His proof was based on the theory of algebras. All the material in this section is closely related to the work of R. Brauer [2].

Throughout this section $\mathfrak{F}$ is a field of characteristic 0, $\mathfrak{H}$ is an $\mathfrak{F}$-elementary group and $\mathfrak{A} = \langle A \rangle$, $\mathfrak{P}$ and p have the same meaning as in the definition of $\mathfrak{F}$-elementary groups.

(14.1) Let $q$ be a prime, $q \neq p$. Let $|\mathfrak{H}| = q^a h_0$, where $q \nmid h_0$, and let $\mathfrak{K} = \mathbf{Q}_{h_0}$. If $\chi$ is an irreducible character of $\mathfrak{H}$ then $m_{\mathfrak{K}}(\chi) = 1$.

Proof. It may be assumed that $\chi$ is faithful. By (9.13) $\chi(1)$ is a power of p. By (10.2) $\chi = \lambda^*$, where $\lambda$ is a linear character of some subgroup $\mathfrak{L}$ of $\mathfrak{H}$. Thus $|\mathfrak{H}:\mathfrak{L}|$ is a power of p and so $\mathfrak{A} \subseteq \mathfrak{L}$. Let $\mathfrak{Q}$ be the $S_q$-group of $\mathfrak{A}$. Since $\lambda$ is linear $\mathfrak{L} \subseteq \mathfrak{C} = \mathbf{C}\mathfrak{Q}$. Let $\zeta$ be the character of $\mathfrak{C}$ induced by $\lambda$. Then $\mathfrak{C} \triangleleft \mathfrak{H}$ and $\chi = \zeta^*$. Furthermore $\mathfrak{C} = \mathfrak{Q} \times \mathfrak{B}$ for some group $\mathfrak{B}$ and so $\zeta = \mu\eta$, where $\mu$ is a linear character of $\mathfrak{Q}$ and $\eta$ is an irreducible character of $\mathfrak{B}$. Let $\chi_1$ be an irreducible constituent of the character of $\mathfrak{B}\mathfrak{P}$ induced by $\eta$. Since $|\mathfrak{B}\mathfrak{P}| \mid h_0$ (10.2) implies that $\chi_1$, and thus also $\chi_1^*$, is afforded by a $\mathfrak{K}$-representation of $\mathfrak{B}\mathfrak{P}$, $\mathfrak{H}$ respectively. $\mathfrak{H}/\mathfrak{C}$ is cyclic since $\mathfrak{H}/\mathfrak{C}$ is a $q'$-group of automorphisms of the cyclic q-group $\mathfrak{Q}$. Thus by (9.12) $\chi_{1|\mathfrak{B}} = \Sigma_i\,\eta_i$, where $\eta = \eta_1, \eta_2, \ldots$ are distinct irreducible characters of $\mathfrak{B}$. Hence $\chi_1^*|_{\mathfrak{C}} = \rho_{\mathfrak{Q}}\,\Sigma_i\,\eta_i$. By the Frobenius reciprocity theorem

$$(\chi, \chi_1^*)_{\mathfrak{H}} = ((\mu\eta)^*, \chi_1^*)_{\mathfrak{H}} = (\mu\eta, \rho_{\mathfrak{Q}} \textstyle\sum_i \eta_1)_{\mathfrak{C}} = 1$$

Therefore by (11.4) $m_{\mathfrak{K}}(\chi) = 1$ as was to be shown.

(14.2) Let $\epsilon$ be a primitive $|\mathfrak{A}|^{th}$ root of unity. For any integer t let $\lambda_t(A^i) = \epsilon^{ti}$ and let $\mathfrak{P}_t = \mathbf{C}_{\mathfrak{P}}(A^t)$. Define $\varphi_t(A^i) = \mathrm{Tr}_{\mathfrak{F}(\epsilon)/\mathfrak{F}}(\lambda_t(A^i))$. Let

$$\theta_t(A^iP) = \varphi_t(A^i) \quad \text{if} \quad P \in \mathfrak{P}_t$$

$$= 0 \quad \text{if} \quad P \in \mathfrak{P} - \mathfrak{P}_t$$

Then $\theta_t$ is a character afforded by some $\mathfrak{F}$-irreducible $\mathfrak{F}$-representation of $\mathfrak{H}$.

Proof. There exists a linear character $\mu$ of $\mathfrak{A}\mathfrak{P}_t$ such that $\mathfrak{P}_t$ is in the kernel of $\mu$ and $\mu_{|\mathfrak{A}} = \lambda_t$. Let $\chi = \mu^*$. Then $Tr_{\mathfrak{F}(\chi)/\mathfrak{F}}(\chi) = \theta_t$. Furthermore $\chi$ is an irreducible character of $\mathfrak{H}$. Since $\chi_{|\mathfrak{P}} = \rho_{\mathfrak{P}/\mathfrak{P}_t}$ we see that $(1_{\mathfrak{P}}^*, \chi)_{\mathfrak{H}} = (1_{\mathfrak{P}}, \chi_{|\mathfrak{P}})_{\mathfrak{P}} = 1$. As $1_{\mathfrak{P}}^*$ is afforded by an $\mathfrak{F}$-representation of $\mathfrak{H}$ (11.4) implies that $m_{\mathfrak{F}}(\chi) = 1$. Thus by (11.4) $\theta_t$ is afforded by an $\mathfrak{F}$-irreducible $\mathfrak{F}$-representation of $\mathfrak{H}$.

The following well known fact is required for the proof of the next result. See M. Hall p. 189.

If $\mathfrak{P}$ is a p-group which contains a unique subgroup of order p then either $\mathfrak{P}$ is cyclic or $p = 2$ and $\mathfrak{P}$ is a quaternion group.

(14.3) Let $\mathfrak{F} = \mathbf{Q}$. Let $\pi(\mathfrak{A}) = \{p_i\}$. Let $\mathcal{K}$ be a field of characteristic 0 which contains a primitive $\Pi p_i$ th root of unity. Suppose that one of the following hypotheses is satisfied

(i) $p \neq 2$.

(ii) $p = 2$ and $\sqrt{-1} \in \mathcal{K}$.

(iii) $p = 2$ and $\mathfrak{P}$ does not contain a cyclic subgroup of index 2.

Then if $\chi$ is a nonlinear irreducible faithful character of $\mathfrak{H}$ there exists $\mathfrak{H}_0 \lhd \mathfrak{H}$ and a character $\zeta$ of $\mathfrak{H}_0$ such that $|\mathfrak{H}:\mathfrak{H}_0| = p$, $\chi = \zeta^*$ and $\mathcal{K}(\chi) = \mathcal{K}(\zeta)$.

Proof. Assume that the result is false. The following statement will be proved first.

(*) There exist normal subgroups $\mathfrak{B}$, $\mathfrak{C}$ of $\mathfrak{H}$ such that $|\mathfrak{H}:\mathfrak{B}|$ is a power of p, $|\mathfrak{B}:\mathfrak{C}| = p$, $\chi_{|\mathfrak{B}} = \Sigma_\sigma \lambda^\sigma$, where $\lambda$ is an irreducible character of $\mathfrak{B}$ and $\sigma$ ranges over $\mathcal{G}_{\mathcal{K}(\lambda)/\mathcal{K}(\chi)}$

and $|\mathfrak{G}_{\mathcal{K}(\lambda)/\mathcal{K}(\chi)}| = |\mathfrak{H}:\mathfrak{E}|$. Furthermore $\lambda_{|\mathfrak{C}} = \Sigma_{i=1}^{p} \mu_i$, where $\mu_1, \ldots, \mu_p$ are distinct irreducible characters of $\mathfrak{C}$ and $\mathcal{K}(\mu_1) = \mathcal{K}(\lambda)$ for $i = 1, \ldots, p$.

Let $\mathfrak{E}$ be a minimal subgroup of $\mathfrak{H}$ such that $\chi_{|\mathfrak{E}} = \Sigma_\sigma \varphi^\sigma$, where $\varphi$ is an irreducible character of $\mathfrak{E}$, $\sigma$ ranges over $\mathfrak{G}(\varphi) = \mathfrak{G}_{\mathcal{K}(\varphi)/\mathcal{K}(\chi)}$ and $|\mathfrak{G}(\varphi)| = |\mathfrak{H}:\mathfrak{B}|$. If $\{G_i\}$ is a complete set of coset representatives of $\mathfrak{E}$ in $\mathfrak{H}$ then $\chi_{|\mathfrak{E}} = \Sigma_i \varphi^{G_i}$. Let $\sigma_i$ be defined by $\varphi^{\sigma_i} = \varphi^{G_i}$. Since $(\varphi^G)^\sigma = (\varphi^\sigma)^G$ we see that

$$\varphi^{G_iG_j} = (\varphi^{\sigma_i})^{G_j} = (\varphi^{G_j})^{\sigma_i} = \varphi^{\sigma_j\sigma_i} = \varphi^{\sigma_i\sigma_j}$$

Thus the mapping sending $G_i$ into $\sigma_i$ is an isomorphism of $\mathfrak{H}/\mathfrak{E}$ onto $\mathfrak{G}(\varphi)$. By the Frobenius reciprocity theorem $\chi \subseteq \varphi^*$. Since $\chi(1) = |\mathfrak{H}:\mathfrak{E}|\,\varphi(1) = \varphi^*(1)$ this implies that $\chi = \varphi^*$. Thus by (9.13) $|\mathfrak{H}:\mathfrak{E}|$ is a power of p.

Assume first that $\varphi$ is nonlinear. By (10.2) there exists a subgroup $\mathfrak{F}$ of $\mathfrak{E}$ with $|\mathfrak{E}:\mathfrak{F}| = p$ such that $\varphi = \tilde{\psi}$ is induced by the character $\psi$ of $\mathfrak{F}$. Let $\mathfrak{T}$ be the intersection of all conjugates of $\mathfrak{F}$ in $\mathfrak{H}$. Since $\mathfrak{A} \subseteq \mathfrak{F}$ and $\mathfrak{A} \lhd \mathfrak{H}$ we get that $\mathfrak{A} \subseteq \mathfrak{T}$. Thus $\mathfrak{T} \lhd \mathfrak{H}$ and $\mathfrak{H}/\mathfrak{T}$ is a p-group. Since $\varphi = \tilde{\psi}$, $\varphi$ vanishes on $\mathfrak{E} - \mathfrak{F}$. Hence for each i $\varphi^{\sigma_i} = \varphi^{G_i}$ vanishes on $\mathfrak{E} - \mathfrak{F}^{G_i}$ and so $\varphi$ vanishes on $\mathfrak{E} - \mathfrak{T}$. There exists $\mathfrak{C} \lhd \mathfrak{H}$ such that $\mathfrak{T} \subseteq \mathfrak{C} \subset \mathfrak{E}$ and $|\mathfrak{E}:\mathfrak{C}| = p$. Since $\varphi$ vanishes on $\mathfrak{E} - \mathfrak{C}$, $\|\varphi_{|\mathfrak{C}}\|^2_{\mathfrak{C}} = p\,\|\varphi\|^2_{\mathfrak{E}}$. Thus $\varphi_{|\mathfrak{C}}$ is reducible. By (9.12) $\varphi_{|\mathfrak{C}} = \Sigma_{i=1}^{p} \mu_i$, where $\mu_1, \ldots, \mu_p$ are distinct irreducible characters of $\mathfrak{C}$. If $\mathcal{K}(\mu_i) \neq \mathcal{K}(\varphi)$ for some i then there exists $\sigma \in \mathfrak{G}_{\mathcal{K}(\mu_i)/\mathcal{K}(\varphi)}$ such that $\mu_i^\sigma = \mu_i^E$, where $\langle E\,\mathfrak{C}\rangle = \mathfrak{E}/\mathfrak{C}$. Thus $\mu_i^{\sigma^j} = \mu_i^{E^j}$. This implies that $\chi_{|\mathfrak{C}} = \Sigma\,\mu^\sigma$, where $\mu = \mu_1$ and $\sigma$ ranges over $\mathfrak{G}_{\mathcal{K}(\mu)/\mathcal{K}(\chi)}$ contrary to the minimality of $\mathfrak{C}$. Thus $\mathcal{K}(\mu_i) =$

$\mathcal{K}(\varphi)$ for $i = 1, \ldots, p$. Now let $\mathfrak{E} = \mathfrak{B}$ and $\varphi = \lambda$. (*) is proved in this case.

Assume next that $\varphi$ is linear. Since $\varphi$ and $\varphi^{\sigma}$ have the same kernel this implies that $\varphi$ is faithful and so $\mathfrak{E}$ is cyclic. Let $\mathfrak{E} = \langle AP \rangle$, where $P \in \mathfrak{P}$. Let $\varphi(A) = \omega$ and $\varphi(P) = \epsilon$. Thus $\omega \in \mathcal{K}(\varphi)$. Since $[\mathcal{K}(\omega):\mathcal{K}] \,\big|\, |\mathfrak{A}|$ and $\mathcal{G}(\varphi)$ is a p-group this implies that $\omega \in \mathcal{K}(\chi)$.

If $\mathfrak{P}$ contains a cyclic subgroup of index 2 and order $2^m$ then hypothesis (ii) holds. Thus $\sqrt{-1} \in \mathcal{K}$. If $\chi(P) = \varphi^*(P) = \epsilon + \epsilon^{-1}$ or $\chi(P) = \epsilon + \epsilon^{-1+2^{m-1}}$ then $\mathcal{K}(\chi) = \mathcal{K}(\epsilon) = \mathcal{K}(\varphi)$ contrary to hypothesis. Thus it may be assumed that $\chi(P) = \epsilon + \epsilon^{1+2^{m-1}}$. Hence in particular $\mathfrak{P}$ is not a quaternion group and so there exists an involution $T \in \mathfrak{P} - \langle P \rangle$. Thus $T^{-1}PT = P^{1+2^{m-1}}$. If $p = 2$ and $|\mathfrak{P}:\langle P \rangle| \neq 2$ then there also exists an element $T \in \mathfrak{P} - \langle P \rangle$ such that $T^{-1}PT = P^{1+2^{m-1}}$ and once again it may be assumed that $T$ is an involution.

Suppose now that $\mathfrak{P}/\langle P \rangle$ is cyclic. Let $|\langle P \rangle| = p^m$ and $|\mathfrak{P}:\langle P \rangle| = p^n$. Thus $\mathfrak{P} = \langle P, B \rangle$ where $T$ can be chosen of order $p$ so that $B^{p^{n-1}} = T$. Furthermore $B^{-1}PB = P^{1+p^{m-n}}$ with $m > n \geq 1$. Then $T^{-1}P^pT = P^{p(1+p^{m-1})} = P^p$. Thus $\langle T, P^p \rangle$ is an abelian group. Since $|\langle T, P \rangle : \langle T, P^p \rangle| = p$, $\langle T, P^p \rangle \lhd \langle T, P \rangle$. As $B^{-1}TB = T$ this implies that $\langle T, P^p \rangle \lhd \mathfrak{P}$. Let $\lambda$ be the character of $\mathfrak{A}\langle T, P \rangle$ induced by $\varphi$. Thus $\lambda(P) = \operatorname{Tr}_{\mathcal{Q}(\epsilon)/\mathcal{Q}(\epsilon^p)}(\epsilon) = 0$. Therefore $\lambda$ vanishes outside $\mathfrak{A}\langle T, P^p \rangle$. Thus $\lambda_{|\mathfrak{A}\langle T, P^p \rangle}$ is reducible. Hence by (9.11) $\lambda_{|\mathfrak{A}\langle T, P^p \rangle} = \Sigma_{i=1}^{p} \mu_i$, where $\mu_1, \ldots, \mu_p$ are distinct irreducible characters of $\mathfrak{A}\langle T, P^p \rangle$. Since the maximal order of any element in $\langle T, P^p \rangle$ is $p^{m-1}$ we get that $\mathcal{K}(\mu_i) \subseteq \mathcal{K}(\omega, \epsilon^p)$. As $[\mathcal{K}(\varphi): \mathcal{K}(\lambda)] = p$ this implies that $\mathcal{K}(\lambda) = \mathcal{K}(\omega, \epsilon^p)$ and so $\mathcal{K}(\lambda) = \mathcal{K}(\mu_1)$. Setting $\mathfrak{B} = \mathfrak{A}\langle T, P \rangle$, $\mathfrak{E} = \mathfrak{A}\langle T, P^p \rangle$ we see that (*) is proved in this case.

Suppose finally that $\mathfrak{P}/\langle P \rangle$ is not cyclic. Since $\mathfrak{P}/\langle P \rangle$ is isomorphic to $\mathcal{G}(\varphi)$ neither hypothesis (i) nor (ii) can hold. Thus

$p = 2$ and $|\langle P\rangle| = 2^m \geq 8$. There exist elements $B, S \in \mathfrak{P}$ such that $S^{-1}PS = P^{-1}$, $B^{-1}PB = P^{1+2^{m-n}}$ where $|\langle B, P\rangle| = 2^{m+n}$, $m - 1 > n \geq 1$ and $|\mathfrak{P}| = 2^{m+n+1}$. Since $\langle B, P\rangle$ is not a quaternion group there exists an element T of order 2 in $\langle B, P\rangle - \langle P\rangle$. Thus it may be assumed that $B^{2^{n-1}} = T$. Let $\varphi(P) = \epsilon$. Thus $\epsilon$ is a primitive $2^m$th root of unity. Hence $\mathfrak{K}(\varphi) = \mathfrak{K}(\omega, \epsilon)$. Since $\mathfrak{P}/\langle P\rangle$ is abelian $\langle T, P\rangle \lhd \mathfrak{P}$. Thus every conjugate of T in $\mathfrak{P}$ is contained in $\langle T, P\rangle$. $TPT = P^{1+2^{m-1}}$. Thus if $(TP^j)^2 = 1$ then $1 = TP^jTP^j = P^{j(2+2^{m-1})}$ and so $P^j$ is an involution. Thus the only involutions in $\langle T, P\rangle$ are T, $P^{2^{m-1}}$ and $TP^{2^{m-1}}$. Hence T has at most 2 conjugates in $\mathfrak{P}$. Thus $|\mathfrak{H}:\mathfrak{A}C_{\mathfrak{P}}(T)| = 2$ and $P \notin C_{\mathfrak{P}}(T)$. Let $\widetilde{\varphi}$ be the character of $\mathfrak{A}\langle T, P\rangle$ induced by $\varphi$. Thus $\widetilde{\varphi}(P) = Tr_{\mathbb{Q}(\epsilon)/\mathbb{Q}(\epsilon^2)}(\epsilon) = 0$. This implies that $\widetilde{\varphi}$ vanishes outside $\mathfrak{A}\langle T, P^2\rangle$. Therefore $\widetilde{\varphi}_{|\mathfrak{A}\langle T, P^2\rangle}$ is reducible. Hence by (9.11) $\widetilde{\varphi}_{|\mathfrak{A}\langle T, P^2\rangle} = \psi_1 + \psi_2$, where $\psi_1$, $\psi_2$ are distinct irreducible characters of $\mathfrak{A}\langle T, P^2\rangle$. Since the order of any element in $\langle T, P^2\rangle$ is at most $2^{m-1}$ we see that $\mathcal{K}(\psi_i) \subseteq \mathcal{K}(\omega, \epsilon^2)$. Let $\mathfrak{C} = \mathfrak{A}C_{\mathfrak{P}}(T)$ and let $\lambda$ be the character of $\mathfrak{C}$ induced by $\psi_1$. Then $[\mathcal{K}(\psi_1): \mathcal{K}(\lambda)] = 2^n$ and so $[\mathcal{K}(\omega, \epsilon): \mathcal{K}(\lambda)] \geq 2^{n+1}$. Since $\chi \subseteq \mathcal{K}(\lambda)$ this implies that $\mathcal{K}(\chi) = \mathcal{K}(\lambda)$. (*) now follows by setting $\mathfrak{B} = \mathfrak{H}$. This completes the proof of (*) in all cases.

By (*) $\chi_{|\mathfrak{C}} = \Sigma_{i=1}^p \Sigma_\sigma \mu_i^\sigma$, where $\sigma$ ranges over $\mathcal{G}_{\mathcal{K}(\mu_1)/\mathcal{K}(\chi)}$ and no two of $\mu_i$, $\mu_j$ are algebraically conjugate. Let $\mathfrak{H}_0$ be the subgroup of $\mathfrak{H}$ consisting of all elements G such that $\mu_1^G = \mu_1^\sigma$ for some $\sigma$. Let $\zeta$ be the character of $\mathfrak{H}_0$ induced by $\mu_1$. Then $|\mathfrak{H}:\mathfrak{H}_0| = p$, $\zeta^* = \chi$ and $\mathcal{K}(\chi) = \mathcal{K}(\zeta)$ as required.

(14.4) <u>Let</u> $\mathfrak{F} = \mathbb{Q}$. <u>Let</u> $\pi(\mathfrak{A}) = \{p_i\}$. <u>Let</u> $\mathcal{K}$ <u>be a field of characteristic</u> 0 <u>which contains a primitive</u> $\Pi_i p_i$ th <u>root of unity. If</u> $p = 2$ <u>assume that also</u> $\sqrt{-1} \in \mathcal{K}$. <u>If</u> $\chi$ <u>is an irre-</u>

ducible character of $\mathfrak{H}$ then there exists a subgroup $\mathfrak{E}$ and a linear character $\lambda$ of $\mathfrak{E}$ such that $\lambda^* = \chi$ and $\mathcal{K}(\chi) = \mathcal{K}(\lambda)$. Thus in particular $m_{\mathcal{K}}(\chi) = 1$.

Proof. The proof is by induction on $|\mathfrak{H}|$. If $\chi(1) = 1$ the result is clear. If $\chi(1) > 1$ then by (14.3) there exists a subgroup $\mathfrak{H}_0$ of $\mathfrak{H}$ with $\mathfrak{H}_0 \neq \mathfrak{H}$ and an irreducible character $\zeta$ of $\mathfrak{H}_0$ such that $\chi = \zeta^*$ and $\mathcal{K}(\chi) = \mathcal{K}(\zeta)$. Since $\mathfrak{H}_0$ is Q-elementary the result follows by induction.

(14.5) Suppose that $\mathfrak{H}$ is a nilpotent group and $\chi$ is an irreducible character of $\mathfrak{H}$. Then there exists a subgroup $\mathfrak{E}$ of $\mathfrak{H}$ and a linear character $\lambda$ of $\mathfrak{E}$ such that $\lambda^* = \chi$ and either $\mathcal{Q}(\lambda) = \mathcal{Q}(\chi)$ or $|\mathfrak{H}|$ is even and $\mathcal{Q}(\lambda) = \mathcal{Q}(\chi, \sqrt{-1})$. Furthermore either $m_{\mathcal{Q}}(\chi) = 1$ or $|\mathfrak{H}|$ is even and $m_{\mathcal{Q}(\sqrt{-1})}(\chi) = m_{\mathcal{Q}(\sqrt{-3})}(\chi) = 1$.

Proof. Let $\mathfrak{H} = \mathfrak{P}_1 \times \cdots \times \mathfrak{P}_n$, where $\mathfrak{P}_i$ is a $p_i$-group and $p_1, \ldots, p_n$ is a set of primes. Thus $\chi = \Pi_{i=1}^n \chi_i$ and $\mathcal{Q}(\chi) = \mathcal{Q}(\chi_1, \ldots, \chi_n)$, where $\chi_i$ is an irreducible character of $\mathfrak{P}_i$. If $\chi_i = \lambda_i^*$ then $\chi = (\Pi_{i=1}^n \lambda_i)^*$ and $\mathcal{Q}(\Pi_{i=1}^n \lambda_i) = \mathcal{Q}(\lambda_1, \ldots \lambda_n)$. Thus it may be assumed that $\mathfrak{G} = \mathfrak{P}$ is a p-group. The first statement follows from (14.4) with $\mathcal{K} = \mathcal{Q}(\chi)$ or $\mathcal{Q}(\sqrt{-1}, \chi)$ since $\chi(P) = \epsilon\chi(1)$ with $\epsilon$ a primitive p th root of 1 for P an element of order p in $\mathbf{Z}(\mathfrak{G})$. This implies that $m_{\mathcal{Q}}(\chi) = 1$ if $p \neq 2$ and $m_{\mathcal{Q}(\sqrt{-1})}(\chi) = 1$ if $p = 2$.

Assume now that $p = 2$. We will prove by induction on $|\mathfrak{P}|$ that $m_{\mathcal{Q}(\sqrt{-3})}(\chi) = 1$. If $\chi(1) = 1$ this is clear. If $\mathfrak{P}$ has a cyclic subgroup of index 2 this follows from (11.7) and (11.9). Otherwise by (14.3) there exists a subgroup $\mathfrak{P}_0$ of $\mathfrak{P}$ and a character $\zeta$ of $\mathfrak{P}_0$ such that $\zeta^* = \chi$ and $\mathcal{Q}(\sqrt{-3}, \chi) = \mathcal{Q}(\sqrt{-3}, \zeta)$. Thus $m_{\mathcal{Q}(\sqrt{-3})}(\chi) \leq m_{\mathcal{Q}(\sqrt{-3})}(\zeta) = 1$ by induction.

## §15. THE CHARACTER RING

Throughout this section the following notation will be used.

$\mathfrak{G}$ is a group and $\mathfrak{F}$ is a field of characteristic 0. $\mathfrak{D}$ is an integral domain whose quotient field has characteristic 0. $\mathfrak{K}$ is an extension field of the quotient field of $\mathfrak{D}$ which contains subfields isomorphic to $\mathfrak{F}$ and to $\mathfrak{Q}_{|\mathfrak{G}|}$. Thus by choosing suitable isomorphisms it may be assumed that $\mathfrak{F} \subseteq \mathfrak{K}$ and $\mathfrak{Q}_{|\mathfrak{G}|} \subseteq \mathfrak{K}$. Thus any character is a $\mathfrak{K}$-valued function on $\mathfrak{G}$ and a $\mathfrak{D}$-linear combination of characters is well defined.

$\mathfrak{Ch}_{\mathfrak{D}}(\mathfrak{G}, \mathfrak{F})$ is the ring of all $\mathfrak{D}$-linear combinations of characters afforded by $\mathfrak{F}$-representations of $\mathfrak{G}$.

$\mathfrak{Ch}_{\mathfrak{D}}(\mathfrak{G}, \mathfrak{F})'$ is the ring of all $\mathfrak{D}$-linear combinations of characters $\theta \in \mathfrak{F}$.

$\mathfrak{U}_{\mathfrak{D}}(\mathfrak{G}, \mathfrak{F}), \mathfrak{U}_{\mathfrak{D}}(\mathfrak{G}, \mathfrak{F})'$ is the ring of all $\mathfrak{K}$-valued class functions $\theta$ on $\mathfrak{G}$ such that $\theta_{|\mathfrak{H}} \in \mathfrak{Ch}_{\mathfrak{D}}(\mathfrak{H}, \mathfrak{F}), \mathfrak{Ch}_{\mathfrak{D}}(\mathfrak{H}, \mathfrak{F})'$ respectively for every $\mathfrak{F}$-elementary subgroup $\mathfrak{H}$ of $\mathfrak{G}$.

Observe that, as the notation indicates, $\mathfrak{U}_{\mathfrak{D}}(\mathfrak{G}, \mathfrak{F})$ and $\mathfrak{U}_{\mathfrak{D}}(\mathfrak{G}, \mathfrak{F})'$ do not depend on $\mathfrak{K}$.

$\mathfrak{V}_{\mathfrak{D}}(\mathfrak{G}, \mathfrak{F}), \mathfrak{V}_{\mathfrak{D}}(\mathfrak{G}, \mathfrak{F})'$ is the ring of all $\mathfrak{D}$-linear combinations of functions $\theta^*$, where $\theta \in \mathfrak{Ch}_{\mathfrak{D}}(\mathfrak{H}, \mathfrak{F}), \mathfrak{Ch}_{\mathfrak{D}}(\mathfrak{H}, \mathfrak{F})'$ respectively for some $\mathfrak{F}$-elementary subgroup $\mathfrak{H}$ of $\mathfrak{G}$.

If p is a rational prime then $\mathfrak{V}_{\mathfrak{D}}(\mathfrak{G}, \mathfrak{F}, p)$ is the ring of all $\mathfrak{D}$-linear combinations of functions $\theta^*$ where $\theta \in \mathfrak{Ch}_{\mathfrak{D}}(\mathfrak{H}, \mathfrak{F})$ and $\mathfrak{H}$ is a subgroup of $\mathfrak{G}$ which is $\mathfrak{F}$-elementary with respect to p.

In all these cases if $\mathfrak{D}$ is the domain of rational integers the subscript $\mathfrak{D}$ will be omitted. In case $\mathfrak{F}$ is a splitting field of $\mathfrak{G}$ we write

$$\mathfrak{Ch}_{\mathfrak{D}}(\mathfrak{G}) = \mathfrak{Ch}_{\mathfrak{D}}(\mathfrak{G}, \mathfrak{F}) = \mathfrak{Ch}_{\mathfrak{D}}(\mathfrak{G}, \mathfrak{F})'$$

The ring $\mathfrak{Ch}(\mathfrak{G})$ is <u>the character ring of</u> $\mathfrak{G}$. The elements of $\mathfrak{Ch}(\mathfrak{G})$ are called <u>generalized characters of</u> $\mathfrak{G}$. Thus a generalized character of $\mathfrak{G}$ is a rational integral linear combination of irreducible characters of $\mathfrak{G}$. Or equivalently a generalized character of $\mathfrak{G}$ is a difference of two characters of $\mathfrak{G}$.

The following results might well be called the fundamental theorems of character theory.

(15.1) $\mathcal{U}_{\mathfrak{D}}(\mathfrak{G}, \mathfrak{F}) = \mathcal{C}h_{\mathfrak{D}}(\mathfrak{G}, \mathfrak{F}) = \mathcal{V}_{\mathfrak{D}}(\mathfrak{G}, \mathfrak{F})$

(15.2) $\mathcal{U}_{\mathfrak{D}}(\mathfrak{G}, \mathfrak{F})' = \mathcal{C}h_{\mathfrak{D}}(\mathfrak{G}, \mathfrak{F})' = \mathcal{V}_{\mathfrak{D}}(\mathfrak{G}, \mathfrak{F})'$

These results have applications in number theory and group theory. The most important special case occurs when $\mathfrak{D}$ is the ring of rational integers and $\mathfrak{F}$ is a splitting field of $\mathfrak{G}$. This special case was first discovered by Brauer who was also the first to realize the importance of results of this type. Roquette [1] simplified Brauer's proof. Berman, Witt and Brauer all independently generalized the original result. In case $\mathfrak{F} = \mathbb{Q}$ Swan also obtained (15.1) independently. See Curtis and Reiner p. 301 for references. The original result was given a new and elegant proof by Brauer and Tate [1] who made use of Roquette's simplifications. Using their methods Solomon [1] gave a proof of (15.1) and (15.2) and also of a related result of Brauer [2]. He also obtained a new result concerning splitting fields. This last approach will be followed here.

Before proving (15.1) and (15.2) we will deduce a result that will be of use later.

(15.3) Let $\theta$ be a complex valued function on $\mathfrak{G}$. Then $\theta$ is a generalized character of $\mathfrak{G}$ if and only if the following conditions are satisfied.

(i) $\theta$ is a class function on $\mathfrak{G}$.

(ii) For every elementary subgroup $\mathfrak{H}$ of $\mathfrak{G}$, $\theta_{|\mathfrak{H}}$ is a generalized character of $\mathfrak{H}$.

Proof. This is a restatement of the fact that $\mathfrak{U}(\mathfrak{G}, \mathfrak{F}) = \mathcal{Ch}(\mathfrak{G}, \mathfrak{F})$, where $\mathfrak{F}$ is the field of complex numbers.

(15.4) Let $\theta$ be a complex valued function on $\mathfrak{G}$. Then $\theta$ is an irreducible character of $\mathfrak{G}$ if and only if $\theta$ satisfies conditions (i), (ii) of (15.3) as well as

(iii) $||\theta||^2 = 1$.

(iv) $\theta(1) > 0$.

Proof. If $\theta$ is an irreducible character of $\mathfrak{G}$ then (i) – (iv) are clearly satisfied. Assume that (i) – (iv) are satisfied. By (15.3) $\theta = \Sigma a_i \chi_i$, where each $\chi_i$ is an irreducible character of $\mathfrak{G}$ and each $a_i$ is a rational integer. By (iii) $1 = \Sigma a_i^2$. Thus there is exactly one nonzero $a_i = \pm 1$. Hence $\theta = \pm \chi_i$ for some i. By (iv) $\theta = \chi_i$ as required.

We will prove several lemmas and then use them to give a proof of (15.1) and (15.2). Throughout the remainder of this section n denotes the exponent of $\mathfrak{G}$ and $\mathfrak{R}$ is the ring of integer in $\mathfrak{Q}_n$.

(15.5) To prove (15.1) and (15.2) it suffices to show that $1_{\mathfrak{G}} \in \mathfrak{V}(\mathfrak{G}, \mathfrak{F})$.

Proof. By definition

$$\mathfrak{U}_{\mathfrak{D}}(\mathfrak{G}, \mathfrak{F}) \supseteq \mathcal{Ch}_{\mathfrak{D}}(\mathfrak{G}, \mathfrak{F}) \supseteq \mathfrak{V}_{\mathfrak{D}}(\mathfrak{G}, \mathfrak{F}) \supseteq \mathfrak{V}(\mathfrak{G}, \mathfrak{F})$$

$$\mathfrak{U}_{\mathfrak{D}}(\mathfrak{G}, \mathfrak{F})' \supseteq \mathcal{Ch}_{\mathfrak{D}}(\mathfrak{G}, \mathfrak{F})' \supseteq \mathfrak{V}_{\mathfrak{D}}(\mathfrak{G}, \mathfrak{F})' \supseteq \mathfrak{V}(\mathfrak{G}, \mathfrak{F})$$

By (9.3) $\mathfrak{V}_{\mathfrak{D}}(\mathfrak{G}, \mathfrak{F})$, $\mathfrak{V}_{\mathfrak{D}}(\mathfrak{G}, \mathfrak{F})'$ is an ideal of $\mathfrak{U}_{\mathfrak{D}}(\mathfrak{G}, \mathfrak{F})$, $\mathfrak{U}_{\mathfrak{D}}(\mathfrak{G}, \mathfrak{F})'$ respectively. The result follows.

(15.6) Let $\mathfrak{H} = \mathfrak{A}\mathfrak{P}$ be an $\mathfrak{F}$-elementary group with respect to p where $\mathfrak{A} = \langle A \rangle$ is a p′-group and $\mathfrak{P}$ is a p-group.

Let $a = |\mathfrak{A}|$ and let $\mathcal{S}$ be the ring of integers in $\mathcal{Q}_a$. Then there exists $\eta \in \mathcal{C}h_{\mathcal{S}}(\mathfrak{H}, \mathfrak{F})$ such that $\eta(A^i) = a$ or $0$ according to whether $A^i$ is $\mathfrak{F}$-conjugate to $A$ or not.

Proof. Let $\mathfrak{F}_a$ be the extension field of $\mathfrak{F}$ generated by a primitive a th root of unity. Define the function $\zeta$ on $\mathfrak{A}$ by $\zeta(A^i) = a$ or $0$ according to whether $A^i$ is $\mathfrak{F}$-conjugate to A or not. Thus $\zeta = \Sigma_{j=0}^{a-1} c_j \lambda_j$, where $\lambda_j = \lambda^j$ $\lambda$ is a faithful irreducible character of $\mathfrak{A}$ and the $c_j$ are complex numbers. By the orthogonality relations

$$c_j = \frac{1}{a}\sum_{i=0}^{a-1} \zeta(A^i)\,\overline{\lambda_j(A^i)} = \mathrm{Tr}_{\mathfrak{F}_a/\mathfrak{F}}\,\overline{(\lambda_j(A))}$$

Thus $c_j \in \mathcal{S}$ and $\zeta = \Sigma_t c_t \,\mathrm{Tr}_{\mathfrak{F}_a/\mathfrak{F}}(\lambda_t)$, where t ranges over a suitable index set. Let $\theta_t$ be the function defined in (14.2). Let $\eta = \Sigma_t c_t \theta_t$. Then $\eta \in \mathcal{C}h_{\mathcal{S}}(\mathfrak{H}, \mathfrak{F})$ and $\eta(A^i) = \zeta(A^i)$ for $i = 1, \ldots, a$. The proof is complete.

Let $G \in \mathfrak{G}$ the $\mathfrak{F}$-normalizer $\mathbf{N}_{\mathfrak{F}}(G)$ is the set of all elements $H \in \mathfrak{G}$ such that $H^{-1}GH = G^i$, where G is $\mathfrak{F}$-conjugate to $G^i$ in $\langle G\rangle$. The definition implies that $\mathbf{N}_{\mathcal{Q}}(G) = \mathbf{N}(\langle G\rangle)$ and $\mathbf{N}_{\mathfrak{F}}(G) = \mathbf{C}(G)$ if $\mathfrak{F}$ contains a primitive $|\mathfrak{G}|$ th root of unity. If A is a p′-element of $\mathfrak{G}$ and $\mathfrak{P}$ is a $S_p$-group of $\mathbf{N}_{\mathfrak{F}}(A)$ then $\langle A\rangle\mathfrak{P}$ is an $\mathfrak{F}$-elementary group with respect to p.

(15.7) Let $A \in \mathfrak{G}$ and let p be a prime. There exists $\psi \in \mathcal{V}_{\mathcal{R}}(\mathfrak{G}, \mathfrak{F}, p)$ such that $\psi(G) = |\mathbf{N}_{\mathfrak{F}}(A)|$ or $0$ according to whether G is $\mathfrak{F}$-conjugate to A or not.

Proof. The cyclic group $\langle A\rangle$ is $\mathfrak{F}$-elementary with respect to p. Let $\alpha = \alpha_{\mathfrak{A}}$ be the function defined in (13.1). Thus $\alpha^* \in \mathcal{V}_{\mathcal{R}}(\mathfrak{G}, \mathfrak{F}, p)$. The definition of $\alpha$ implies directly that $\psi = \alpha^*$ has the required properties.

(15.8) Let p be a rational prime and let $\mathfrak{p}$ be a prime divisor of p in $\mathfrak{R}$. Let A be a p′-element in $\mathfrak{G}$ of order a. Then there exists $\theta \in \mathfrak{V}_{\mathfrak{R}}(\mathfrak{G}, \mathfrak{F}, p)$ such that $\theta(G) = 0$ if G is a p′-element of $\mathfrak{G}$ which is not $\mathfrak{F}$-conjugate to A and $\theta(A) \equiv 1 \pmod{\mathfrak{p}}$.

Proof. Let $\mathfrak{A} = \langle A \rangle$. Let $\mathfrak{P}$ be a $S_p$-group of $\mathbf{N}_{\mathfrak{F}}(A)$ and let $\mathfrak{H} = \mathfrak{A}\mathfrak{P}$. Thus $\mathfrak{H}$ is $\mathfrak{F}$-elementary. Let $\mathcal{S}$ be the ring of integers in $\mathcal{Q}_a$ and let $\eta$ be the function defined in (15.6). Since $\mathcal{S} \subseteq \mathfrak{R}$, $\eta^* \in \mathfrak{V}_{\mathfrak{R}}(\mathfrak{G}, \mathfrak{F}, p)$. The only p′-elements of $\mathfrak{H}$ are in $\mathfrak{A}$ thus the definition of $\eta^*$ yields directly that $\eta^*(G) = 0$ if G is a p′-element which is not $\mathfrak{F}$-conjugate to A and

$$\eta^*(A) = \frac{1}{|\mathfrak{H}|} \sum_{\mathfrak{G}} \eta(G^{-1}AG) = \frac{a}{|\mathfrak{H}|} |\mathbf{N}_{\mathfrak{F}}(A)| = |\mathbf{N}_{\mathfrak{F}}(A):\mathfrak{P}|$$

Since $\mathfrak{P}$ is a $S_p$-group of $\mathbf{N}_{\mathfrak{F}}(A)$, $p \nmid \eta^*(A)$. Hence there exists a rational integer b such that $b\eta^*(A) \equiv 1 \pmod{p}$. Then $\theta = b\eta^*$ has the required properties.

(15.9) Let p be a rational prime and let $\mathfrak{p}$ be a prime divisor of p in $\mathfrak{R}$. There exists $\zeta \in \mathfrak{V}_{\mathfrak{R}}(\mathfrak{G}, \mathfrak{F}, p)$ such that $\zeta(G) \equiv 1 \pmod{\mathfrak{p}}$ for all $G \in \mathfrak{G}$.

Proof. Let $\{A_i\}$ be a complete system of representatives of the $\mathfrak{F}$-conjugate classes of $\mathfrak{G}$ which consists of p′-elements. Let $\theta_i$ be the function defined in (15.8) corresponding to $A_i$ and let $\zeta = \Sigma\theta_i$. Then $\zeta(A) \equiv 1 \pmod{\mathfrak{p}}$ for all p′-elements A of $\mathfrak{G}$. If $G \in \mathfrak{G}$ then $G = AP = PA$, where P is a p-element and A is a p′-element. By (6.4) $\zeta(G) \equiv 1 \pmod{\mathfrak{p}}$.

(15.10) Let $|\mathfrak{G}| = p^c b$, where $(p,b) = 1$. Then $b1_{\mathfrak{G}} \in \mathfrak{V}_{\mathfrak{R}}(\mathfrak{G}, \mathfrak{F}, p)$.

Proof. Let $\zeta$ be the function constructed in (15.9). By induction $\zeta(G)^{p^s} \equiv 1 \pmod{\mathfrak{p}^s}$ for all s and all $G \in \mathfrak{G}$. The construction of $\zeta$ was independent of the choice of the prime divisor $\wp$ of p. Thus for suitable s $\zeta(G)^{p^s} \equiv 1 (\mathrm{mod}\ p^c)$ for all $G \in \mathfrak{G}$. Clearly $b\zeta^{p^s} \in \mathfrak{V}_{\mathfrak{R}}(\mathfrak{G}, \mathfrak{F}, p)$. It remains to show that $b(1_{\mathfrak{G}} - \zeta^{p^s}) \in \mathfrak{V}_{\mathfrak{R}}(\mathfrak{G}, \mathfrak{F}, p)$.

Let $A_1, A_2, \ldots$ be a complete system of representatives of the $\mathfrak{F}$-conjugate classes of $\mathfrak{G}$. Let $\psi_i$ be the function defined in (15.7) corresponding to $A_i$. Then

$$b(1_{\mathfrak{G}} - \zeta^{p^s}) = \sum_i \frac{b\{1 - \zeta^{p^s}(A_i)\}}{|\mathbf{N}_{\mathfrak{F}}(A_i)|} \psi_i$$

Since $\zeta^{p^s} \equiv 1 \ (\mathrm{mod}\ p^c)$ it follows that

$$\frac{b\{1 - \zeta^{p^s}(A_i)\}}{|\mathbf{N}_{\mathfrak{F}}(A_i)|} \in \mathfrak{R}$$

Thus by (15.7) $b(1_{\mathfrak{G}} - \zeta^{p^s}) \in \mathfrak{V}_{\mathfrak{R}}(\mathfrak{G}, \mathfrak{F}, p)$ as required.

(15.11) <u>Let</u> $|\mathfrak{G}| = p^c b$, <u>where</u> $(p, b) = 1$. <u>Then</u> $b1_{\mathfrak{G}} \in \mathfrak{V}(\mathfrak{G}, \mathfrak{F}, p)$.

<u>Proof.</u> Let $\epsilon$ be a primitive $n^{th}$ root of unity. Then $\{\epsilon^i \mid 0 \leq i < \varphi(n)\}$ is a basis of $\mathfrak{R}$ as a module over the rational integers. By (15.10) $b1_{\mathfrak{G}} = \Sigma a_i \psi_i^*$, where $a_i \in \mathfrak{R}$ and $\psi_i$ is a character of some subgroup which is $\mathfrak{F}$-elementary with respect to p. Let $a_i = \Sigma_j a_{ij} \epsilon^j$, where $a_{ij}$ is a rational integer for all i, j. Thus $b1_{\mathfrak{G}} = \Sigma_{i,j} a_{ij} \epsilon^j \psi_i^*$. Let $\chi_1 = 1_{\mathfrak{G}}, \chi_2, \ldots$ be all the irreducible characters of $\mathfrak{G}$. Then

$$b\,\delta_{sl} = (b1_{\mathfrak{G}}, \chi_s) = \sum_j \epsilon^j \left\{ \sum_i a_{ij}(\psi_i^*, \chi_s) \right\}$$

This implies that $\Sigma_i a_{io} (\psi_i^*, \chi_s) = b\delta_{sl}$. Thus $b1_{\mathfrak{G}} = \Sigma_i a_{io} \psi_i^*$ proving the result.

The proof of (15.1) and (15.2) is now very simple. Let $\{p_i\}$ be the set of distinct primes dividing $|\mathfrak{G}|$. For each i let $|\mathfrak{G}| = p_i^{c_i} b_i$, where $p_i \nmid b_i$. By (15.11) $b_i 1_{\mathfrak{G}} \in \mathfrak{V}(\mathfrak{G}, \mathfrak{F})$. There exist rational integers $a_i$ such that $\Sigma a_i b_i = 1$. Thus

$$1_{\mathfrak{G}} = \sum_i a_i b_i 1_{\mathfrak{G}} \in \mathfrak{V}(\mathfrak{G}, \mathfrak{F})$$

By (15.5) the proof is complete.

The following lemma is of use in computing Schur indices.

(15.12) Let $\chi$ be an irreducible character of $\mathfrak{G}$. Let $\mathfrak{L}$ be a field such that $\mathfrak{F}(\chi) \subset \mathfrak{L} \subset \mathfrak{F}(\epsilon)$, where $\epsilon$ is a primitive $n^{th}$ root of unity and $[\mathfrak{F}(\epsilon):\mathfrak{L}]$ is a power of p. Then there exists a subgroup $\mathfrak{H}$ of $\mathfrak{G}$ which is $\mathfrak{L}$-elementary with respect to p and an irreducible character $\xi$ of $\mathfrak{H}$ such that $\xi \in \mathfrak{L}$ and $p \nmid (\chi, \xi^*)$.

Proof. Let $|\mathfrak{G}| = p^c b$, where $(p, b) = 1$. By (15.11) there exist subgroups $\mathfrak{H}_j$ of $\mathfrak{G}$ which are $\mathfrak{L}$-elementary with respect to p such that $b1_{\mathfrak{G}} = \Sigma a_j \varphi_j^*$, where $\varphi_j$ is a character of $\mathfrak{H}_j$ and $\varphi_j \in \mathfrak{L}$. By (9.3) this implies that $\chi_{|\mathfrak{H}_j} \varphi_j \in \mathfrak{L}$ and

$$b\chi = \sum a_j \chi \varphi_j^* = \sum a_j (\chi_{|\mathfrak{H}_j} \varphi_j)^*$$

For any irreducible character $\xi$ of $\mathfrak{H}_j$ let $T(\xi) = Tr_{\mathfrak{L}(\xi)/\mathfrak{L}}(\xi)$.

Thus there exists subgroups $\mathfrak{H}_i$ of $\mathfrak{G}$ which are $\mathfrak{L}$-elementary with respect to p and irreducible characters $\xi_i$ of $\mathfrak{H}_i$ such that $b\chi = \Sigma d_i T(\xi_i)^*$. Hence

$$b = (b\chi, \chi) = \sum_i d_i (\chi, T(\xi_i)^*) = \sum_i d_i |\mathfrak{L}(\xi_i):\mathfrak{L}| (\chi, \xi_i^*)$$

Since $(b, p) = 1$ this implies that for some $\xi = \xi_i$ and $\mathfrak{H} = \mathfrak{H}_i$

$$|\mathfrak{L}(\xi): \mathfrak{L}| (\chi, \xi^*) \not\equiv 0 \pmod{p}$$

Since $\xi \in \mathfrak{F}(\epsilon)$ and $|\mathfrak{F}(\epsilon) : \mathfrak{L}|$ is a power of p this implies that $\mathfrak{L}(\xi) = \mathfrak{L}$. Hence $\xi \in \mathfrak{L}$ and $(\chi, \xi^*) \not\equiv 0 \pmod{p}$ as required.

## §16. SCHUR INDICES AND SPLITTING FIELDS

By combining the results of the last two sections we can now derive some information concerning Schur indices and splitting fields.

(16.1) (Brauer [2]) Let $\mathfrak{F}$ be a field of characteristic 0. Let $\chi$ be an irreducible character of $\mathfrak{G}$. For each rational prime p there exists a finite extension field $\mathfrak{L}$ of $\mathfrak{F}$, a subgroup $\mathfrak{H}$ of $\mathfrak{G}$ which is $\mathfrak{L}$-elementary with respect to p and an irreducible character $\xi$ of $\mathfrak{H}$ with $\xi \in \mathfrak{L}$ such that if $p^a | m_{\mathfrak{F}}(\chi)$ then $p^a | m_{\mathfrak{F}}(\xi)$.

Proof. Let n be the exponent of $\mathfrak{G}$. Let $\mathfrak{F} \subseteq \mathfrak{L} \subseteq \mathfrak{F}(\epsilon)$ such that $[\mathfrak{F}(\epsilon): \mathfrak{L}]$ is a power of p and $p \nmid |\mathfrak{L}: \mathfrak{F}|$. Let $\xi$ be the character constructed in (15.12). Then $m_{\mathfrak{F}}(\xi)\, \xi^*$ is afforded by an $\mathfrak{L}$-representation of $\mathfrak{G}$. Hence by (11.4) $m_{\mathfrak{L}}(\chi) | (\chi, m_{\mathfrak{F}}(\xi)\, \xi^*)$. Since $m_{\mathfrak{F}}(\chi) | m_{\mathfrak{L}}(\chi)\, |\mathfrak{L}: \mathfrak{F}|$ and $p \nmid (\chi, \xi^*) \times |\mathfrak{L}: \mathfrak{F}|$ this yields that $p^a | m_{\mathfrak{F}}(\xi)$ as was asserted.

The following special case of (16.1) is useful.

(16.2) Let $\mathfrak{F}$ be a field of characteristic 0. Assume that for any $\mathfrak{F}$-elementary subgroup $\mathfrak{H}$ of $\mathfrak{G}$ and any irreducible character $\varphi$ of $\mathfrak{H}$, $m_{\mathfrak{F}}(\varphi) = 1$. Then $m_{\mathfrak{F}}(\chi) = 1$ for any irreducible character $\chi$ of $\mathfrak{G}$.

The next result was an open question for about 40 years. For this result the argument can be considerably simplified. See Brauer and Tate [1] and Curtis and Reiner p. 294.

(16.3) (Brauer) Let n be the exponent of $\mathfrak{G}$. Then $\mathbf{Q}_n$ is a splitting field of $\mathfrak{G}$.

Proof. By (16.2) it suffices to prove the result in case $\mathfrak{G}$ is $\mathbf{Q}_n$-elementary. Since $\mathbf{Q}_n$-elementary groups are nilpotent every character of $\mathfrak{G}$ is monomial. The result follows.

(16.3) has been strengthened as follows.

(16.4) (Solomon [1]) Let $\pi(\mathfrak{G}) = \{p_i\}$. Let $\mathfrak{F}$ be a field of characteristic 0 which contains a primitive $\Pi p_i$th root of unity. If $|\mathfrak{G}|$ is even assume also that $\sqrt{-1} \in \mathfrak{F}$. Then $m_{\mathfrak{F}}(\chi) = 1$ for any irreducible character $\chi$ of $\mathfrak{G}$. Thus in particular $m_{\mathbf{Q}}(\chi) | 2\,\Pi_i (p_i - 1)$ and if $|\mathfrak{G}|$ is odd then $m_{\mathbf{Q}}(\chi) | \Pi_i (p_i - 1)$.

Proof. By (16.2) it may be assumed that $\mathfrak{G}$ is $\mathfrak{F}$-elementary. The result follows from (14.4) and (11.3).

(16.5) (Fong [1]) Let p be a prime and let $|\mathfrak{G}| = p^c b$, where $(p,b) = 1$. Let $\mathfrak{F}$ be a field of characteristic 0 which contains a primitive $b$th root of unity. If $p = 2$ assume also that either $\sqrt{-1} \in \mathfrak{F}$ or $\sqrt{-3} \in \mathfrak{F}$. Then $m_{\mathfrak{F}}(\chi) = 1$ for every irreducible character $\chi$ of $\mathfrak{G}$.

Proof. By (16.2) it may be assumed that $\mathfrak{G}$ is $\mathfrak{F}$-elementary with respect to some prime q. If $q \neq p$ the result follows from (14.1). Suppose that $p = q$. Thus $\mathfrak{G}$ is nilpotent since $\mathbf{Q}_b \subseteq \mathfrak{F}$ and the result follows from (14.5).

The special case below which motivated (16.5) was first

proved by using the theory of algebras and parts of the class field theory. It was of great importance in applications of the theory of modular characters.

(16.6) (Brauer) Let p be a prime. There exists an algebraic number field $\mathfrak{F}$ in which p does not ramify such that $m_{\mathfrak{F}}(\chi) = 1$ for every irreducible character $\chi$ of $\mathfrak{G}$.

## §17. EQUATIONS IN GROUPS

The next result is due to Frobenius. The proof given here is due to Brauer [3].

(17.1) Let $\mathfrak{g}$ be an integral domain which contains a primitive $|\mathfrak{G}|$ th root of unity and whose quotient field has characteristic 0. Let n be a positive integer. For any subset $\mathfrak{K}$ of $\mathfrak{G}$ which is a union conjugate classes define $\theta_{\mathfrak{K}}(G) = \theta_{\mathfrak{K}}(G:\mathfrak{G})$ for $G \in \mathfrak{G}$ by

$$\theta_{\mathfrak{K}}(G) = \frac{|\mathfrak{G}|}{(|\mathfrak{G}|, n)} \qquad \text{if} \quad G^n \in \mathfrak{K}$$

$$\theta_{\mathfrak{K}}(G) = 0 \qquad \text{if} \quad G^n \notin \mathfrak{K}$$

Then $\theta_{\mathfrak{K}} \in \mathfrak{Ch}_{\mathfrak{g}}(\mathfrak{G})$.

Proof. If $\mathfrak{H}$ is a subgroup of $\mathfrak{G}$ then the quotient of $|\mathfrak{G}|/(|\mathfrak{G}|, n)$ by $|\mathfrak{H}|/(|\mathfrak{H}|, n)$ is a rational integer c and $\mathfrak{K} \cap \mathfrak{H}$ is a union of conjugate classes of $\mathfrak{H}$. Thus for $H \in \mathfrak{H}$

$$\theta_{\mathfrak{K}}(H;\mathfrak{G}) = c\, \theta_{\mathfrak{K} \cap \mathfrak{H}}(H;\mathfrak{H})$$

If the result has been proved for elementary groups then since $\theta_{\mathfrak{K}}$ is clearly a class function the result follows in general from (15.1). Thus it may be assumed that $\mathfrak{G}$ is an elementary group.

Let $\mathfrak{K}_1 = \{1\}, \mathfrak{K}_2, \ldots, \mathfrak{K}_k$ be all the conjugate classes of $\mathfrak{G}$. If $\mathfrak{K} = \cup \mathfrak{K}_i$, where i ranges over some index set then $\theta_{\mathfrak{K}} = \Sigma\, \theta_{\mathfrak{K}_i}$. Thus it may be assumed that $\mathfrak{K} = \mathfrak{K}_i$ for some i since the result is trivial in case $\mathfrak{K}$ is empty. Furthermore

$$\sum_{i=1}^{k} \theta_{\mathfrak{K}_i} = \frac{|\mathfrak{G}|}{(|\mathfrak{G}|, n)} \qquad 1_{\mathfrak{G}} \in \mathcal{C}h_{\mathfrak{g}}(\mathfrak{G})$$

Thus it suffices to prove the result in case $\mathfrak{K} = \mathfrak{K}_i$ with $i \neq 1$.

If $\mathfrak{G} = \mathfrak{G}_1 \times \mathfrak{G}_2$ with $(|\mathfrak{G}_1|, |\mathfrak{G}_2|) = 1$ then every element in $\mathfrak{K}$ is of the form $K_1K_2$, where $\mathfrak{K}_i$ ranges over a conjugate class $\mathfrak{K}^{(i)}$ of $\mathfrak{G}_i$ for $i = 1,2$. Thus for $G_i \in \mathfrak{G}_i$, $i = 1,2$

$$\theta_{\mathfrak{K}}(G_1 G_2; \mathfrak{G}) = \theta_{\mathfrak{K}_1}(G_1; \mathfrak{G}_1)\, \theta_{\mathfrak{K}_2}(G_2; \mathfrak{G}_2)$$

Since $\mathfrak{G}$ is elementary it thus may be assumed that $\mathfrak{G}$ is a p-group for some prime p.

Let $\theta = \theta_{\mathfrak{K}}$. We need to show that if $\chi$ is any irreducible character of $\mathfrak{G}$ then $(\theta,\chi) \in \mathfrak{g}$. By (10.2) $\chi = \lambda^*$ where $\lambda$ is a linear character of some subgroup $\mathfrak{H}$ of $\mathfrak{G}$. By the Frobenius reciprocity theorem $(\theta_{|\mathfrak{H}}, \lambda)_{\mathfrak{H}} = (\theta, \chi)$. Let $s = \Sigma_{\mathfrak{H}}\theta(H) \times \lambda(H^{-1})$. It remains to show that $s/|\mathfrak{H}| \in \mathfrak{g}$. Let $|\mathfrak{G}| = p^a$. It may be assumed that $n = p^b$ is a power of p. If $b \geq a$ then $H^n = 1$ for $H \in \mathfrak{H}$ and so $\theta(H) = 0$ for $H \in \mathfrak{H}$. Suppose that $b < a$. Then $s = p^{a-b}\Sigma\lambda(H^{-1})$ where H ranges over these elements in $\mathfrak{H}$ such that $H^n \in \mathfrak{K}$. Distribute these elements into pairwise disjoint sets as follows. $H_1$ and $H_2$ are in the same set if and only if each is a power of the other and $H_1^n = H_2^n \in \mathfrak{K}$. It suffices to show that for any such set $\mathfrak{A}$ $\Sigma_{\mathfrak{A}}\lambda(H^{-1}) \equiv 0 (\text{mod } p^b)$. If $A \in \mathfrak{A}$ and A has order

$p^d$ then $d > b$ since $\mathfrak{K} \neq \{1\}$. Furthermore $A^j \in \mathfrak{A}$ if and only if $jp^b \equiv p^b \pmod{p^d}$, that is $j \equiv 1 \pmod{p^{d-b}}$. Hence if $\lambda(A^{p^{d-b}}) = \epsilon$

$$\Sigma_{\mathfrak{A}} \lambda(H^{-1}) = \sum_{i=0}^{p^b-1} \lambda(A^{-1+ip^{d-b}}) = \lambda(A^{-1}) \sum_{i=0}^{p^b-1} \epsilon^i$$

Since $\epsilon$ is a $p^b$-th root of unity this implies that $\Sigma_{\mathfrak{A}}\lambda(H^{-1}) = 0$ or $\lambda(A^{-1})p^b$. Hence in any case $\Sigma_{\mathfrak{A}} \lambda(H^{-1}) \equiv 0 \pmod{p^b}$ as required.

(17.2) Let $\theta_{\mathfrak{K}}$ be defined as in (17.1). Then $\theta_{\{1\}}$ is a generalized character of $\mathfrak{G}$.

Proof. Let $\{\chi_i\}$ be the set of irreducible characters of $\mathfrak{G}$. Let $\theta = \theta_{\{1\}} = \Sigma a_i \chi_i$. By (17.1) each $a_i$ is an algebraic integer in $\mathfrak{Q}_{|\mathfrak{G}|}$. Let $\sigma \in \mathcal{G}_{\mathfrak{Q}_{|\mathfrak{G}|}/\mathfrak{Q}}$. Then $\epsilon^\sigma = \epsilon^c$ for some c with $(c, |\mathfrak{G}|) = 1$ where $\epsilon$ is a primitive $|\mathfrak{G}|$-th root of unity. Since $\theta(G) = \theta(G^c)$ for $G \in \mathfrak{G}$ this implies that

$$a_i^\sigma = \frac{1}{|\mathfrak{G}|} \Sigma_{\mathfrak{G}}\, \theta(G)\, \chi_i(G^{-c})$$

$$= \frac{1}{|\mathfrak{G}|} \Sigma_{\mathfrak{G}}\, \theta(G^c)\, \chi_i(G^{-c})$$

$$= a_i$$

Thus $a_i \in \mathfrak{Q}$ as required.

(17.3) Let n be a positive integer and let $\mathfrak{K}$ be a union of conjugate classes of $\mathfrak{G}$. Let $\mathfrak{A}_{\mathfrak{K}} = \{G \mid G^n \in \mathfrak{K}\}$. If $\chi$ is a character of $\mathfrak{G}$ then $[1/(|\mathfrak{G}|, n)] \Sigma_{\mathfrak{A}_{\mathfrak{K}}} \chi(G)$ is an algebraic integer. Furthermore $(|\mathfrak{G}|, n) \,|\, |\mathfrak{A}_{\mathfrak{K}}|$.

Proof. Let $\theta_{\mathfrak{K}}$ be defined as in (17.1). It suffices to prove the result in case $\chi$ is an irreducible character. Then

$$\frac{1}{(|\mathfrak{G}|, n)} \sum_{\mathfrak{A}_{\mathfrak{K}}} \chi(G) = (\theta_{\mathfrak{K}}, \overline{\chi})$$

The first statement follows from (17.1). The last statement follows by setting $\chi = 1_{\mathfrak{G}}$.

By using different methods Solomon [3] has shown that in case $\mathfrak{K} = \{1\}$ in (17.3) then even

$$\frac{1}{(|\mathfrak{G}|, n)} \frac{1}{m_{\mathbf{Q}}(\chi)} \Sigma_{\mathfrak{A}_{\{1\}}} \chi(G)$$

is an algebraic integer.

Frobenius has conjectured that if $(|\mathfrak{G}|, n) = |\mathfrak{A}_{\{1\}}|$ then $\mathfrak{A} \triangleleft \mathfrak{G}$. Only special cases of this conjecture have so far been proved.

As an application of these results we prove here a theorem that arises more naturally in the theory of modular representations.

(17.4) Let $|\mathfrak{G}| = g_1 g_2$ with $(g_1, g_2) = 1$. Let $\chi$ be an irreducible character of $\mathfrak{G}$. If $g_1 | \chi(1)$ then $\chi(G) = 0$ unless $G^{g_2} = 1$. Conversely if $\chi(G) = 0$ whenever $G^{g_1} = 1$, $G \neq 1$ then $g_1 | \chi(1)$.

Proof. Suppose first that $\chi(G) = 0$ whenever $G^{g_1} = 1$, $G \neq 1$. Let p be a prime such that $p | g_1$ and let $\mathfrak{P}$ be a

$S_p$-group of $\mathfrak{G}$. Thus $\chi(G) = 0$ for $G \in \mathfrak{P}^{\#}$. Hence by (6.2) $|\mathfrak{P}|\,|\,\chi(1)$. Therefore $g_1 | \chi(1)$.

Assume now that $g_1 | \chi(1)$. Let $\mathfrak{A} = \{G | G^{g_2} = 1\}$. By (17.3) $g_2 | \Sigma_{\mathfrak{A}} |\chi(G)|^2$. Let $\mathfrak{A} = \cup\, \mathfrak{K}_i$ where each $\mathfrak{K}_i$ is a conjugate class of $\mathfrak{G}$ and let $G_i \in \mathfrak{K}_i$. Thus $\Sigma_{\mathfrak{A}} |\chi(G)|^2 = \Sigma_i |\mathfrak{K}_i| \chi(G_i) \times \overline{\chi(G_i)}$. Hence by (2.17) $\chi(1) | \Sigma_{\mathfrak{A}} |\chi(G)|^2$. Therefore

$$g_1 g_2 \,|\, \sum_{\mathfrak{A}} |\chi(G)|^2$$

As $\chi(1) > 0$, $|\chi(G)|^2 \geq 0$ for all $G \in \mathfrak{G}$ and $\Sigma_{\mathfrak{A}} |\chi(G)|^2$ is a rational integer, this yields that

$$\sum_{\mathfrak{A}} |\chi(G)|^2 \leq \sum_{\mathfrak{G}} |\chi(G)|^2 = |\mathfrak{G}| \leq \sum_{\mathfrak{A}} |\chi(G)|^2$$

Therefore $\Sigma_{\mathfrak{G} - \mathfrak{A}} |\chi(G)|^2 = 0$ and so $\chi(G) = 0$ for $G \in \mathfrak{G} - \mathfrak{A}$ as was to be shown.

As an immediate consequence of (17.4) we get

(17.5) <u>Let</u> $|\mathfrak{G}| = g_1 g_2$ <u>with</u> $(g_1 g_2) = 1$. <u>Let</u> $\chi$ <u>be an irreducible character of</u> $\mathfrak{G}$. <u>If</u> $\chi(G) = 0$ <u>whenever</u> $G^{g_1} = 1, G \neq 1$ <u>then</u> $\chi(G) = 0$ <u>whenever</u> $G^{g_2} \neq 1$.

# CHAPTER III

## § 18. CRITERIA FOR SOLVABILITY

Throughout the rest of these notes we will to a large extent be concerned with applying the theory of character to questions concerning the structure of finite groups. We begin with one of the earliest and most elegant results of this kind due to Burnside which also forms the starting point of P. Hall's theory of solvable groups. Only elementary properties of characters will be used in this section. The first four results are due to Burnside. The remaining results in this section are due to P. Hall.

(18.1) *Suppose that* $(|\mathfrak{K}|, \chi(1)) = 1$ *for some conjugate class of* $\mathfrak{K}$ *of* $\mathfrak{G}$ *and some irreducible character* $\chi$ *of* $\mathfrak{G}$. *Then for* $G \in \mathfrak{K}$ *either* $\chi(G) = 0$ *or* $|\chi(G)| = \chi(1)$.

*Proof.* There exist rational integers $s, t$ such that $s|\mathfrak{K}| + t\chi(1) = 1$. Hence $s|\mathfrak{K}|\chi(G) + t\chi(1)\chi(G) = \chi(G)$. Thus by (2.17) $a = \chi(G)/\chi(1)$ is an algebraic integer. Let $a_1 = a, a_2, \ldots$, be all the algebraic conjugates of $a$. Since every algebraic conjugate of a root of unity is again a root of unity it follows that each $a_i$ is a sum of $\chi(1)$ roots of unity divided by $\chi(1)$. Thus $|a_i| \leq 1$ for all $i$. Therefore $|\Pi a_i| \leq 1$. Since $\Pi a_i$ is a rational integer this yields that $|\Pi a_i| = 0$ or $1$. In the first case $a = 0$ and thus $\chi(G) = 0$. In the second case $|a| = 1$ and so $|\chi(G)| = \chi(1)$.

(18.2) *Suppose that* $|\mathfrak{K}|$ *is a power of a prime for some conjugate class* $\mathfrak{K} \neq \{1\}$ *of* $\mathfrak{G}$. *Then* $\mathfrak{G}$ *is not a noncyclic simple group.*

Proof. Let $|\mathfrak{K}| = p^c$ where p is a prime. Let $G \in \mathfrak{K}$. If $c = 0$ then $G \in \mathbf{Z}(\mathfrak{G})$ and the result follows. Suppose that $c > 0$ and $\mathfrak{G}$ is a noncyclic simple group. Then every nonprincipal irreducible character of $\mathfrak{G}$ is faithful. Let $\chi_1 = 1_{\mathfrak{G}}, \chi_2, \ldots$ be all the irreducible characters of $\mathfrak{G}$. Then

$$1 + \sum_{i \neq 1} \chi_i(1)\chi_i(G) = 0$$

Thus there exists $i \neq 1$ such that $\chi_i(1)\chi_i(G) \not\equiv 0 \pmod{p}$. Hence $(|\mathfrak{K}|, \chi_i(1)) = 1$ and $\chi_i(G) \neq 0$. Thus by (18.1) $|\chi_i(G)| = \chi_i(1)$. Therefore by (6.7) $G \in \mathbf{Z}(\mathfrak{G})$ contrary to the fact that $\mathfrak{G}$ is a noncyclic simple group.

(18.3) *If $|\mathfrak{G}| = p^a q^b$ where p, q are primes then $\mathfrak{G}$ is solvable.*

Proof. The proof is by induction on $|\mathfrak{G}|$. It may be assumed that $p \neq q$. If $a = 0$ or $b = 0$ the result is clear. Assume that $ab \neq 0$. Let $\mathfrak{P}$ be a $S_p$-group of $\mathfrak{G}$. Let $P \in \mathbf{Z}(\mathfrak{P})^\#$ and let $\mathfrak{K}$ be the conjugate class of $\mathfrak{G}$ with $P \in \mathfrak{K}$. Since $\mathfrak{P} \subseteq \mathbf{C}(P)$ it follows that $|\mathfrak{K}| = |\mathfrak{G}:\mathbf{C}(P)|$ is a power of q. Hence by (18.2) there exists $\mathfrak{H} \lhd \mathfrak{G}$ with $\langle 1 \rangle \neq \mathfrak{H} \neq \mathfrak{G}$. By induction $\mathfrak{H}$ and $\mathfrak{G}/\mathfrak{H}$ are solvable. Thus $\mathfrak{G}$ is solvable.

The following consequence of (18.1) was also observed by Burnside.

(18.4) *Suppose that $\mathfrak{G}$ has an irreducible character $\chi$ with $\chi(1) = p$ for p a prime. Let $\mathfrak{P}$ be a $S_p$-group of $\mathfrak{G}$. If $\mathfrak{G}$ is simple then $|\mathfrak{P}| = p$.*

Proof. Suppose that $\mathfrak{G}$ is simple. Thus $\chi$ is faithful. If $\mathfrak{P}$ is nonabelian then $\chi_{|\mathfrak{P}}$ is irreducible. Thus by (6.7) $|\chi(G)| = \chi(1)$ for $G \in \mathbf{Z}(\mathfrak{P})^\#$ and so $\mathbf{Z}(\mathfrak{P}) \subseteq \mathbf{Z}(\mathfrak{G})$ contrary to the simplicity of $\mathfrak{G}$. Thus $\mathfrak{P}$ is abelian. Hence if $P \in \mathfrak{P}^\#$ and $\mathfrak{K}$ is the conjugate class of $\mathfrak{G}$ with $P \in \mathfrak{K}$ we see that $(|\mathfrak{K}|, \chi(1)) = (|\mathfrak{G}:\mathbf{C}(P)|, p) = 1$. Thus by (18.1) $\chi(P) = 0$ or $|\chi(P)| = \chi(1)$. By (6.7) the latter case implies that $P \in Z(\mathfrak{G})$

contrary to the simplicity of $\mathfrak{G}$. Therefore $\chi(P) = 0$ for $P \in \mathfrak{R}^{\#}$. Hence $|\mathfrak{P}| \mid \chi(1)$ by (6.2) which implies that $|\mathfrak{P}| = p$.

The next three results are elementary preliminaries.

(18.5) If $\mathfrak{G}$ is solvable and $|\mathfrak{G}| > 1$ then there exists a prime p and a p-group $\mathfrak{P}$ such that $\langle 1 \rangle \neq \mathfrak{P} \triangleleft \mathfrak{G}$.

Proof. Induction on $|\mathfrak{G}|$. If $|\mathfrak{G}|$ is a prime let $\mathfrak{P} = \mathfrak{G}$. Suppose that $\mathfrak{G}$ is not a prime. Since $\mathfrak{G}$ is solvable, there exists $\mathfrak{H} \triangleleft \mathfrak{G}$ such that $|\mathfrak{G}:\mathfrak{H}|$ is a prime. By induction $\mathfrak{H}$ contains a normal subgroup distinct from $\langle 1 \rangle$ which is a p-group for some prime p. Let $\mathfrak{P}$ be a maximal normal p-subgroup of $\mathfrak{H}$. Thus $\mathfrak{P} \neq \langle 1 \rangle$. Since $\mathfrak{P}$ is the intersection of all the $S_p$-subgroups of $\mathfrak{H}$ it follows that $\mathfrak{P}$ is characteristic in $\mathfrak{H}$ and thus $\mathfrak{P} \triangleleft \mathfrak{G}$.

(18.6) Let $|\mathfrak{G}| = \Pi p_i^{c_i}$, where $\{p_i\} = \pi(\mathfrak{G})$. Suppose that $\mathfrak{H}_1$ and $\mathfrak{H}_2$ are subgroups of $\mathfrak{G}$ such that for each i, $p_i^{c_i} \mid |\mathfrak{H}_1|$ or $p_i^{c_i} \mid |\mathfrak{H}_2|$. Then $\mathfrak{G} = \mathfrak{H}_1\mathfrak{H}_2$ and $|\mathfrak{H}_1 \cap \mathfrak{H}_2| = (h_1, h_2)$.

Proof. Since $\mathfrak{H}_1\mathfrak{H}_2$ is a union of cosets of $\mathfrak{H}_1$ and also a union of cosets of $\mathfrak{H}_2$ it follows that for each i, $p_i^{c_i} \mid |\mathfrak{H}_1\mathfrak{H}_2|$. Hence $|\mathfrak{G}| \mid |\mathfrak{H}_1\mathfrak{H}_2|$ and so $\mathfrak{G} = \mathfrak{H}_1\mathfrak{H}_2$. By counting cosets it is easily shown that $|\mathfrak{H}_1||\mathfrak{H}_2| = |\mathfrak{H}_1\mathfrak{H}_2||\mathfrak{H}_1 \cap \mathfrak{H}_2|$. Since $|\mathfrak{G}| = |\mathfrak{H}_1\mathfrak{H}_2|$ is the least common multiple of $|\mathfrak{H}_1|$ and $|\mathfrak{H}_2|$ the result follows.

(18.7) Let $|\mathfrak{G}| = \Pi_{i=1}^{s} p_i^{c_i}$ where $\pi(\mathfrak{G}) = \{p_1, \ldots, p_s\}$. Suppose that for each $i = 1, \ldots, s$, $\mathfrak{G}$ contains a subgroup $\mathfrak{H}_i$ with $|\mathfrak{G}:\mathfrak{H}_i| = p_i^{c_i}$. Let $\mathfrak{T}_j = \mathfrak{H}_j \cap \ldots \cap \mathfrak{H}_s$ for $j = 1, \ldots, s$. Then $|\mathfrak{T}_j| = \Pi_{i=1}^{j-1} p_i^{c_i}$.

Proof. The proof is by induction on $s-j$. If $s-j = 0$ then $\mathfrak{T}_j = \mathfrak{H}_s$ and the result follows. Suppose now that

$|\mathfrak{D}_{j+1}| = \Pi_{i=1}^{j} p_i^{c_i}$. Since $\mathfrak{D}_j = \mathfrak{D}_{j+1} \cap \mathfrak{H}_j$ the result follows from (18.6).

(18.8) Let $|\mathfrak{G}| = p_1^{c_1} p_2^{c_2} m$, where $p_1$ and $p_2$ are primes not dividing m. Suppose that $\mathfrak{G}$ contains a subgroup $\mathfrak{D}$ with $|\mathfrak{D}| = p_1^{c_1} p_2^{c_2}$ and $\mathfrak{G}$ contains subgroups $\mathfrak{H}_i$ for i = 1,2 such that $|\mathfrak{G}:\mathfrak{H}_i|$ is a power of $p_i$ and $|\mathfrak{G}:\mathfrak{H}_i| > 1$. Then $\mathfrak{G}$ is not simple.

Proof. By (18.3) $\mathfrak{D}$ is solvable. Hence by (18.5) there exists a p-group $\mathfrak{P}$ with $\langle 1 \rangle \neq \mathfrak{P} \lhd \mathfrak{D}$ and $p = p_1$ or $p_2$. Without loss of generality it may be assumed that $p = p_2$. Replacing $\mathfrak{H}_1$ by a conjugate if necessary it may be assumed that some $S_p$-group of $\mathfrak{D}$ is contained in $\mathfrak{H}_1$. Thus $\mathfrak{P} \subseteq \mathfrak{H}_1$ since $\mathfrak{P}$ is contained in every $S_p$-group of $\mathfrak{D}$. By (18.6) $\mathfrak{D}\mathfrak{H}_1 = \mathfrak{G}$. Thus every conjugate of $\mathfrak{H}_1$ is of the form $D^{-1}\mathfrak{H}_1 D$ for some $D \in \mathfrak{D}$. Therefore $D^{-1}\mathfrak{P}D = \mathfrak{P}$ since $\mathfrak{P} \lhd \mathfrak{D}$. Consequently $\mathfrak{P} \subseteq \bigcap_{\mathfrak{G}} G^{-1}\mathfrak{H}_1 G \lhd \mathfrak{G}$. The group $\bigcap_{\mathfrak{G}} G^{-1}\mathfrak{H}_1 G$ is a proper normal subgroup of $\mathfrak{G}$ and so $\mathfrak{G}$ is not simple.

(18.9) Let $|\mathfrak{G}| = \Pi_{i=1}^{s} p_i^{c_i}$ where $\pi(\mathfrak{G}) = \{p_1, \ldots, p_s\}$. Suppose that for each $i = 1, \ldots, s$, $\mathfrak{G}$ contains a subgroup $\mathfrak{H}_i$ with $|\mathfrak{G}:\mathfrak{H}_i| = p_i^{c_i}$. Then $\mathfrak{G}$ is solvable.

Proof. Induction on $|\mathfrak{G}|$. If $s \leq 1$ the result is clear. Suppose that $s > 1$. Let $\mathfrak{D} = \bigcap_{i=3}^{s} \mathfrak{H}_i$. By (18.7) $|\mathfrak{D}| = p_1^{c_1} p_2^{c_2}$. Thus by (18.8) $\mathfrak{G}$ is not simple. Let $1 \neq \mathfrak{A} \lhd \mathfrak{G}$ with $\mathfrak{A} \neq \mathfrak{G}$ and let $|\mathfrak{A}| = \Pi_{i=1}^{s} p_i^{b_i}$. Since $\mathfrak{A}$ and $\mathfrak{H}_j$ are subgroups of $\mathfrak{A}\mathfrak{H}_j$ which satisfy the hypotheses of (18.6) it follows from (18.6) that $|\mathfrak{A} \cap \mathfrak{H}_j| = \Pi_{i \neq j} p_i^{b_i}$. Thus for each j, $|\mathfrak{A}:\mathfrak{A} \cap \mathfrak{H}_j| = p_j^{b_j}$ and $\mathfrak{A}$ is solvable by induction. Since $\mathfrak{H}_j\mathfrak{A}/\mathfrak{A}$ is isomorphic to $\mathfrak{H}_j/\mathfrak{H}_j \cap \mathfrak{A}$ we also get that for each j $|\mathfrak{G}/\mathfrak{A}:\mathfrak{H}_j\mathfrak{A}/\mathfrak{A}| = p_j^{c_j - b_j}$. Thus $\mathfrak{G}/\mathfrak{A}$ is solvable by induction. Hence $\mathfrak{G}$ is solvable as was to be shown.

Let $\pi$ be a set of primes. P. Hall has introduced the following propositions:

$E_\pi$ $\mathfrak{G}$ contains a $S_\pi$-subgroup.
$C_\pi$ $\mathfrak{G}$ satisfies $E_\pi$ and any two $S_\pi$-subgroups of $\mathfrak{G}$ are conjugate.
$D_\pi$ $\mathfrak{G}$ satisfies $C_\pi$ and any $\pi$-subgroup of $\mathfrak{G}$ is contained in some $S_\pi$-subgroup of $\mathfrak{G}$.

The next result which includes the converse of (18.9) is the beginning of a systematic investigation of solvable groups.

(18.10) Every solvable group satisfies $D_\pi$ for every set of primes $\pi$.

Proof. Let $\mathfrak{G}$ be a solvable group and let $\pi$ be a set of primes. The proof is by induction on $|\mathfrak{G}|$. If $|\mathfrak{G}|$ is a p-group the result is trivial. Suppose that the result has been proved for solvable groups of order strictly less than $|\mathfrak{G}|$. By (18.5) there exists a prime p and a p-group $\mathfrak{P}$ such that $\langle 1 \rangle \neq \mathfrak{P} \lhd \mathfrak{G}$. By induction $\mathfrak{G}/\mathfrak{P}$ satisfies $C_\pi$. Let $\mathfrak{H}_0^*$ be a $S_\pi$-subgroup of $\mathfrak{G}/\mathfrak{P}$ and let $\mathfrak{H}_0$ be the inverse image of $\mathfrak{H}_0^*$ in $\mathfrak{G}$. Suppose first that $p \in \pi$. Thus $\mathfrak{H} = \mathfrak{H}_0$ is a $S_\pi$-subgroup of $\mathfrak{G}$ and so $\mathfrak{G}$ satisfies $E_\pi$. Let $\mathfrak{A}$ be any $\pi$-subgroup of $\mathfrak{G}$ and let $\mathfrak{A}^*$ be the image of $\mathfrak{A}$ in $\mathfrak{A}/\mathfrak{P}$. By induction $\mathfrak{A}^*$ is conjugate to a subgroup of $\mathfrak{H}_0^*$. Thus $\mathfrak{A}\mathfrak{P}$ is conjugate to a subgroup of $\mathfrak{H}$. Since $\mathfrak{A} \subseteq \mathfrak{A}\mathfrak{P}$ this implies $\mathfrak{A}$ is conjugate to a subgroup of $\mathfrak{H}$ and so $\mathfrak{G}$ satisfies $D_\pi$.

Assume next that $p \notin \pi$. By the Schur-Zassenhaus theorem $\mathfrak{H}_0$ contains a subgroup $\mathfrak{H}$ such that $\mathfrak{H}_0 = \mathfrak{H}\mathfrak{P}$ and $\mathfrak{H} \cap \mathfrak{P} = \langle 1 \rangle$. Thus $\mathfrak{G}$ satisfies $E_\pi$. Let $\mathfrak{A}$ be a $\pi$-subgroup of $\mathfrak{G}$ and let $\mathfrak{A}^*$ be the image of $\mathfrak{A}$ in $\mathfrak{G}/\mathfrak{P}$. By induction $\mathfrak{A}^*$ is conjugate to a subgroup of $\mathfrak{H}_0^*$. Without loss of generality it may be assumed that $\mathfrak{A}^* \subseteq \mathfrak{H}_0^*$. Thus $\mathfrak{A}\mathfrak{P} \subseteq \mathfrak{H}_0$. Since $\mathfrak{A}\mathfrak{P} = (\mathfrak{A}\mathfrak{P} \cap \mathfrak{H})\mathfrak{P}$ it follows from the Schur-Zassenhaus theorem that $\mathfrak{A}$ is conjugate to $\mathfrak{A}\mathfrak{P} \cap \mathfrak{H}$ in $\mathfrak{A}\mathfrak{P}$. Thus $\mathfrak{G}$ satisfies $D_\pi$ in this case also.

## § 19. QUOTIENT GROUPS

Let $\mathfrak{H}$ be a subgroup of $\mathfrak{G}$ and suppose that $\mathfrak{H}_0 \triangleleft \mathfrak{H} \subseteq \mathfrak{G}$. A normal complement of $\mathfrak{H}$ over $\mathfrak{H}_0$ in $\mathfrak{G}$ is a subgroup $\mathfrak{G}_0$ of $\mathfrak{G}$ such that $\mathfrak{G} = \mathfrak{G}_0\mathfrak{H}$ and $\mathfrak{H}_0 = \mathfrak{G}_0 \cap \mathfrak{H}$. If $\mathfrak{H}_0 = \langle 1 \rangle$ a normal complement of $\mathfrak{H}$ over $\mathfrak{H}_0$ in $\mathfrak{G}$ is called a normal complement of $\mathfrak{H}$ in $\mathfrak{G}$. If $\mathfrak{H}$ is a $S_\pi$-subgroup of $\mathfrak{G}$ for a set of primes $\pi$ then a normal complement of $\mathfrak{H}$ in $\mathfrak{G}$ is called a normal $\pi$-complement in $\mathfrak{G}$. In these definitions the phrase "in $\mathfrak{G}$" will often be omitted when the context determines the group $\mathfrak{G}$.

There are many theorems by many authors which assert that under various conditions on $\mathfrak{H}$ and $\mathfrak{H}_0$ there exists a normal complement of $\mathfrak{H}$ over $\mathfrak{H}_0$ in $\mathfrak{G}$. We will here follow a paper of Brauer [7] which has several of these theorems as consequences. The proofs given here make use of the results of Section 15, in particular (15.4). In most of the applications these results can be avoided. If $\mathfrak{H}/\mathfrak{H}_0$ is abelian then the normal complement of $\mathfrak{H}$ over $\mathfrak{H}_0$ can often be constructed by more explicit methods which do not make use of the character theory. If $\mathfrak{H}/\mathfrak{H}_0$ is solvable then generally a routine induction argument may be used to reduce the problems to the case that $\mathfrak{H}/\mathfrak{H}_0$ is abelian.

If $G \in \mathfrak{G}$ and $\pi$ is a set of primes then G has a unique decomposition in the form $G = G_\pi G_{\pi'} = G_{\pi'} G_\pi$, where $G_\pi$, $G_{\pi'}$ is respectively a $\pi$-element, $\pi'$-element. The element $G_\pi$, $G_{\pi'}$ respectively is the $\pi$-factor, $\pi'$-factor of G. If $\pi = \{p\}$ let $G_p = G_\pi$.

Throughout this section the following notation will be used:

$\mathfrak{H}_0 \triangleleft \mathfrak{H} \subseteq \mathfrak{G}$, where $\mathfrak{H}$ is a subgroup of $\mathfrak{G}$ and $\pi = \pi(\mathfrak{H}/\mathfrak{H}_0)$.

$\mathfrak{H}_1, \ldots, \mathfrak{H}_n$ are the inverse images in $\mathfrak{H}$ of the conjugate classes of $(\mathfrak{H}/\mathfrak{H}_0)^\#$.

For $i = 1, \ldots, n$, $\mathfrak{G}_i$ is the set of $G \in \mathfrak{G}$ such that $G_\pi$ is conjugate to an element of $\mathfrak{H}_i$. $\mathfrak{G}_0 = \mathfrak{G} - \cup_{i=1}^n \mathfrak{G}_i$.

The sets $\mathfrak{H}_i$ are pairwise disjoint. This is not the case in general for the $\mathfrak{G}_i$. It is clear that each $\mathfrak{G}_i$ is a union of conjugate classes of $\mathfrak{G}$.

We will be concerned with groups in which the following hypotheses are satisfied.

(19.1) $(|\mathfrak{G}:\mathfrak{H}|, |\mathfrak{H}:\mathfrak{H}_0|) = 1$

(19.2) *If $H_1, H_2 \in \mathfrak{H}$ and $H_1$ is conjugate to $H_2$ in $\mathfrak{G}$ then $H_1\mathfrak{H}_0$ and $H_2\mathfrak{H}_3$ are conjugate in $\mathfrak{H}/\mathfrak{H}_0$.*

(19.3) *If $H$ is a $\pi$-element of $\mathfrak{H}-\mathfrak{H}_0$ and if $p \in \pi$ such that $p \nmid |\langle H\rangle|$. Then*

$$p \nmid |\mathbf{C}_{\mathfrak{G}}(H):\mathbf{C}_{\mathfrak{H}}(H)|$$

(19.4) $|\mathfrak{G}_i| = |\mathfrak{G}:\mathfrak{H}|\,|\mathfrak{H}_i|$ *for* $i = 0, \ldots, n$.

The main purpose of this section is to prove the following result.

(19.5) *Assume that (19.1) – (19.4) are satisfied. Then $\mathfrak{G}_0$ is the unique normal complement of $\mathfrak{H}$ over $\mathfrak{H}_0$ in $\mathfrak{G}$.*

The proof of (19.5) will be given in a series of short steps. Throughout this section it will be assumed that (19.1) – (19.4) are satisfied.

If $p \in \pi$ then by (19.1) $\mathfrak{H}$ contains a $S_p$-subgroup $\mathfrak{P}$ of $\mathfrak{G}$. Hence by the Sylow theorems every p-element $G$ of $\mathfrak{G}$ is conjugate to an element $H \in \mathfrak{P} \subseteq \mathfrak{H}$. $G$ is of the *first kind* or the *second kind* according to whether $H \in \mathfrak{H}-\mathfrak{H}_0$ or not. By (19.2) this definition is independent of the choice of $H$.

For any $G \in \mathfrak{G}$ let $\alpha(G)$ be the product of all factors $G_p$ with $p \in \pi$ which are of the first kind and let $\beta(G)$ be the product of all factors $G_p$ with $p \in \pi$ which are of the second kind. Thus $G = \alpha(G)\beta(G)G_{\pi'}$.

(19.6) *The sets $\mathfrak{G}_i$ are pairwise disjoint. For* $i = 0, \ldots, n$, $\mathfrak{H}_i = \mathfrak{G}_i \cap \mathfrak{H}$.

*Proof.* Suppose that $\mathfrak{G}_i \cap \mathfrak{G}_j$ is nonempty. If $i = 0$ then $j = 0$ by definition. Suppose that $i, j > 0$. If $G \in$

$\mathfrak{G}_i \cap \mathfrak{G}_j$ let $\mathfrak{K}$ be the conjugate class of $\mathfrak{G}$ with $G_\pi \in \mathfrak{K}$. Thus $\mathfrak{K} \cap \mathfrak{H}_i$ and $\mathfrak{K} \cap \mathfrak{H}_j$ are both nonempty. Let $H_i \in \mathfrak{K} \cap \mathfrak{H}_i$, $H_j \in \mathfrak{K} \cap \mathfrak{H}_j$. By (19.2) $H_i \mathfrak{H}_0$ is conjugate to $H_j \mathfrak{H}_0$ in $\mathfrak{H}/\mathfrak{H}_0$ and so $i = j$. The first statement is proved.

By definition $\mathfrak{H}_i \subseteq \mathfrak{G}_i \cap \mathfrak{H}$ for $i > 0$. If $H \in \mathfrak{G}_i \cap \mathfrak{H}$ with $i > 0$ then $H_\pi$ is conjugate in $\mathfrak{G}$ to some element of $\mathfrak{H}_i$. Thus by (19.2) $H_\pi \in \mathfrak{H}_i$. Since $\mathfrak{H}/\mathfrak{H}_0$ is a $\pi$-group $H_{\pi'} \in \mathfrak{H}_0$ and so $H = H_\pi H_{\pi'} \in \mathfrak{H}_i \mathfrak{H}_0 = \mathfrak{H}_i$. This shows that $\mathfrak{H}_i = \mathfrak{G}_i \cap \mathfrak{H}$ for $i > 0$. Therefore

$$\mathfrak{G}_0 \cap \mathfrak{H} = \mathfrak{H} - \bigcup_{i=1}^{n} (\mathfrak{G}_i \cap \mathfrak{H}) = \mathfrak{H} - \bigcup_{i=1}^{n} \mathfrak{H}_i = \mathfrak{H}_0$$

The proof is complete.

(19.7) *If* $\alpha(G) \neq 1$ *then* $G_\pi$ *is conjugate to an element of* $\mathfrak{H} - \mathfrak{H}_0$.

Proof. If $G_\pi$ is a p-element for some prime $p \in \pi$ this follows from the definition. The proof is by induction on the number of distinct primes dividing the order of $G_\pi$. If $G_\pi$ is not a p-element then $G_\pi = HG_p$ where H is the $p'$-factor of $G_\pi$ and where p may be chosen so that $\alpha(H) \neq 1$. Thus by induction H is conjugate to an element of $\mathfrak{H} - \mathfrak{H}_0$. Replacing G by a conjugate it may be assumed that $H \in \mathfrak{H} - \mathfrak{H}_0$. By (19.3) $\mathbf{C}_{\mathfrak{H}}(H)$ contains a $S_p$-subgroup $\mathfrak{P}_0$ of $\mathbf{C}_{\mathfrak{G}}(H)$. Since $G_p \in \mathbf{C}_{\mathfrak{G}}(H)$ it is conjugate in $\mathbf{C}_{\mathfrak{G}}(H)$ to an element of $\mathfrak{P}_0 \subseteq \mathfrak{H}$ and so $G_\pi = HG_p$ is conjugate to an element $K \in \mathfrak{H}$. If $K \in \mathfrak{H}_0$ so is every power of K and thus $\alpha(G) = 1$ contrary to assumption. The proof is complete.

(19.8) (i) $G \in \mathfrak{G}_0$ *if and only if* $\alpha(G) = 1$.

(ii) *If* $G \in \mathfrak{G}$ *then the elements* $G, G_\pi$ *and* $\alpha(G)$ *lie in the same* $\mathfrak{G}_i$.

(iii) *If* $G \in \mathfrak{G}_0$ *then every power of* G *is in* $\mathfrak{G}_0$.

(iv) *All* $\pi'$*-elements of* $\mathfrak{G}$ *lie in* $\mathfrak{G}_0$.

Proof. If $\alpha(G) \neq 1$ then $G \notin \mathfrak{G}_0$ by (19.7). Suppose that $G \in \mathfrak{G}_i$ with $i \neq 0$. Then $G_\pi$ is conjugate to some $H \in \mathfrak{H}_i$.

Thus $\alpha(G)$ is conjugate to $\alpha(H)$ and $\beta(G)$ is conjugate to $\beta(H)$. Let $H_p$ be the p-factor of $\beta(H)$ for some prime p. By definition $H_p$ is conjugate in $\mathfrak{G}$ to an element of $\mathfrak{H}_0$. Thus by (19.2) $H_p \in \mathfrak{H}_0$. This yields that $\beta(H) \in \mathfrak{H}_0$. Hence $H = \alpha(H)\beta(H) \in \alpha(H)\mathfrak{H}_0$ and so $\alpha(H) \in \mathfrak{H}_i\mathfrak{H}_0 = \mathfrak{H}_i$. Thus $\alpha(H) \neq 1$ and so $\alpha(G) \neq 1$. This proves (i).

If $G \in \mathfrak{G}_i'$ with $i > 0$ then we have just shown that $\alpha(G)$ is conjugate to an element $\alpha(H) \in \mathfrak{H}_i$. Since $\alpha(G) = (\alpha(G))_\pi$ we see that $\alpha(G) \in \mathfrak{G}_i$. If $G \in \mathfrak{G}_0$ then $\alpha(G) \in \mathfrak{G}_0$ by (i). By definition G and $G_\pi$ lie in the same $\mathfrak{G}_i$. (ii) is proved.

Statements (iii) and (iv) are immediate consequences of (i).

(19.9) <u>Suppose that</u> $\mathfrak{E} = \mathfrak{A} \times \mathfrak{P}$ <u>is a</u> $\pi$<u>-group where</u> $\mathfrak{P}$ <u>is a p-group for some</u> $p \in \pi$ <u>and</u> $\mathfrak{A} = \langle A \rangle$ <u>is a cyclic</u> $p'$<u>-group. If</u> $\alpha(A) \neq 1$ <u>then</u> $\mathfrak{E}$ <u>is conjugate to a subgroup of</u> $\mathfrak{H}$.

<u>Proof.</u> By (19.7) A is conjugate to an element of $\mathfrak{H}$. Thus it may be assumed that $A \in \mathfrak{H}$. By (19.3) $\mathbf{C}_{\mathfrak{H}}(A)$ contains a $S_p$-group of $\mathbf{C}_{\mathfrak{G}}(A)$. Thus $\mathfrak{P}$ is conjugate in $\mathbf{C}_{\mathfrak{G}}(A)$ to a subgroup of $\mathfrak{H}$ and so $\mathfrak{E}$ is conjugate to a subgroup of $\mathfrak{H}$.

(19.10) <u>Let</u> $\zeta$ <u>be an irreducible character of</u> $\mathfrak{H}/\mathfrak{H}_0$. <u>Define the function</u> $\theta = \theta_\zeta$ <u>on</u> $\mathfrak{G}$ <u>by</u> $\theta(G) = \zeta(H)$ <u>if</u> $G \in \mathfrak{G}_i$ <u>and</u> $H \in \mathfrak{H}_i$. <u>Then</u> $\theta$ <u>is an irreducible character of</u> $\mathfrak{G}$.

<u>Proof.</u> Since $\zeta$ is constant on each $\mathfrak{H}_i$ we remark that by (19.6) $\theta$ is well defined. Since each $\mathfrak{G}_i$ is a union of conjugate classes of $\mathfrak{G}$, $\theta$ is a class function on $\mathfrak{G}$. The result will be proved by showing that $\theta$ satisfies conditions (i)-(iv) of (15.4). We have just observed that condition (i) is satisfied. Since $\theta(1) = \zeta(1) > 1$ so is condition (iv).

We next verify condition (ii). Let $\mathfrak{E}$ be an elementary subgroup $\mathfrak{G}$. Then $\mathfrak{E} = \mathfrak{E}_0 \times \mathfrak{E}_1$, where $\mathfrak{E}_0$ is a $\pi$-group and $\mathfrak{E}_1$ is a $\pi'$-group. It suffices to show that $\theta|_{\mathfrak{E}_0}$ is a generalized character of $\mathfrak{E}_0$ because in that case $\theta|_{\mathfrak{E}}$ is a generalized character of $\mathfrak{E}/\mathfrak{E}_1$ since $\theta(E_0E_1) = \theta(E_0)$ for $E_i \in \mathfrak{E}_i$, $i = 0, 1$ by (19.8) (ii). The $\pi$-group $\mathfrak{E}_0$ is elementary. Let $\mathfrak{E}_0 = \mathfrak{A} \times \mathfrak{P}$ where $\mathfrak{A} = \langle A \rangle$ is a $p'$-group and $\mathfrak{P}$ is a p-group for some $p \in \pi$. If $\alpha(A) \neq 1$ then by (19.9)

$\mathfrak{E}_0$ is conjugate to a subgroup of $\mathfrak{H}$. Hence it may be assumed that $\mathfrak{E}_0 \subseteq \mathfrak{H}$, thus $\theta_{|\mathfrak{E}_0} = \zeta_{|\mathfrak{E}_0}$ and so $\theta_{|\mathfrak{E}_0}$ is a generalized character of $\mathfrak{E}_0$. Assume that $\alpha(A) = 1$. Thus by (19.8) (iii) $\alpha(A^j) = 1$ for all j and if $P \in \mathfrak{P}$ then $\alpha(A^jP) = \alpha(P)$. Thus by (19.8) (ii) $\theta(A^jP) = \theta(P)$. Hence it suffices to show that $\theta|_{\mathfrak{P}}$ is a generalized character of $\mathfrak{P}$. By the Sylow theorems and (19.1) $\mathfrak{P}$ is conjugate to a subgroup of $\mathfrak{H}$. Hence it may be assumed that $\mathfrak{P} \subseteq \mathfrak{H}$. Therefore $\theta_{|\mathfrak{P}} = \zeta_{|\mathfrak{P}}$ which shows that condition (ii) is satisfied.

Let $H_i \in \mathfrak{H}_i$ for $i = 0, \ldots, n$. Then by (19.4)

$$\|\theta\|^2_{\mathfrak{G}} = \frac{1}{|\mathfrak{G}|} \sum_{i=0}^{n} |\mathfrak{G}_i|\,|\zeta(H_i)|^2$$

$$= \frac{1}{|\mathfrak{H}|} \sum_{i=0}^{n} |\mathfrak{H}_i|\,|\zeta(H_i)|^2$$

$$= \|\zeta\|^2_{\mathfrak{H}} = 1$$

Thus condition (iii) is verified and by (15.4) $\theta$ is an irreducible character of $\mathfrak{G}$.

(19.11) $\mathfrak{G}_0$ <u>is a normal complement of</u> $\mathfrak{H}$ <u>over</u> $\mathfrak{H}_0$ <u>in</u> $\mathfrak{G}$.

<u>Proof.</u> Let $\zeta_1, \zeta_2, \ldots$ be all the irreducible characters of $\mathfrak{H}/\mathfrak{H}_0$. Let $\theta_i = \theta_{\zeta_i}$ be defined as in (19.10). Then the definition of $\theta_i$ yields that $\theta_i(G) = \theta_i(1)$ for all i if and only if $G \in \mathfrak{G}_0$. Hence by (19.10) $\mathfrak{G}_0 \triangleleft \mathfrak{G}$. By (19.6) $\mathfrak{H}_0 = \mathfrak{G}_0 \cap \mathfrak{H}$. Since $\mathfrak{G}_0$ contains all $\pi'$-elements of $\mathfrak{G}$ it follows from (19.1) that $\mathfrak{G}_0\mathfrak{H} = \mathfrak{G}$ which proves the statement.

Let $\mathfrak{A}$ be a normal complement of $\mathfrak{H}$ over $\mathfrak{H}_0$ in $\mathfrak{G}$. To prove (19.5) it is now sufficient to show that $\mathfrak{A} = \mathfrak{G}_0$.

Suppose that $G \in \mathfrak{A}$. If $p \in \pi$ then by (19.1) $G_p$ is conjugate to an element H of $\mathfrak{H}$. Since $\mathfrak{A} \triangleleft \mathfrak{G}$ this implies that $H \in \mathfrak{A} \cap \mathfrak{H} = \mathfrak{H}_0$. Hence $\alpha(G) = 1$. Thus by (19.8) (i) $\mathfrak{A} \subseteq \mathfrak{G}_0$. Since

$$|\mathfrak{G}:\mathfrak{G}_0| = |\mathfrak{H}:\mathfrak{H}_0| = |\mathfrak{G}:\mathfrak{A}|$$

this yields that $\mathfrak{A} = \mathfrak{G}_0$ as was to be shown.

## §20. NONSIMPLICITY CRITERIA

The results in this section are all consequences of (19.5). We begin with a theorem of Wielandt [1] which generalizes a classical result of Frobenius.

(20.1) Let $\mathfrak{A}$ be a subgroup of $\mathfrak{G}$, let $\mathfrak{A}_0 \lhd \mathfrak{A}$ and let $\mathfrak{H} = \mathbf{N}_{\mathfrak{G}}(\mathfrak{A})$. Assume that $(|\mathfrak{H}:\mathfrak{A}|, |\mathfrak{A}:\mathfrak{A}_0|) = 1$ and $\mathfrak{A} \cap \mathfrak{A}^G \subseteq \mathfrak{A}_0$ for $G \in \mathfrak{G} - \mathfrak{H}$. Then $\mathfrak{G}$ and $\mathfrak{H}$ each have at most one normal complement of $\mathfrak{A}$ over $\mathfrak{A}_0$. $\mathfrak{G}$ has a normal complement $\mathfrak{G}_0$ of $\mathfrak{A}$ over $\mathfrak{A}_0$ if and only if $\mathfrak{H}$ has a normal complement $\mathfrak{H}_0$ of $\mathfrak{A}$ over $\mathfrak{A}_0$. In that case $\mathfrak{G}_0 = \mathfrak{G} - \bigcup_{\mathfrak{G}} (\mathfrak{H} - \mathfrak{H}_0)^G$.

Proof. Suppose that $\mathfrak{G}_0$ exists. Let $\mathfrak{H}_0 = \mathfrak{G}_0 \cap \mathfrak{H}$. Then

$$\mathfrak{H}_0 \cap \mathfrak{A} = \mathfrak{G}_0 \cap \mathfrak{H} \cap \mathfrak{A} = \mathfrak{G}_0 \cap \mathfrak{A} = \mathfrak{A}_0$$

Since $\mathfrak{G} = \mathfrak{A}\mathfrak{G}_0 \subseteq \mathfrak{H}\mathfrak{G}_0$,

$$|\mathfrak{H}:\mathfrak{H}_0| = |\mathfrak{G}:\mathfrak{G}_0| = |\mathfrak{A}:\mathfrak{A}_0| = |\mathfrak{A}:\mathfrak{H}_0 \cap \mathfrak{A}| = |\mathfrak{A}\mathfrak{H}_0 : \mathfrak{H}_0|$$

Thus $\mathfrak{H} = \mathfrak{A}\mathfrak{H}_0$. The uniqueness of $\mathfrak{H}_0$ follows directly from the fact that $(|\mathfrak{H}_0:\mathfrak{A}_0|, |\mathfrak{A}:\mathfrak{A}_0|) = 1$.

Assume that $\mathfrak{H}_0$ exists. Suppose that $H \in \mathfrak{H} \cap \mathfrak{H}^G$ with $G \in \mathfrak{G} - \mathfrak{H}$. Let $a = |\mathfrak{H}:\mathfrak{A}|$. Thus $H^a \in \mathfrak{A} \cap \mathfrak{A}^G \subseteq \mathfrak{A}_0 \subseteq \mathfrak{H}_0$. Since $(a, |\mathfrak{H}:\mathfrak{H}_0|) = 1$ this implies that $H \in \mathfrak{H}_0$. Consequently $\mathfrak{H} \cap \mathfrak{H}^G \subseteq \mathfrak{H}_0$ for $G \in \mathfrak{G} - \mathfrak{H}$.

Let $\pi$, $\mathfrak{G}_i$, $\mathfrak{H}_i$ be defined as in section 19. Suppose that conditions (19.1) – (19.4) have been verified. Then (19.5) implies that $\mathfrak{G}_0$ is the unique complement of $\mathfrak{H}$ over $\mathfrak{H}_0$. If $G \in \mathfrak{G}$ then by (19.1) $G_\pi$ is conjugate to an element of $\mathfrak{H}$. Thus $\bigcup_{\mathfrak{G}} (\mathfrak{H} - \mathfrak{H}_0)^G = \bigcup_{i=1}^{n} \mathfrak{G}_i$ and $\mathfrak{G}_0$ has the required form. It remains to verify conditions (19.1) – (19.4).

Let $\mathfrak{B}$ be a subset of $\mathfrak{H}$, $\mathfrak{B} \nsubseteq \mathfrak{H}_0$. If $\mathfrak{B}^G \subseteq \mathfrak{H}$ for $G \in \mathfrak{G}$ then $\mathfrak{B} \subseteq \mathfrak{H} \cap \mathfrak{H}^{G^{-1}} \nsubseteq \mathfrak{H}_0$ and so $G \in \mathfrak{H}$. If $\mathfrak{P}$ is a $S_p$-subgroup of $\mathfrak{H}$ for some $p \in \pi$ this implies that $\mathbf{N}_{\mathfrak{G}}(\mathfrak{P}) \subseteq \mathfrak{H}$ and so $\mathfrak{P}$ is a $S_p$-subgroup of $\mathfrak{G}$. This verifies (19.1). If $\mathfrak{B} = \{H\}$ for some $H \in \mathfrak{H} - \mathfrak{H}_0$ we get that $\mathbf{C}_{\mathfrak{G}}(H) = \mathbf{C}_{\mathfrak{H}}(H)$. Furthermore if $H' \in \mathfrak{H}$ and $H'$ is conjugate to $H$ in $\mathfrak{G}$ then $H'$ is conjugate to $H$ in $\mathfrak{H}$. Thus in particular (19.2) and (19.3) are proved.

Since $|\mathfrak{G}| = \Sigma_{i=0}^{n} |\mathfrak{G}_i|$ and $|\mathfrak{H}| = \Sigma_{i=0}^{n} |\mathfrak{H}_i|$ it suffices to show that $|\mathfrak{G}_i| = |\mathfrak{G}:\mathfrak{H}||\mathfrak{H}_i|$ for $i > 0$ in verifying (19.4). If $\mathfrak{K}$ is a conjugate class of $\mathfrak{G}$ with $\mathfrak{K} \subseteq \mathfrak{G}_i$ for some $i > 0$ then we have just shown that $\mathfrak{K} \cap \mathfrak{H}$ is a conjugate class and $\mathfrak{K} \cap \mathfrak{H} \subseteq \mathfrak{H} - \mathfrak{H}_0$. Thus for $H \in \mathfrak{K}$

$$|\mathfrak{K}| = |\mathfrak{G}:\mathbf{C}_{\mathfrak{H}}(H)| = |\mathfrak{G}:\mathfrak{H}||\mathfrak{H}:\mathbf{C}_{\mathfrak{H}}(H)|$$

$$= |\mathfrak{G}:\mathfrak{H}||\mathfrak{K} \cap \mathfrak{H}|$$

This implies that $|\mathfrak{G}_i| = |\mathfrak{G}:\mathfrak{H}||\mathfrak{G}_i|$ for $i > 0$ and completes the proof.

Due to its importance in many applications we state a special case of (20.1) explicitly. As will be seen later more direct proofs can be given of this theorem.

(20.2) <u>(Frobenius) Let</u> $\mathfrak{H}$ <u>be a subgroup of</u> $\mathfrak{G}$. <u>Assume that</u> $\mathfrak{H} \cap \mathfrak{H}^G = \langle 1 \rangle$ <u>for</u> $G \in \mathfrak{G} - \mathfrak{H}$ <u>Then there exists a normal complement of</u> $\mathfrak{H}$ <u>in</u> $\mathfrak{G}$.

As an application of (20.1) we will prove a special case of the Frobenius conjecture mentioned in section 17. See Feit [1], Wielandt [1].

(20.3) <u>Let</u> $\mathfrak{A}$ <u>be a subgroup of</u> $\mathfrak{G}$ <u>and let</u> $\mathfrak{A}_0 \triangleleft \mathfrak{A}$. <u>Let</u> $|\mathfrak{A}:\mathfrak{A}_0| = a$ <u>and</u> $|\mathfrak{G}| = ma$. <u>Assume that</u> $\mathfrak{A} \cap \mathfrak{A}^G \subseteq \mathfrak{A}_0$ <u>for</u> $G \in \mathfrak{G} - \mathbf{N}_{\mathfrak{G}}(\mathfrak{A})$ <u>and</u> $(a, m) = 1$. <u>Let</u> $\mathfrak{M} = \{G | G \in \mathfrak{G}, G^m = 1\}$. <u>If</u> $|\mathfrak{M}| = m$ <u>then</u> $\mathfrak{M} \triangleleft \mathfrak{G}$.

Proof. Let $\mathfrak{H} = \mathbf{N}_{\mathfrak{G}}(\mathfrak{A})$ and let $\mathfrak{M}_0 = \mathfrak{H} \cap \mathfrak{M}$. Since $(|\mathfrak{A}_0|, |\mathfrak{A}:\mathfrak{A}_0|) = 1$ and $\mathfrak{A}_0 \lhd \mathfrak{A}$ it follows that $\mathfrak{A}_0 \lhd \mathfrak{H}$. Furthermore $\mathfrak{A}/\mathfrak{A}_0 \lhd \mathfrak{H}/\mathfrak{A}_0$. By the Schur-Zassenhaus theorem there exists a complement of $\mathfrak{A}/\mathfrak{A}_0$ in $\mathfrak{H}/\mathfrak{A}_0$. Thus there exists a subgroup $\mathfrak{H}_0$ of $\mathfrak{H}$ such that $\mathfrak{A}_0 \subseteq \mathfrak{H}_0$ and $|\mathfrak{H}:\mathfrak{H}_0| = a$. Suppose we know that $\mathfrak{H}_0 \lhd \mathfrak{H}$ then by (20.1) there exists a normal complement $\mathfrak{G}_0$ of $\mathfrak{A}$ over $\mathfrak{A}_0$. Since $|\mathfrak{G}:\mathfrak{G}_0| = a$ we get that $|\mathfrak{G}_0| = m$ and so $\mathfrak{G}_0 = \mathfrak{M} \lhd \mathfrak{G}$. It remains to show that $\mathfrak{H}_0 \lhd \mathfrak{H}$. This will be done by showing that $\mathfrak{H}_0 = \mathfrak{M}_0$.

Since $|\mathfrak{H}_0| \mid m$, $\mathfrak{H}_0 \subseteq \mathfrak{M}_0$. Let $|\mathfrak{H}:\mathfrak{A}| = h$ and let $|\mathfrak{A}_0| = a_0$. Thus $|\mathfrak{H}| = haa_0$ and $|\mathfrak{M}_0| \geq ha_0$ since $\mathfrak{H}_0 \subseteq \mathfrak{M}_0$. It suffices to show that $|\mathfrak{M}_0| = ha_0$.

Let $G \in \mathfrak{G} - \mathfrak{M}$. Then some power $H$ of $G$ has prime order $p$, where $p \nmid m$. Let $\mathfrak{P}$ be a $S_p$-subgroup of $\mathfrak{G}$ with $H \in \mathfrak{P}$. Let $\mathfrak{P}_0$ be a $S_p$-subgroup of $\mathfrak{A}$. Then $\mathfrak{P}_0$ is a $S_p$-subgroup of $\mathfrak{G}$ since $p \nmid |\mathfrak{G}:\mathfrak{A}|$. Thus $\mathfrak{P} = \mathfrak{P}_0{}^A$ for some $A \in \mathfrak{G}$. Hence

$$H^{A^{-1}} = H^{GA^{-1}} \in (\mathfrak{P}_0{}^A \cap \mathfrak{P}_0{}^{AG})^{A^{-1}}$$

$$= \mathfrak{P}_0 \cap \mathfrak{P}_0{}^{AGA^{-1}} \subseteq \mathfrak{A} \cap \mathfrak{A}^{AGA^{-1}}$$

Thus $AGA^{-1} \in \mathfrak{H}$ by assumption. Consequently $\mathfrak{G} - \mathfrak{M} = \cup_{\mathfrak{G}} (\mathfrak{H} - \mathfrak{M}_0)^G$. The number of distinct conjugates of $\mathfrak{H}$ is at most $|\mathfrak{G}:\mathfrak{H}|$ and $|\mathfrak{H} - \mathfrak{M}_0| \leq ha_0(a-1)$. Therefore

$$m(a-1) = |\mathfrak{G} - \mathfrak{M}| \leq |\mathfrak{G}:\mathfrak{H}||\mathfrak{H} - \mathfrak{M}_0| = m(a-1)$$

Thus we must have equality and so $|\mathfrak{H} - \mathfrak{M}_0| = ha_0(a-1)$. Therefore $|\mathfrak{M}_0| = ha_0$ as was to be shown.

If $H$ is a $\pi$-element of $\mathfrak{G}$, the $\pi$-section $\mathfrak{S}_{\mathfrak{G},\pi}(H)$ is the set of all elements $G \in \mathfrak{G}$ such that $G_\pi$ is conjugate to $H$ in $\mathfrak{G}$. Either or both of the subscripts will be omitted if $\mathfrak{G}$ and/or $\pi$ is specified. Let $r_\pi(\mathfrak{H}) = |\mathfrak{S}_{\mathfrak{H},\pi}(1)|$ for any group $\mathfrak{H}$. The following two lemmas will be needed.

(20.4) $|\mathfrak{S}_{\mathfrak{G}, \pi}(H)| = |\mathfrak{G} : \mathbf{C}_{\mathfrak{G}}(H)| r_{\pi}(\mathbf{C}_{\mathfrak{G}}(H))$

Proof. If $G \in \mathfrak{S}(H)$ there are $|\mathfrak{G} : \mathbf{C}_{\mathfrak{G}}(H)|$ possibilities for $G_{\pi}$. If $H' = G_{\pi}$ then $G = H' G_{\pi'}$, where $G_{\pi'}$ may be any $\pi'$-element in $\mathbf{C}_{\mathfrak{G}}(H')$. Since $\mathbf{C}_{\mathfrak{G}}(H)$ is isomorphic to $\mathbf{C}_{\mathfrak{G}}(H')$ the result follows.

(20.5) Let p be a prime. Then $r_p(\mathfrak{H}) \not\equiv 0 \pmod{p}$ for any group $\mathfrak{H}$.

Proof. Let $\mathfrak{P}$ be a $S_p$-subgroup of $\mathfrak{H}$. Distribute the p'-elements of $\mathfrak{H}$ into equivalence classes where H is equivalent to H' if and only if $P^{-1} HP = H'$ for some $P \in \mathfrak{P}$. The number of elements in any equivalence class is a power of p and $\{H\}$ forms an equivalence class if and only if $H \in \mathbf{C}_{\mathfrak{G}}(\mathfrak{P})$. Thus $r_p(\mathfrak{H}) \equiv r_p(\mathbf{C}_{\mathfrak{H}}(\mathfrak{P})) \pmod{p}$. Thus it may be assumed that $\mathfrak{H} = \mathbf{C}_{\mathfrak{H}}(\mathfrak{P})$. This yields that for $P \in \mathfrak{P}, \mathfrak{S}(P)$ consists of all elements PG where G is any p'-element of $\mathfrak{H}$. Thus $|\mathfrak{S}(P)| = r_p(\mathfrak{H})$ for $P \in \mathfrak{P}$. Since $\mathfrak{S}(P_1)$ is disjoint from $\mathfrak{S}(P_2)$ for $P_1 \neq P_2$ and $\mathfrak{H} = \cup_{P \in \mathfrak{P}} \mathfrak{S}(P)$ we get that $|\mathfrak{H}| = |\mathfrak{P}| r_p(\mathfrak{H})$ which implies the result.

(20.6) Let $\mathfrak{H}$ be a subgroup of $\mathfrak{G}$, let $\mathfrak{H}_0 \triangleleft \mathfrak{H}$ and let $\pi = \pi(\mathfrak{H}/\mathfrak{H}_0)$. Assume that if $\mathfrak{A}$ is any abelian $\pi$-subgroup of $\mathfrak{H}$ (including $\mathfrak{A} = \langle 1 \rangle$), every conjugate class of $\mathbf{C}_{\mathfrak{G}}(\mathfrak{A})$ consisting of $\pi$-elements meets $\mathfrak{H}$ in a conjugate class of $\mathbf{C}_{\mathfrak{H}}(\mathfrak{A})$. Then there exists a normal complement of $\mathfrak{H}$ over $\mathfrak{H}_0$ in $\mathfrak{G}$.

Proof. If H is a $\pi$-element of $\mathfrak{H}$ let $\mathfrak{G}^* = \mathbf{C}_{\mathfrak{G}}(H)$ and $\mathfrak{H}^* = \mathbf{C}_{\mathfrak{H}}(H)$. Then $\mathfrak{H}^* = \mathfrak{G}^* \cap \mathfrak{H}$. If $\mathfrak{A}^*$ is an abelian $\pi$-subgroup of $\mathfrak{H}^*$ then $\mathfrak{A} = \langle H, \mathfrak{A}^* \rangle$ is an abelian subgroup of $\mathfrak{H}$ and

$$\mathbf{C}_{\mathfrak{G}}(\mathfrak{A}) = \mathbf{C}_{\mathfrak{G}}(H) \cap \mathbf{C}_{\mathfrak{G}}(\mathfrak{A}^*)$$

$$= \mathfrak{G}^* \cap \mathbf{C}_{\mathfrak{G}}(\mathfrak{A}^*) = \mathbf{C}_{\mathfrak{G}^*}(\mathfrak{A}^*)$$

$$\mathbf{C}_{\mathfrak{H}}(\mathfrak{A}) = \mathbf{C}_{\mathfrak{G}}(\mathfrak{A}) \cap \mathfrak{H}$$

$$= \mathbf{C}_{\mathfrak{G}^*}(\mathfrak{A}^*) \cap \mathfrak{H} = \mathbf{C}_{\mathfrak{H}^*}(\mathfrak{A}^*)$$

If $\mathfrak{K}^*$ is a conjugate class of $\mathbf{C}_{\mathfrak{G}^*}(\mathfrak{A}^*) = \mathbf{C}_{\mathfrak{G}}(\mathfrak{A})$ consisting of $\pi$-elements then $\mathfrak{K}^* \subseteq \mathfrak{G}^*$ and so

$$\mathfrak{K}^* \cap \mathfrak{H} = \mathfrak{K}^* \cap \mathfrak{G}^* \cap \mathfrak{H} = \mathfrak{K}^* \cap \mathfrak{H}^*$$

Then by assumption $\mathfrak{K}^* \cap \mathfrak{H}^*$ is a conjugate class of $\mathbf{C}_{\mathfrak{H}^*}(\mathfrak{A}^*)$. Hence the pair $\mathfrak{G}^*$, $\mathfrak{H}^*$ satisfy the same assumption on $\mathfrak{G}$ and $\mathfrak{H}$ for the same $\pi$. Observe also that this assumption is satisfied for any subset $\pi_1$ of $\pi$.

Let $H_0 = 1, H_1, \ldots, H_m$ be a complete set of representatives of the conjugate classes of $\mathfrak{H}$ which consist of $\pi_1$-elements for $\pi_1 \subseteq \pi$. We next prove by induction on $|\mathfrak{G}|$ that

$$\text{(20.7)} \qquad \frac{r_{\pi_1}(\mathfrak{G})}{|\mathfrak{G}|} = \frac{r_{\pi_1}(\mathfrak{H})}{|\mathfrak{H}|}$$

By letting $\mathfrak{A} = \langle 1 \rangle$ we see that $\mathfrak{G} = \bigcup_{i=0}^{m} \mathfrak{S}_{\mathfrak{G}}(H_i)$ and $\mathfrak{H} = \bigcup_{i=0}^{m} \mathfrak{S}_{\mathfrak{H}}(H_i)$, where the sets $\mathfrak{S}_{\mathfrak{G}}(H_i)$ are pairwise disjoint. Thus by (20.4)

$$\sum_{i=0}^{m} \frac{r_{\pi_1}(\mathbf{C}_{\mathfrak{G}}(H_i))}{|\mathbf{C}_{\mathfrak{G}}(H_i)|} = 1 = \sum_{i=0}^{m} \frac{r_{\pi_1}(\mathbf{C}_{\mathfrak{H}}(H_i))}{|\mathbf{C}_{\mathfrak{H}}(H_i)|}$$

If $H_i \notin \mathbf{Z}(\mathfrak{G})$ then since $\mathfrak{G}^* = \mathbf{C}_{\mathfrak{G}}(H_i)$, $\mathfrak{H}^* = \mathbf{C}_{\mathfrak{H}}(H_i)$ satisfy the same assumptions as $\mathfrak{G}$ and $\mathfrak{H}$ and $|\mathfrak{G}^*| < |\mathfrak{G}|$ we get by induction that

$$\frac{r_{\pi_1}(\mathbf{C}_{\mathfrak{G}}(H_i))}{|\mathbf{C}_{\mathfrak{G}}(H_i)|} = \frac{r_{\pi_1}(\mathbf{C}_{\mathfrak{H}}(H_i))}{|\mathbf{C}_{\mathfrak{H}}(H_i)|}$$

Thus if exactly k of the $H_i$ lie in $\mathbf{Z}(\mathfrak{G})$ it follows that

$$k\,\frac{r_{\pi_1}(\mathfrak{G})}{|\mathfrak{G}|} = k\,\frac{r_{\pi_1}(\mathfrak{H})}{|\mathfrak{H}|} \quad \text{which implies (20.7)}$$

The result will be proved by showing that (19.1) – (19.4) are satisfied and then using (19.5)

Let $p \in \pi$ and let H be a $\pi$-element in $\mathfrak{H}$. Let $\pi_1 = \{p\}$. Applying (20.5) and (20.7) to the pair $\mathbf{C}_{\mathfrak{G}}(H)$, $\mathbf{C}_{\mathfrak{H}}(H)$ yields that $p \nmid |\mathbf{C}_{\mathfrak{G}}(H)|:\mathbf{C}_{\mathfrak{H}}(\mathfrak{H})$. Thus (19.3) is satisfied. Letting $H = 1$ yields (19.1). (19.2) follows from letting $\mathfrak{A} = \langle 1 \rangle$. It remains to verify (19.4). Each $\mathfrak{G}_i$ is a union of $\pi$-sections. Thus it suffices to show that $|\mathfrak{S}_{\mathfrak{G}}(H_i)| = |\mathfrak{G}:\mathfrak{H}||\mathfrak{S}_{\mathfrak{H}}(H_i)|$ for $i = 0, \ldots, m$ and this follows from (20.4) and (20.7) applied to the pair $\mathbf{C}_{\mathfrak{G}}(H_i)$, $\mathbf{C}_{\mathfrak{H}}(H_i)$.

The next result due to Brauer [7] is a generalization of earlier results of Grün and P. Hall. If $\mathfrak{A} \subseteq \mathfrak{H} \subseteq \mathfrak{G}$ where $\mathfrak{A}$ and $\mathfrak{H}$ are subgroups of $\mathfrak{G}$ then $\mathfrak{A}$ is <u>weakly closed in</u> $\mathfrak{H}$ <u>with respect to</u> $\mathfrak{G}$ if $\mathfrak{A}^G \subseteq \mathfrak{H}$ for some $G \in \mathfrak{G}$ implies that $\mathfrak{A}^G = \mathfrak{A}$.

(20.8) <u>Let $\pi$ be a nonempty set of primes. Assume that the following conditions are satisfied.</u>

(i) <u>$\mathfrak{B}$ is a $S_\pi$-subgroup of $\mathfrak{G}$. $\mathfrak{C} \subseteq \mathbf{Z}(\mathfrak{B})$ and $\mathfrak{C}$ is weakly closed in $\mathfrak{B}$ with respect to $\mathfrak{G}$.</u>

(ii) <u>If $\mathfrak{A}$ is any abelian $\pi$-subgroup of $\mathfrak{H} = \mathbf{N}_{\mathfrak{G}}(\mathfrak{C})$, then $D_\pi$ holds for $\mathbf{C}_{\mathfrak{G}}(\mathfrak{A})$.</u>

<u>Let $\mathfrak{H}/\mathfrak{H}_0$ be the maximal $\pi$-quotient group of $\mathfrak{H}$. Then there exists a normal complement of $\mathfrak{H}$ over $\mathfrak{H}_0$ in $\mathfrak{G}$.</u>

<u>Proof.</u> Let $\mathfrak{A}$ be an abelian $\pi$-subgroup of $\mathfrak{H}$ and set $\mathfrak{G}^* = \mathbf{C}_{\mathfrak{G}}(\mathfrak{A})$, $\mathfrak{H}^* = \mathbf{C}_{\mathfrak{H}}(\mathfrak{A}) = \mathfrak{G}^* \cap \mathfrak{H}$. Thus $\langle \mathfrak{A}, \mathfrak{C} \rangle$ is a $\pi$-subgroup

of $\mathfrak{G}$ and since $D_\pi$ holds for $\mathfrak{G} = \mathbf{C}_{\mathfrak{G}}(1)$, $\langle \mathfrak{A}, \mathfrak{C} \rangle \subseteq \mathfrak{B}^G$ for some $G \in \mathfrak{G}$. Thus $\mathfrak{C} = \mathfrak{C}^G \subseteq \mathbf{Z}(\mathfrak{B})$ as $\mathfrak{C}$ is weakly closed in $\mathfrak{B}$. Since $\mathfrak{A} \subseteq \mathfrak{B}^G$ this implies that $\mathfrak{C} \subseteq \mathbf{C}_{\mathfrak{G}}(\mathfrak{A}) = \mathfrak{G}^*$. By (ii) there exists a $S_\pi$-subgroup $\mathfrak{B}^*$ of $\mathfrak{G}^*$ with $\mathfrak{C} \subseteq \mathfrak{B}^*$. As $\mathfrak{B}^* \subseteq \mathfrak{B}^H$ for some $H \in \mathfrak{G}$ we conclude that $\mathfrak{C} \subseteq \mathbf{Z}(\mathfrak{B}^*)$. Clearly $\mathfrak{C}$ is weakly closed in $\mathfrak{B}^*$. Thus (i) is satisfied if $\mathfrak{G}, \mathfrak{B}, \mathfrak{C}$ are replaced by $\mathfrak{G}^*, \mathfrak{B}^*, \mathfrak{C}$.

If $\mathfrak{A}^*$ is an abelian $\pi$-subgroup of $\mathfrak{H}^* = \mathbf{N}_{\mathfrak{G}^*}(\mathfrak{C})$ then $\mathfrak{A}_1 = \langle \mathfrak{A}, \mathfrak{A}^* \rangle$ is an abelian $\pi$-subgroup of $\mathfrak{H}$ and

$$\mathbf{C}_{\mathfrak{G}}(\mathfrak{A}_1) = \mathbf{C}_{\mathfrak{G}}(\mathfrak{A}) \cap \mathbf{C}_{\mathfrak{G}}(\mathfrak{A}^*)$$

$$= \mathfrak{G}^* \cap \mathbf{C}_{\mathfrak{G}}(\mathfrak{A}^*) = \mathbf{C}_{\mathfrak{G}^*}(\mathfrak{A}^*)$$

Thus $D_\pi$ holds for $\mathbf{C}_{\mathfrak{G}^*}(\mathfrak{A}^*)$ by (ii). Since $\mathbf{N}_{\mathfrak{G}^*}(\mathfrak{C}) = \mathfrak{G}^* \cap \mathfrak{H} = \mathfrak{H}^*$ we see that also (ii) is satisfied if $\mathfrak{G}, \mathfrak{B}, \mathfrak{C}$ is replaced by $\mathfrak{G}^*, \mathfrak{B}^*, \mathfrak{C}$.

We will next show that (i) and (ii) imply that if $\mathfrak{K}$ is a conjugate class of $\mathfrak{G}$ consisting of $\pi$-elements, then $\mathfrak{K} \cap \mathfrak{H}$ is a conjugate class of $\mathfrak{H}$. By $D_\pi$, $\mathfrak{K} \cap \mathfrak{B}$ is nonempty. Hence $\mathfrak{K} \cap \mathfrak{H}$ is nonempty. Let $H_1, H_2 \in \mathfrak{K} \cap \mathfrak{H}$ and let $\mathfrak{A} = \langle H_i \rangle$ with $i = 1$ or $2$. Thus as was remarked above $\mathfrak{C} \subseteq \mathbf{C}_{\mathfrak{G}}(H_i)$. By (ii) there exists a $S_\pi$-subgroup $\mathfrak{D}_i$ of $\mathbf{C}_{\mathfrak{G}}(H_i)$ such that $\langle \mathfrak{C}, H_i \rangle \subseteq \mathfrak{D}_i$. Let $G^{-1} H_1 G = H_2$. Then $G^{-1} \mathfrak{D}_1 G$ and $\mathfrak{D}_2$ are both $S_\pi$-groups of $\mathbf{C}_{\mathfrak{G}}(H_2)$. Hence by $D_\pi$ in $\mathbf{C}_{\mathfrak{G}}(H_2)$ it may be assumed that $G^{-1}\mathfrak{D}_1 G = \mathfrak{D}_2$. Thus $\langle \mathfrak{C}, \mathfrak{C}^G \rangle \subseteq \mathfrak{D}_2$. As $\mathfrak{D}_2 \subseteq \mathfrak{B}^H$ for some $H \in \mathfrak{G}$ the weak closure of $\mathfrak{C}$ in $\mathfrak{B}$ implies that $\mathfrak{C} = \mathfrak{C}^G$. Therefore $G \in \mathfrak{H}$. Thus $\mathfrak{K} \cap \mathfrak{H}$ is a conjugate class of $\mathfrak{H}$.

In view of the first part of the proof this may be applied to $\mathfrak{G}^* = \mathbf{C}_{\mathfrak{G}}(\mathfrak{A})$ and $\mathfrak{H}^* = \mathbf{C}_{\mathfrak{H}}(\mathfrak{A})$ for any abelian subgroup $\mathfrak{A} \subseteq \mathfrak{H}$. Thus the hypothesis of (20.6) is satisfied and the result follows from (20.6).

The next result is essentially due to Grün and P. Hall. See M. Hall, Theorem 14.4.6.

(20.9) <u>Let p be a prime and let $\mathfrak{P}$ be a $S_p$-subgroup of $\mathfrak{G}$. Let $\mathfrak{C}$ be a subgroup of $\mathbf{Z}(\mathfrak{P})$ which is weakly closed in $\mathfrak{P}$. Let $\mathfrak{H} = \mathbf{N}_{\mathfrak{G}}(\mathfrak{C})$ and let $\mathfrak{H}/\mathfrak{H}_0$ be the maximal p-quotient group of $\mathfrak{H}$. Then there exists a normal complement of $\mathfrak{H}$ over $\mathfrak{H}_0$ in $\mathfrak{G}$.</u>

<u>Proof.</u> This is an immediate consequence of (20.8) with $\pi = \{p\}$ since (20.8) (ii) is satisfied by the Sylow theorems.

(20.10) <u>Let p be a prime. Assume that a $S_p$-subgroup $\mathfrak{P}$ of $\mathfrak{G}$ is abelian. Let $\mathfrak{H} = \mathbf{N}_{\mathfrak{G}}(\mathfrak{P})$ and let $\mathfrak{H}/\mathfrak{H}_0$ be the maximal p-quotient group of $\mathfrak{H}$. Then there exists a normal complement of $\mathfrak{H}$ over $\mathfrak{H}_0$ in $\mathfrak{G}$.</u>

<u>Proof.</u> Let $\mathfrak{P} = \mathfrak{C}$ in (20.9).

(20.11) <u>Let p be a prime. Assume that the $S_p$-group $\mathfrak{P}$ of $\mathfrak{H}$ is abelian and $\mathfrak{P} \triangleleft \mathfrak{H}$. Let $\mathfrak{Z} = \mathfrak{P} \cap \mathbf{Z}(\mathfrak{H})$. Then there exists a subgroup $\mathfrak{P}_0$ of $\mathfrak{P}$ such that $\mathfrak{P}_0 \triangleleft \mathfrak{H}$ and $\mathfrak{P} = \mathfrak{P}_0 \times \mathfrak{Z}$.</u>

<u>Proof.</u> Let $H_1, \ldots, H_m$ be a complete system of coset representatives of $\mathfrak{P}$ in $\mathfrak{H}$. For $P \in \mathfrak{P}$ let $t(P) = \Pi_{i=1}^{m} H_i^{-1} P H_i$. Since $\mathfrak{P}$ is abelian $t(P)$ is independent of the choice of the $H_i$. Furthermore $t(P_1 P_2) = t(P_1) t(P_2)$, $t(P_1) = t(P_2)$ in case $P_1$ is conjugate to $P_2$ in $\mathfrak{H}$ and $t(\mathfrak{P}) \subseteq \mathfrak{Z}$. Let $\mathfrak{P}_0$ be the kernel of t. If $Z \in \mathfrak{P}_0 \cap \mathfrak{Z}$ then $1 = t(Z) = Z^m$. Hence $Z = 1$ since $(p, m) = 1$. Thus $\mathfrak{P}_0 \cap \mathfrak{Z} = \langle 1 \rangle$ and so $\mathfrak{P}_0 \mathfrak{Z} = \mathfrak{P}_0 \times \mathfrak{Z} \subseteq \mathfrak{P}$. Thus

$$|\mathfrak{P}_0||\mathfrak{Z}| \leq |\mathfrak{P}| = |\mathfrak{P}_0||t(\mathfrak{P})| \leq |\mathfrak{P}_0||\mathfrak{Z}|$$

Hence we must have equality and so $\mathfrak{P}_0 \times \mathfrak{Z} = \mathfrak{P}$. Clearly $\mathfrak{P}_0 \lhd \mathfrak{H}$. The proof is complete.

(20.12) Let p be a prime. Suppose that a $S_p$-subgroup $\mathfrak{P}$ of $\mathfrak{G}$ is abelian. Let $\mathfrak{Z} = \mathfrak{P} \cap \mathbf{Z}(\mathbf{N}_{\mathfrak{G}}(\mathfrak{P}))$. Then there exists a normal complement of $\mathfrak{Z}$ in $\mathfrak{G}$.

Proof. Let $\mathfrak{H} = \mathbf{N}_{\mathfrak{G}}(\mathfrak{P})$. Let $\mathfrak{P}_0$ be defined as in (20.11). Then $\mathfrak{H}/\mathfrak{P}_0$ is isomorphic to $\mathfrak{H}_0/\mathfrak{P}_0 \times \mathfrak{P}/\mathfrak{P}_0$, where $\mathfrak{H}_0$ is a subgroup of $\mathfrak{H}$ whose $S_p$-subgroup is $\mathfrak{P}_0$. Hence $\mathfrak{H}_0$ is a normal complement of $\mathfrak{Z}$ in $\mathfrak{H}$. It is easily seen that $\mathfrak{H}/\mathfrak{H}_0$ is the maximal p-quotient group of $\mathfrak{H}$. Thus by (20.10) there exists a normal complement $\mathfrak{G}_0$ of $\mathfrak{H}$ over $\mathfrak{H}_0$. Then

$$\mathfrak{G}_0 \cap \mathfrak{Z} = \mathfrak{G}_0 \cap \mathfrak{H} \cap \mathfrak{Z} = \mathfrak{H}_0 \cap \mathfrak{Z} = \langle 1 \rangle$$

Since $|\mathfrak{G} : \mathfrak{G}_0| = |\mathfrak{H} : \mathfrak{H}_0| = |\mathfrak{Z}|$ this implies that $\mathfrak{G}_0 \mathfrak{Z} = \mathfrak{G}$. The result is proved.

As a special case of (20.12) we get one of the earliest results of this type.

(20.13) (Burnside) Let p be a prime and let $\mathfrak{P}$ be a $S_p$-subgroup of $\mathfrak{G}$. Assume that $\mathfrak{P} \subseteq \mathbf{Z}(\mathbf{N}_{\mathfrak{G}}(\mathfrak{P}))$. Then there exists a normal p-complement in $\mathfrak{G}$.

(20.14) Let p be the smallest prime in $\pi(\mathfrak{G})$. Assume that a $S_p$-subgroup of $\mathfrak{G}$ is cyclic. Then $\mathfrak{G}$ has a normal p-complement.

Proof. Let $\mathfrak{P}$ be a $S_p$-subgroup of $\mathfrak{G}$ and let $\mathfrak{H} = \mathbf{N}_{\mathfrak{G}}(\mathfrak{P})/\mathbf{C}_{\mathfrak{P}}(\mathfrak{P})$. Thus $\mathfrak{H}$ is a p′-group of automorphisms of the cyclic p-group $\mathfrak{P}$. Hence $|\mathfrak{H}| \mid (p-1, |\mathfrak{G}|)$. As p is the smallest prime in $\pi(\mathfrak{G})$ this implies that $|\mathfrak{H}| = 1$. Hence $\mathbf{N}_{\mathfrak{G}}(\mathfrak{P}) = \mathbf{C}_{\mathfrak{G}}(\mathfrak{P})$ and the result follows from (20.13).

A group in which every Sylow subgroup is cyclic is called a Z-group.

(20.15) Let $\mathfrak{G}$ be a Z-group. Then $\mathfrak{G}'$ is cyclic. In particular $\mathfrak{G}$ is solvable.

Proof. By repeated application of (20.14) one gets a normal series of $\mathfrak{G}$ in which every factor is a Sylow group. Hence $\mathfrak{G}$ is solvable. Since every abelian subgroup of $\mathfrak{G}$ is cyclic it suffices to show that $\mathfrak{G}'' = \langle 1 \rangle$. Assume that $\mathfrak{G}'' \neq \langle 1 \rangle$. Then by solvability $\mathfrak{G}'' \neq \mathfrak{G}'''$. Hence by factoring out $\mathfrak{G}'''$ it may be assumed that $\mathfrak{G}''$ is abelian and therefore cyclic. Let $\mathfrak{G}'' = \langle G \rangle$. Since $\mathfrak{G}/\mathbf{C}_{\mathfrak{G}}(G)$ is an automorphism group of the cyclic group $\langle G \rangle$ it is abelian. Hence $\mathfrak{G}' \subseteq \mathbf{C}_{\mathfrak{G}}(G)$. Choose $H \in \mathfrak{G}'$ such that $\langle H\mathfrak{G}'' \rangle = \mathfrak{G}'/\mathfrak{G}''$ Thus $\mathfrak{G}' = \langle H, G \rangle$ is abelian and so $\mathfrak{G}'' = \langle 1 \rangle$ contrary to assumption.

(20.16) Let $\mathfrak{G}$ be a nonabelian Z-group. There exist integers m, n, s all greater than 1 such that $s^n \equiv 1 \pmod{m}$, $((s-1)n, m) = 1$, $mn = |\mathfrak{G}|$ where $\mathfrak{G} = \langle A, B \rangle$ with $A^m = 1 = B^n$, $B^{-1}AB = A^s$ and $\mathfrak{G}' = \langle A \rangle$. Conversely given positive integers m, n, s satisfying these conditions then the group generated by two elements satisfying these relations is a nonabelian Z-group.

Proof. The converse is immediate since $(|\mathfrak{G} : \mathfrak{G}'|, |\mathfrak{G}'|) = 1$ and $\mathfrak{G}'$ and $\mathfrak{G}/\mathfrak{G}'$ are cyclic.

Suppose that $\mathfrak{G}$ is a Z-group. By (20.15) $\mathfrak{G}' = \langle A \rangle$ for some $A \in \mathfrak{G}$. Choose $B \in \mathfrak{G}$ such that $\mathfrak{G}/\mathfrak{G}' = \langle B\mathfrak{G}' \rangle$. Then $\mathfrak{G} = \langle A, B \rangle$ and $B^{-1}AB = A^s$ for some positive integer s. Thus $B^{-n}AB^n = A^{s^n} = A$ and so $s^n \equiv 1 \pmod{m}$. Since $B^{-b}A^{-a}B^bA^a = A^{a(1-s^b)}$, every commutator is a power of $B^{-1}A^{-1}BA = A^{1-s}$. Thus $(s-1, m) = 1$. Since $B^n \in \mathfrak{G}'$ there exists k such that $B^n = A^k$. Hence $A^k = B^{-1}A^kB = A^{sk}$. Consequently $k(s-1) \equiv 0 \pmod{m}$ and so $k \equiv 0 \pmod{m}$. Therefore $B^n = 1$. If a prime p divides both m and n then $\langle A^{m/p}, B^{n/p} \rangle$ is a noncyclic p-group contrary to assumption. Therefore (m, n) = 1 and the proof is complete.

It was observed by Frobenius that (20.13) can be used to prove the following special case of the conjecture mentioned in Section 17.

(20.17) Let $|\mathfrak{G}| = m_1 m_2$ with $(m_1, m_2) = 1$. Let $\mathfrak{M}_i = \{G \mid G^{m_i} = 1\}$ for i = 1, 2. Assume that $|\mathfrak{M}_i| = m_i$ for i = 1, 2. Then $\mathfrak{M}_i \lhd \mathfrak{G}$ for i = 1, 2 and $\mathfrak{G} = \mathfrak{M}_1 \times \mathfrak{M}_2$.

Proof. By symmetry it suffices to show that $\mathfrak{M}_2 \lhd \mathfrak{G}$. As the normality is obvious it is sufficient to show that $\mathfrak{M}_2$ is a subgroup of $\mathfrak{G}$. If $G \in \mathfrak{G}$ then $G = G_1 G_2 = G_2 G_1$ where $G_i \in \mathfrak{M}_i$ for i = 1, 2. Since $|\mathfrak{G}| = |\mathfrak{M}_1|\,|\mathfrak{M}_2|$ this implies that $G_1, G_2$ range independently over $\mathfrak{M}_1, \mathfrak{M}_2$ respectively. Thus $\mathfrak{M}_2 \subseteq \mathbf{C}_{\mathfrak{G}}(\mathfrak{M}_1)$. Let $\mathfrak{H} = \cap\, \mathbf{C}_{\mathfrak{G}}(\mathfrak{A})$ where $\mathfrak{A}$ ranges over all $S_p$-subgroups of $\mathfrak{G}$ and all prime divisors p of $m_1$. Thus $\mathfrak{M}_2 \subseteq \mathfrak{H}$. Let p be a prime such that $p \mid m_1$ and let $\mathfrak{P}$ be a $S_p$-subgroup of $\mathfrak{H}$. Thus $\mathfrak{P} \subseteq \mathbf{Z}(\mathfrak{G})$. Hence by (20.13) there exists a normal p-complement $\mathfrak{G}_p$ in $\mathfrak{G}$. Since $\mathfrak{M}_2 = \cap\, \mathfrak{G}_p$ the result follows.

## §21. NORMAL $\pi$-COMPLEMENTS

(21.1) (Brauer [7], Suzuki [3]) Let $\pi$ be a set of primes. $\mathfrak{G}$ contains a normal $\pi$-complement if and only if the following conditions are satisfied.

(i) $\mathfrak{G}$ contains a $S_\pi$-subgroup $\mathfrak{H}$.

(ii) If two elements of $\mathfrak{H}$ are conjugate in $\mathfrak{G}$ then they are also conjugate in $\mathfrak{H}$.

(iii) If $\mathfrak{E}$ is an elementary $\pi$-subgroup of $\mathfrak{G}$ then $\mathfrak{E}$ is conjugate to a subgroup of $\mathfrak{H}$.

Proof. If $\mathfrak{G}$ contains a normal $\pi$-complement $\mathfrak{G}_0$ then (i) and (iii) follow from the Schur-Zassenhaus theorem. Let $H_1, H_2 \in \mathfrak{H}$ and $G^{-1} H_1 G = H_2$. Then $G = HG_0$ with

$H \in \mathfrak{H}$ and $G_0 \in \mathfrak{G}_0$. Replacing $H_1$ by $H^{-1}H_1H$ it may be assumed that $G_0^{-1}H_1G_0 = H_2$. Thus

$$H_2\mathfrak{G}_0 \subseteq \mathfrak{G}_0H_1\mathfrak{G}_0 = H_1\mathfrak{G}_0$$

and so $H_1^{-1}H_2 \in \mathfrak{H} \cap \mathfrak{G}_0 = \langle 1 \rangle$. Hence $H_1 = H_2$ and (ii) is satisfied.

Conversely suppose that (i), (ii) and (iii) are satisfied. We will verify that (19.1)–(19.4) hold with $\mathfrak{H}_0 = \langle 1 \rangle$. The result will then follow from (19.5). Clearly (19.1) is satisfied and (ii) yields (19.2). Let $H \in \mathfrak{H}^\#$ and let $\mathfrak{P}$ be a $S_p$-subgroup of $\mathbf{C}_{\mathfrak{G}}(H)$ for some prime $p \in \pi$ such that $p \not| \; |\langle H \rangle|$. Thus $\mathfrak{E} = \langle H \rangle \times \mathfrak{P}$ is elementary and by (iii) $\mathfrak{E}^G \subseteq \mathfrak{H}$ for some $G \in \mathfrak{G}$. Hence $H^G \in \mathfrak{H}$ and so by (ii) there exists $A \in \mathfrak{H}$ with $H^{GA} = H$. Since $\mathfrak{P}^{GA} \subseteq \mathbf{C}_{\mathfrak{H}}(H)$ (19.3) is satisfied.

To verify (19.4) observe that since $\mathfrak{H}_0 = \langle 1 \rangle$, each $\mathfrak{H}_i$ is a conjugate class of $\mathfrak{H}$. Let $H_i \in \mathfrak{H}_i$ and let $c_i = r_{\pi'}(\mathbf{C}_{\mathfrak{G}}(H_i))$. Then $|\mathfrak{G}_i| = |\mathfrak{G}: \mathbf{C}_{\mathfrak{G}}(H_i)| c_i$. Let $|\mathbf{C}_{\mathfrak{G}}(H_i)| = a_i b_i$ where $a_i = |\mathbf{C}_{\mathfrak{G}}(H_i)|_\pi$. By (17.3) $c_i \geq b_i$ and so $|\mathfrak{G}_i| \geq |\mathfrak{G}|/(a_i b_i) b_i = |\mathfrak{G}|/a_i$. By (ii) $|\mathfrak{H}_i| = |\mathfrak{H}: \mathbf{C}_{\mathfrak{H}}(H_i)|$ and by (19.3) $|\mathbf{C}_{\mathfrak{H}}(H_i)| = a_i$. Hence $|\mathfrak{G}_i| \geq |\mathfrak{G}:\mathfrak{H}||\mathfrak{H}_i|$ for $i = 0, \ldots, n$. Since $\Sigma_{i=0}^n |\mathfrak{G}_i| = |\mathfrak{G}|$ and $\Sigma_{i=0}^n |\mathfrak{H}_i| = |\mathfrak{H}|$ this implies that $|\mathfrak{G}_i| = |\mathfrak{G}:\mathfrak{H}||\mathfrak{H}_i|$ for $i = 0, \ldots, n$ which verifies (19.4) and completes the proof.

(21.2) (Suzuki [3]) Let $\mathfrak{H}$ be a $S_\pi$-subgroup of $\mathfrak{G}$. Then $\mathfrak{G}$ has a normal $\pi$-complement if and only if the following conditions are satisfied.

(i) Every elementary $\pi$-subgroup of $\mathfrak{G}$ is conjugate to a subgroup of $\mathfrak{H}$.

(ii) There exists a set $\mathfrak{A}$ of coset representatives of $\mathfrak{H}$ in $\mathfrak{G}$ such that $\mathfrak{A}^H = \mathfrak{A}$ for $H \in \mathfrak{H}$.

Proof. If $\mathfrak{G}_0$ is a normal $\pi$-complement in $\mathfrak{G}$ then (i) follows from (21.1) and (ii) is satisfied for $\mathfrak{G}_0 = \mathfrak{A}$. Suppose (i) and (ii) are satisfied. Thus (21.1) (i) and (21.1) (iii) are satisfied. Hence by (21.1) it suffices to verify (21.1) (ii). Let $H_1, H_2 \in \mathfrak{H}$ and $G^{-1}H_1G = H_2$. Let $G = HA$ where $A \in \mathfrak{A}$ and $H \in \mathfrak{H}$. Replacing $H_1$ by $H^{-1}H_1H$ it may be assumed that $A^{-1}H_1A = H_2$ and $A \in \mathfrak{A}$. Thus

$$H_1AH_1^{-1} = H_2H_1^{-1}A \in \mathfrak{A} \cap \mathfrak{H}A = \{A\}$$

Therefore $H_1A = AH_1$ and so $H_1 = H_2$ as required.

(21.3) (Frobenius) Let p be a prime and let $\mathfrak{P}$ be a $S_p$-subgroup of $\mathfrak{G}$. $\mathfrak{G}$ contains a normal p-complement if and only if whenever two elements in $\mathfrak{P}$ are conjugate in $\mathfrak{G}$ they are conjugate in $\mathfrak{P}$.

Proof. This is an immediate consequence of (21.1) as conditions (i) and (iii) are automatically satisfied by the Sylow theorem.

The argument used in (21.6) is essentially due to Burnside. Our primary object is (21.8) below. This proof is due to G. Higman and was communicated to the author by J. Alperin. The following property of groups will be considered.

(21.4) Let p be a prime. For any two $S_p$-subgroups $\mathfrak{P}_1$ and $\mathfrak{P}_2$ of $\mathfrak{G}$ there exists $G \in \mathbf{C}_{\mathfrak{G}}(\mathfrak{P}_1 \cap \mathfrak{P}_2)$ with $\mathfrak{P}_1^G = \mathfrak{P}_2$.

(21.5) Let p be a prime. If $\mathfrak{G}$ contains a normal p-complement then $\mathfrak{G}$ satisfies (21.4).

Proof. Let $\mathfrak{M}$ be a normal p-complement in $\mathfrak{G}$. There exists $G \in \mathfrak{M}$ such that $\mathfrak{P}_1^G = \mathfrak{P}_2$. If $P \in \mathfrak{P}_1 \cap \mathfrak{P}_2$ then $\{P, P^G\} \subseteq \mathfrak{P}_1^G = \mathfrak{P}_2$. Thus $[P, G] \in \mathfrak{P}_2 \cap \mathfrak{M} = \langle 1 \rangle$. Hence $G \in \mathbf{C}_G(\mathfrak{P}_1 \cap \mathfrak{P}_2)$.

(21.6) Let p be a prime. Suppose that $\mathfrak{G}$ satisfies (21.4). Assume further that for any p'-group $\mathfrak{H}$ in $\mathfrak{G}$, $\mathbf{N}_{\mathfrak{G}}(\mathfrak{H})/\mathbf{C}_{\mathfrak{G}}(\mathfrak{H})$ is a p-group. Then $\mathfrak{G}$ has a normal p-complement.

Proof. Let $\mathfrak{P}$ be a $S_p$-subgroup of $\mathfrak{G}$ and suppose that for some $H \in \mathfrak{G}$, $\{P, P^H\} \in \mathfrak{P}$. Then $P^H \in \mathfrak{P} \cap \mathfrak{P}^H$. By (21.4) there exists $G \in \mathbf{C}_{\mathfrak{G}}(\mathfrak{P} \cap \mathfrak{P}^H)$ such that $\mathfrak{P}^H = \mathfrak{P}^G$. Hence $\mathfrak{P}^{HG^{-1}} = \mathfrak{P}$ and $P^{HG^{-1}} = P^H$. Let $HG^{-1} = G_1 P_1 = P_1 G_1$, where $P_1$ is a p-element and $G_1$ is a p′-element. Since $G_1 P_1 \in \mathbf{N}_{\mathfrak{G}}(\mathfrak{P})$ this implies that $P_1 \in \mathfrak{P}$ and by assumption $G_1 \in \mathbf{C}_{\mathfrak{G}}(\mathfrak{P}) \subseteq \mathbf{C}_{\mathfrak{G}}(P)$. Therefore

$$P^H = P^{HG^{-1}} = P^{G_1 P_1} = P^{P_1}$$

The result now follows from (21.3).

(21.7) Let p be a prime. Suppose that $\mathfrak{G}$ contains no normal p-subgroup distinct from $\langle 1 \rangle$. Assume that every subgroup $\mathfrak{H}$ of $\mathfrak{G}$ with $\mathfrak{H} \neq \mathfrak{G}$ satisfies (21.4). Then $\mathfrak{G}$ satisfies (21.4).

Proof. Let $\mathfrak{P}_1$ and $\mathfrak{P}_2$ be $S_p$-subgroups of $\mathfrak{G}$. The proof is by induction on $|\mathfrak{P}_1 : \mathfrak{P}_1 \cap \mathfrak{P}_2|$. If $|\mathfrak{P}_1 : \mathfrak{P}_1 \cap \mathfrak{P}_2| = 1$ then $\mathfrak{P}_1 = \mathfrak{P}_2$ and (21.4) is satisfied with $G = 1$.

Given $\mathfrak{P}_1$ and $\mathfrak{P}_2$ let $\mathfrak{D} = \mathfrak{P}_1 \cap \mathfrak{P}_2$. If $\mathfrak{D} = \langle 1 \rangle$ the result is trivial. Suppose that $\langle 1 \rangle \neq \mathfrak{D} \neq \mathfrak{P}_1$. Thus $\mathbf{N}_{\mathfrak{G}}(\mathfrak{D}) \neq \mathfrak{D}$. For $i = 1, 2$, let $\mathfrak{G}_i = \mathfrak{P}_i \cap \mathbf{N}_{\mathfrak{G}}(\mathfrak{D})$, let $\mathfrak{R}_i$ be a $S_p$-subgroup of $\mathbf{N}_{\mathfrak{G}}(\mathfrak{D})$ with $\mathfrak{G}_i \subseteq \mathfrak{R}_i$ and let $\mathfrak{T}_i$ be a $S_p$-subgroup of $\mathfrak{G}$ with $\mathfrak{R}_i \subseteq \mathfrak{T}_i$. Since $\mathfrak{G}_i \subseteq \mathfrak{P}_i \cap \mathfrak{T}_i$ it follows by induction that there exist $G_i \in \mathbf{C}_{\mathfrak{G}}(\mathfrak{P}_i \cap \mathfrak{T}_i) \subseteq \mathbf{C}_{\mathfrak{G}}(\mathfrak{D})$ such that $\mathfrak{P}_i^{G_i} = \mathfrak{T}_i$ for $i = 1, 2$. By assumption there exists $H \in \mathbf{C}_{\mathfrak{G}}(\mathfrak{D})$ such that $\mathfrak{R}_1^H = \mathfrak{R}_2$. Since $\mathfrak{R}_2 \subseteq \mathfrak{T}_1{}^H \cap \mathfrak{T}_2$, induction yields the existence of $K \in \mathbf{C}_{\mathfrak{G}}(\mathfrak{T}_1{}^H \cap \mathfrak{T}_2) \subseteq \mathbf{C}_{\mathfrak{G}}(\mathfrak{D})$ such that $\mathfrak{T}_1{}^{HK} = \mathfrak{T}_2$. Consequently

$$\mathfrak{P}_1^{G_1 HKG_2^{-1}} = \mathfrak{T}_1^{HKG_2^{-1}} = \mathfrak{T}_2^{G_2^{-1}} = \mathfrak{P}_2$$

and $G_1 HKG_2^{-1} \in \mathbf{C}_{\mathfrak{G}}(\mathfrak{D})$ proving the result.

(21.8) (Frobenius) Let p be a prime and let $\mathfrak{P}$ be a

$S_p$-subgroup of $\mathfrak{G}$. Assume that for every subgroup $\mathfrak{H}$ of $\mathfrak{P}$, $\mathbf{N}_{\mathfrak{G}}(\mathfrak{H})/\mathbf{C}_{\mathfrak{G}}(\mathfrak{H})$ is a p-group. Then $\mathfrak{G}$ contains a normal p-complement.

Proof. The proof is by induction on $|\mathfrak{G}|$. If $|\mathfrak{G}| = 1$ there is nothing to prove. The assumption of the theorem is clearly satisfied by every subgroup of $\mathfrak{G}$. Hence by induction it may be assumed that $\mathfrak{G}$ has no p-factor group $\neq \langle 1 \rangle$. If $\langle 1 \rangle \neq \mathfrak{A} \lhd \mathfrak{G}$ where $\mathfrak{A}$ is a p-group then $\mathfrak{G}/\mathfrak{A}$ satisfies the hypothesis of the theorem. Hence by induction $\mathfrak{G}/\mathfrak{A}$ has a normal p-complement. Since $\mathfrak{G}$ has no p-factor group $\neq\langle 1 \rangle$ this implies that $\mathfrak{A} = \mathfrak{P}$ and $\mathbf{C}_{\mathfrak{G}}(\mathfrak{P}) = \mathfrak{G}$. The result follows from (20.13) in this case. Thus it may be assumed that $\langle 1 \rangle$ is the only normal p-subgroup of $\mathfrak{G}$. By induction and (21.5) every proper subgroup of $\mathfrak{G}$ satisfies (21.4). Thus by (21.7) also $\mathfrak{G}$ satisfies (21.4). The result follows from (21.6).

In contrast to (21.8) the answer to the following question is not known.

Let $\pi \subseteq \pi(\mathfrak{G})$. Suppose that for every $\pi$-subgroup, $\pi'$-subgroup $\mathfrak{H}$ of $\mathfrak{G}$, $\mathbf{N}_{\mathfrak{G}}(\mathfrak{H})/\mathbf{C}_{\mathfrak{G}}(\mathfrak{H})$ is a $\pi$-group, $\pi'$-group respectively. Is $\mathfrak{G}$ a direct product of a $\pi$-group and a $\pi'$-group?

If the answer to this question is in the negative then it can be shown by using (20.1) that there exists a simple group $\mathfrak{G}$ such that $\pi_1$ and $\pi_2$ are disjoint nonempty subsets of $\pi(\mathfrak{G})$ with $\pi(\mathfrak{G}) = \pi_1 \cup \pi_2$ and such that every proper subgroup of $\mathfrak{G}$ is either a $\pi_1$-group or a $\pi_2$-group. Baer [1].

## §22. THOMPSON SUBGROUPS

In this section a generalization of (21.8) for odd primes due to Thompson [3] will be proved and some consequences of it will be deduced. The proof of the result is not too long, however a fuller appreciation of the subtlety of the statement of the result may be obtained by studying the difficulties involved in the original proof of a weaker statement (Thompson [2]).

The following elementary result will be needed. We state it here without proof.

(22.1) *Let p be an odd prime. Let* $\mathfrak{G} = SL(2, p)$. *Then the only abelian* $p'$*-subgroups of* $\mathfrak{G}$ *which are normalized by a* $S_p$*-subgroup of* $\mathfrak{G}$ *lie in the center of* $\mathfrak{G}$.

For any group $\mathfrak{G}$ let $m(\mathfrak{G})$ denote the minimal number of generators of $\mathfrak{G}$. Define $d(\mathfrak{G}) = \max m(\mathfrak{A})$ where $\mathfrak{A}$ ranges over all the abelian subgroups of $\mathfrak{G}$. The *Thompson subgroup* $\mathbf{T}(\mathfrak{G})$ is defined to be the subgroup of $\mathfrak{G}$ generated by all abelian subgroups $\mathfrak{A}$ of $\mathfrak{G}$ with $m(\mathfrak{A}) = d(\mathfrak{G})$.

Clearly if $\mathfrak{H}$ is a subgroup of $\mathfrak{G}$ with $\mathbf{T}(\mathfrak{G}) \subseteq \mathfrak{H} \subseteq \mathfrak{G}$, then $\mathbf{T}(\mathfrak{G})$ is a characteristic subgroup of $\mathfrak{H}$.

(22.2) *(Thompson) Let p be an odd prime and let* $\mathfrak{P}$ *be a* $S_p$*-subgroup of* $\mathfrak{G}$. *If* $\mathbf{C}_{\mathfrak{G}}(\mathbf{Z}(\mathfrak{P}))$ *and* $\mathbf{N}_{\mathfrak{G}}(\mathbf{T}(\mathfrak{P}))$ *have normal p-complements, so does* $\mathfrak{G}$.

*Proof*. Induction on $|\mathfrak{G}|$. Suppose that $\mathfrak{G}$ has no normal p-complement. Let $\mathcal{H}$ be the set of nonidentity p-subgroups $\mathfrak{H}$ of $\mathfrak{G}$ such that $\mathbf{N}_{\mathfrak{G}}(\mathfrak{H})$ has no normal p-complement. By (21.8) $\mathcal{H}$ is nonempty.

Define a partial ordering on $\mathcal{H}$ as follows. If $\mathfrak{H}_1, \mathfrak{H}_2 \in \mathcal{H}$ then $\mathfrak{H}_1 < \mathfrak{H}_2$ if and only if one of the following holds:

(i) $|\mathbf{N}_{\mathfrak{G}}(\mathfrak{H}_1)|_p < |\mathbf{N}_{\mathfrak{G}}(\mathfrak{H}_2)|_p$.

(ii) $|\mathbf{N}_{\mathfrak{G}}(\mathfrak{H}_1)|_p = |\mathbf{N}_{\mathfrak{G}}(\mathfrak{H}_2)|_p$ and $|\mathfrak{H}_1| < |\mathfrak{H}_2|$.

(iii) $\mathfrak{H}_1 = \mathfrak{H}_2$.

Let $\mathfrak{H}$ be a maximal element of $\mathcal{H}$ with respect to $<$ and let $\mathfrak{N} = \mathbf{N}_{\mathfrak{G}}(\mathfrak{H})$. It may be assumed that $\mathfrak{H} \subseteq \mathfrak{P}^* \subseteq \mathfrak{P}$, where $\mathfrak{P}^*$ is a $S_p$-subgroup of $\mathfrak{N}$.

If $\mathfrak{H} = \mathfrak{P}$ then $\mathfrak{N} \subseteq \mathbf{N}_{\mathfrak{G}}(\mathbf{T}(\mathfrak{P}))$ and so has a normal p-complement by assumption contrary to the choice of $\mathfrak{H}$. Thus $\mathfrak{H} \neq \mathfrak{P}$.

It is easily verified that the maximality of $\mathfrak{H}$ with respect to $<$ implies that $\mathfrak{N}/\mathfrak{H}$ satisfies the assumptions of the theorem. Thus by induction $\mathfrak{N}/\mathfrak{H}$ has a normal p-complement $\mathfrak{K}/\mathfrak{H}$.

Since $\mathfrak{P}^* \subseteq \mathfrak{P}$ it follows that $\mathbf{Z}(\mathfrak{P}) \subseteq \mathbf{Z}(\mathfrak{P}^*)$ and so

$\mathbf{C}_{\mathfrak{N}}(\mathbf{Z}(\mathfrak{P}^*))$ has a normal p-complement. If $\mathbf{N}_{\mathfrak{N}}(\mathbf{T}(\mathfrak{P}^*))$ does not have a normal p-complement then the maximality of $\mathfrak{H}$ implies that $\mathfrak{P} = \mathfrak{P}^*$ since $\mathbf{T}(\mathfrak{P}^*) \lhd \mathbf{N}_{\mathfrak{P}}(\mathfrak{P}^*)$. Thus $\mathbf{N}_{\mathfrak{N}}(\mathbf{T}(\mathfrak{P}^*))$ has a normal p-complement. If $\mathfrak{N} \neq \mathfrak{G}$ then by induction $\mathfrak{N}$ has a normal p-complement contrary to the choice of $\mathfrak{H}$. Thus $\mathfrak{N} = \mathfrak{G}$. By induction

(22.3) $\langle 1 \rangle$ is the only normal p′-subgroup of $\mathfrak{G}$.

The maximality of $\mathfrak{H}$ implies that

(22.4) $\mathfrak{H}$ is the largest normal p-subgroup of $\mathfrak{G}$.

Let $\mathfrak{L}/\mathfrak{H}$ be a chief factor of $\mathfrak{G}$ with $\mathfrak{L} \subseteq \mathfrak{K}$. If $\mathfrak{L} \neq \mathfrak{K}$ then $\mathfrak{L}\mathfrak{P} \neq \mathfrak{G}$. Hence by induction $\mathfrak{L}\mathfrak{P}$ has a normal p-complement $\mathfrak{T}$. Then $\mathfrak{T}$ is characteristic in $\mathfrak{K}$ and so $\mathfrak{G} = \mathfrak{P}\mathfrak{K} \subseteq \mathbf{N}_{\mathfrak{G}}(\mathfrak{T})$ contrary to (22.3). Thus $\mathfrak{K}/\mathfrak{H}$ is a chief factor of $\mathfrak{G}$.

Since $\mathfrak{K}$ and $\mathfrak{P}$ normalize $\mathbf{C}_{\mathfrak{P}}(\mathfrak{K}/\mathfrak{H})$ it follows from (22.4) that

(22.5) $\mathbf{C}_{\mathfrak{P}}(\mathfrak{K}/\mathfrak{H}) = \mathfrak{H}$

Let $\mathfrak{C} = \mathbf{C}_{\mathfrak{K}}(\mathfrak{H})$ so that $\mathfrak{C} \lhd \mathfrak{G}$. If $\mathfrak{C} \not\subseteq \mathfrak{H}$ then $\mathfrak{K} = \mathfrak{H}\mathfrak{C}$ since $\mathfrak{K}/\mathfrak{H}$ is a chief factor of $\mathfrak{G}$. As $\mathfrak{C} \cap \mathfrak{H} = \mathbf{Z}(\mathfrak{H})$ is a $S_p$-subgroup of $\mathfrak{C}$ it follows by (20.13) or (21.8) that $\mathfrak{C}$ contains a normal p-complement which is thus normal in $\mathfrak{G}$ contrary to (22.3). Hence $\mathfrak{C} \subseteq \mathfrak{H}$. As $\mathfrak{K}$ contains all p′-elements of $\mathfrak{G}$ this implies that $\mathbf{C}_{\mathfrak{G}}(\mathfrak{H})$ is a p-group and so by (22.4) $\mathbf{C}_{\mathfrak{G}}(\mathfrak{H}) = \mathbf{Z}(\mathfrak{H})$. Thus in particular

(22.6) $\mathbf{Z}(\mathfrak{P}) \subseteq \mathbf{Z}(\mathfrak{H}) = \mathbf{C}_{\mathfrak{G}}(\mathfrak{H})$

Let $\mathfrak{M}$ be a maximal subgroup of $\mathfrak{G}$ with $\mathfrak{P} \subseteq \mathfrak{M}$. By induction $\mathfrak{M}$ contains a normal p-complement which necessarily centralizes $\mathfrak{H}$. Thus by (22.6) $\mathfrak{P} = \mathfrak{M}$ is a maximal subgroup of $\mathfrak{G}$. Let q be a prime divisor of $|\mathfrak{K} : \mathfrak{H}|$. The number of $S_q$-subgroups of $\mathfrak{K}/\mathfrak{H}$ is prime to p, so $\mathfrak{P}/\mathfrak{H}$ normalizes some $S_q$-subgroup $\mathfrak{Q}/\mathfrak{H}$ of $\mathfrak{K}/\mathfrak{H}$. Thus $\mathfrak{P}\mathfrak{Q}$ is a group and so $\mathfrak{P}\mathfrak{Q} = \mathfrak{G}$ and $\mathfrak{K} = \mathfrak{Q}$ by the maximality of $\mathfrak{P}$. Since $\mathfrak{K}/\mathfrak{H}$ is a chief factor of $\mathfrak{G}$ this implies that $\mathfrak{K}/\mathfrak{H}$

is an elementary abelian q-group.

Since $\mathbf{N}_{\mathfrak{G}}(\mathbf{T}(\mathfrak{P}))$ has a normal p-complement, it follows that $\mathbf{T}(\mathfrak{P}) \not\subseteq \mathfrak{H}$. Let $d = d(\mathfrak{P})$ and choose an abelian subgroup $\mathfrak{A}$ of $\mathfrak{P}$ with $m(\mathfrak{A}) = d$ and $\mathfrak{A} \not\subseteq \mathfrak{H}$. Let $\mathfrak{A}_0 = \mathfrak{A} \cap \mathfrak{H}$.

Let $\mathfrak{P}_0 = \mathfrak{H}\mathfrak{A}$. By (20.11) $\mathfrak{K}/\mathfrak{H} = \mathfrak{K}_1/\mathfrak{H} \times \mathfrak{K}_2/\mathfrak{H}$ where $\mathfrak{K}_i/\mathfrak{H} \lhd \mathfrak{A}\mathfrak{K}/\mathfrak{H}$ for $i = 1, 2$ and $\mathfrak{K}_2/\mathfrak{H} = \mathbf{C}_{\mathfrak{K}/\mathfrak{H}}(\mathfrak{P}_0/\mathfrak{H})$. By (22.5) $\mathfrak{K}_2 \neq \mathfrak{H}$ and so $\mathfrak{K}_1$ has no normal p-complement in $\mathfrak{K}_1\mathfrak{P}_0$. Let $\mathfrak{G}_0 = \mathfrak{K}_1\mathfrak{P}_0$. Since $\mathfrak{A} \subseteq \mathfrak{P}_0$ it follows that $\mathfrak{A} \subseteq \mathbf{T}(\mathfrak{P}_0)$ and so $\mathbf{N}_{\mathfrak{G}_0}(\mathbf{T}(\mathfrak{P}_0)) = \mathfrak{P}_0$ has a normal p-complement. Since $\mathbf{Z}(\mathfrak{P}) \subseteq \mathbf{Z}(\mathfrak{P}_0)$ by (22.6) also $\mathbf{C}_{\mathfrak{G}_0}(\mathbf{Z}(\mathfrak{P}_0))$ has a normal p-complement. Hence by induction $\mathfrak{G}_0 = \mathfrak{G}$. Thus $\mathfrak{P}_0 = \mathfrak{P}$ and $\mathfrak{K}_1 = \mathfrak{K}$.

The group $\mathfrak{K}/\mathfrak{H}$ is a vector space over the field of q elements and $\mathfrak{P}$ acts on $\mathfrak{K}/\mathfrak{H}$ as a group of linear transformations under the operation of conjugation. Thus we have a representation of $\mathfrak{P}$ on $\mathfrak{K}/\mathfrak{H}$. Since $\mathfrak{P}$ is a maximal subgroup of $\mathfrak{G}$ this representation is irreducible. By (22.5) the kernel of this representation is $\mathfrak{H}$. Thus $\mathfrak{P}/\mathfrak{H}$ which is isomorphic to $\mathfrak{A}/\mathfrak{A}_0$ is an abelian group which has a faithful irreducible representation in a field of characteristic $q \neq p$. By (1.8) $\mathfrak{A}/\mathfrak{A}_0$ is cyclic. In particular $m(\mathfrak{A}_0) \geq d - 1$.

Since $\mathfrak{P}$ is a maximal subgroup of $\mathfrak{G}$ and $\mathbf{C}_{\mathfrak{G}}(\mathbf{Z}(\mathfrak{P})) \neq \mathfrak{G}$ it follows that $\mathbf{C}_{\mathfrak{G}}(\mathbf{Z}(\mathfrak{P})) = \mathfrak{P}$. Let $\mathfrak{W} = \langle \mathbf{Z}(\mathfrak{P})^G \mid G \in \mathfrak{G}\rangle$ so that $\mathfrak{W} \subseteq \mathbf{Z}(\mathfrak{H})$ by (22.6). Thus in particular $\mathfrak{W}$ is abelian. Clearly $\mathfrak{W} \lhd \mathfrak{G}$. Let $\mathfrak{Q}_0$ be a $S_q$-subgroup of $\mathfrak{G}$. Applying (20.11) to $\mathfrak{W}\mathfrak{Q}_0$ we see that $\mathfrak{W} = \mathfrak{W}_1 \times \mathfrak{W}_2$, where $\mathfrak{W}_i \lhd \mathfrak{W}\mathfrak{Q}_0$ for $i = 1, 2$ and $\mathfrak{W}_2 = \mathbf{C}_{\mathfrak{W}}(\mathfrak{Q}_0)$. Since $\mathfrak{Q}_0$ does not centralize $\mathbf{Z}(\mathfrak{P})$ it follows that $\mathfrak{W}_1 \neq \langle 1\rangle$. Let $\mathfrak{V} = \{W \mid W \in \mathfrak{W}_1, W^p = 1\}$. Thus $\mathbf{C}_{\mathfrak{V}}(\mathfrak{Q}_0) = \langle 1\rangle$ and $\mathfrak{V} \lhd \mathfrak{K}$.

Let $\mathfrak{V}_0 = \mathfrak{V} \cap \mathfrak{A}_0 = \mathfrak{V} \cap \mathfrak{A}$ and let $m(\mathfrak{V}/\mathfrak{V}_0) = s$. Since $\mathfrak{V} \subseteq \mathbf{Z}(\mathfrak{H})$, $\langle \mathfrak{V}, \mathfrak{A}_0\rangle$ is abelian. As $\mathfrak{V}$ is elementary it follows that $m(\langle \mathfrak{A}_0, \mathfrak{V}\rangle) = m(\mathfrak{A}_0) + s$. Hence $s \leq 1$ by the definition of $d(\mathfrak{P})$.

Thus if $A \in \mathfrak{A}$ and $G \in \mathfrak{K} - \mathfrak{H}$ then $m(\mathfrak{V}/\mathbf{C}_{\mathfrak{V}}(A)) \leq 1$ and also $m(\mathfrak{V}/\mathbf{C}_{\mathfrak{V}}(G^{-1}AG)) \leq 1$ since $G^{-1}\mathfrak{V}G = \mathfrak{V}$. Consequently $m(\mathfrak{V}/\mathbf{C}_{\mathfrak{V}}(A, G^{-1}AG)) \leq 2$.

Now choose $A \in \mathfrak{A}$ such that $\langle A\mathfrak{A}_0\rangle = \mathfrak{A}/\mathfrak{A}_0$. Let

$G \in \mathfrak{K} - \mathfrak{H}$. If $m(\mathfrak{V}) \geq 3$ then $m(\mathbf{C}_{\mathfrak{V}}(A, G^{-1}AG)) \geq 1$. Thus there exists $V \in \mathfrak{V}^{\#}$ such that $\langle A, G^{-1}AG\rangle \subseteq \mathbf{C}_{\mathfrak{G}}(V)$. Hence $\langle \mathfrak{H}, A, G^{-1}AG\rangle \subseteq \mathbf{C}_{\mathfrak{G}}(V)$. Since $\mathfrak{P} = \langle \mathfrak{H}, A\rangle$ the maximality of $\mathfrak{P}$ implies that

$$\mathfrak{G} = \langle \mathfrak{H}, A, G^{-1}AG\rangle = \mathbf{C}_{\mathfrak{G}}(V)$$

This contradicts the fact that $\mathbf{C}_{\mathfrak{V}}(\mathfrak{D}_0) = \langle 1\rangle$. Hence $m(\mathfrak{V}) \leq 2$. Since $\mathfrak{G}/\mathfrak{H}$ is represented faithfully as a group of linear transformations on $\mathfrak{V}$ this implies that $\mathfrak{G}/\mathfrak{H}$ is isomorphic to a subgroup of $GL(2, p)$. Since $\mathfrak{G}/\mathfrak{H}$ is generated by its p-elements it is isomorphic to a subgroup of $SL(2, p)$. Therefore by (22.1) $\mathfrak{K}/\mathfrak{H} \subseteq \mathbf{Z}(\mathfrak{G}/\mathfrak{H})$ contrary to (22.5). This contradiction completes the proof.

The following corollary of (22.2) had been conjectured for some time however no direct proof of it is known. One major difficulty in attempting a direct proof arises from the fact that unlike (21.8) the hypothesis is not readily amenable to an inductive argument.

(22.7) *(Thompson [2], [3]) Let p be an odd prime and let $\mathfrak{P}$ be a $S_p$-subgroup of $\mathfrak{G}$. Suppose that for every characteristic subgroup $\mathfrak{H}$ of $\mathfrak{P}$, $\mathbf{N}_{\mathfrak{G}}(\mathfrak{H})/\mathbf{C}_{\mathfrak{G}}(\mathfrak{H})$ is a p-group. Then $\mathfrak{G}$ contains a normal p-complement.*

*Proof*. Induction on $|\mathfrak{G}|$. If $\mathfrak{H}$ is a characteristic subgroup of $\mathfrak{P}$, $\mathfrak{H} \neq \langle 1\rangle$ then by induction $\mathbf{N}_{\mathfrak{G}}(\mathfrak{H})/\mathfrak{H}$ has a normal p-complement $\mathfrak{M}/\mathfrak{H}$. By assumption every p′-element in $\mathfrak{M}$ centralizes $\mathfrak{H}$. Thus by (21.8) $\mathfrak{M}$ has a normal p-complement and so also $\mathbf{N}_{\mathfrak{G}}(\mathfrak{H})$ has a normal p-complement. The result now follows from (22.2).

(22.8) *(Thompson [1]) Suppose that $\mathfrak{G}$ contains a maximal subgroup $\mathfrak{M}$ which is nilpotent of odd order. Then $\mathfrak{G}$ is solvable.*

*Proof*. Induction on $|\mathfrak{G}|$. Let $\pi = \pi(\mathfrak{M})$. If $\langle 1\rangle \neq \mathfrak{N} \subseteq \mathfrak{M}$ and $\mathfrak{N} \lhd \mathfrak{G}$ then by induction $\mathfrak{G}/\mathfrak{N}$ is solvable. Thus $\mathfrak{G}$ is solvable since $\mathfrak{N}$ is nilpotent. Assume that no nonidentity subgroup of $\mathfrak{M}$ is normal in $\mathfrak{G}$. Let $p \in \pi$ and let $\mathfrak{P}$ be a $S_p$-subgroup of $\mathfrak{M}$. Since $\mathfrak{M}$ is maximal $\mathbf{N}_{\mathfrak{G}}(\mathfrak{P}) = \mathfrak{M}$. Thus $\mathfrak{P}$ is a $S_p$-subgroup of $\mathfrak{G}$. The maximality of $\mathfrak{M}$ also implies that $\mathfrak{M} = \mathbf{N}_{\mathfrak{G}}(\mathbf{T}(\mathfrak{P}))$ and $\mathfrak{M} = \mathbf{C}_{\mathfrak{G}}(\mathbf{Z}(\mathfrak{P}))$. Thus by (22.2) $\mathfrak{G}$ has a normal p-complement. Applying this to every prime in $\pi$ we see that $\mathfrak{G}$ Has a normal $\pi$-complement $\mathfrak{H}$. Let q be a prime divisor of $|\mathfrak{H}|$. The number of $S_q$-subgroups of $\mathfrak{H}$ is a divisor of $\mathfrak{H}$. Hence by the Schur-Zassenhaus theorem there exists a $S_q$-subgroup $\mathfrak{Q}$ of $\mathfrak{H}$ with $\mathfrak{M} \subseteq \mathbf{N}_{\mathfrak{G}}(\mathfrak{Q})$. Thus $\mathfrak{M}\mathfrak{Q}$ is a group and so $\mathfrak{M}\mathfrak{Q} = \mathfrak{G}$ by the maximality of $\mathfrak{M}$. Therefore $\mathfrak{H} = \mathfrak{Q}$ is solvable. Since $\mathfrak{M}$ is solvable this implies that $\mathfrak{G}$ is solvable as was to be shown.

It should be mentioned that (22.2), (22.7), and (22.8) are all false for $p = 2$. The group $PGL_2(7)$ provides a counter example to all three statements.

# CHAPTER IV

## §23. T. I. SETS

A subset $\mathfrak{A}$ of $\mathfrak{G}$ is a trivial intersection set in $\mathfrak{G}$ or a T. I. set in $\mathfrak{G}$ if $\mathfrak{A} \subseteq \mathbf{N}_{\mathfrak{G}}(\mathfrak{A})$ and $\mathfrak{A}^G \cap \mathfrak{A} \subseteq \langle 1 \rangle$ for $G \in \mathfrak{G} - \mathbf{N}_{\mathfrak{G}}(\mathfrak{A})$. If $\mathfrak{A}$ is a T. I. set in $\mathfrak{G}$ we will also say that $\mathfrak{A}$ has the T. I. property.

The importance of this property and of the following result was first realized by Brauer and independently by Suzuki [1]. The remainder of these notes will to a large extent be concerned with deriving consequences of (23.1) and its generalizations.

(23.1) Let $\mathfrak{A}$ be a T.I. set in $\mathfrak{G}$ and let $\mathfrak{N} = \mathbf{N}_{\mathfrak{G}}(\mathfrak{A})$. Let $\alpha, \beta$ be complex valued class functions on $\mathfrak{N}$ such that $\alpha$ vanishes on $\mathfrak{N} - \mathfrak{A}$ and $\beta$ vanishes on $\{\bigcup_{\mathfrak{G}} \mathfrak{A}^G \cap \mathfrak{N}\} - \mathfrak{A}$. Then $\alpha^*(A) = \alpha(A)$ and $\beta^*(A) = \beta(A)$ for $A \in \mathfrak{A}^{\#}$. If furthermore $\alpha(1) = 0$ then

$$(\alpha, \beta)_{\mathfrak{N}} = (\alpha^*, \beta^*)_{\mathfrak{G}}$$

Proof. The first statement follows directly from the definition of $\alpha^*$ and $\beta^*$. The number of distinct conjugates of $\mathfrak{A}$ in $\mathfrak{G}$ is $|\mathfrak{G} : \mathfrak{N}|$. Thus the T.I. property and the first statement imply that

$$(\alpha^*, \beta^*)_{\mathfrak{G}} = \frac{1}{|\mathfrak{G}|} \sum_{\mathfrak{G}} \alpha^*(G)\overline{\beta^*(G)}$$

$$= \frac{1}{|\mathfrak{N}|} \sum_{\mathfrak{A}} \alpha(A)\overline{\beta(A)} = (\alpha, \beta)_{\mathfrak{N}}$$

It should be observed that if $\mathfrak{A}$ is a S-subgroup of $\mathbf{N}_{\mathfrak{G}}(\mathfrak{A})$ in (23.1) then $\beta$ automatically satisfies the required assumptions.

As a first illustration of how (23.1) is used we give here an alternative proof of Frobenius' theorem (20.2).

(23.2) Suppose that $\mathfrak{E} = \mathbf{N}_{\mathfrak{G}}(\mathfrak{E})$ and $\mathfrak{E}$ is a T.I. set in $\mathfrak{G}$. Then $\mathfrak{E}$ has a normal complement in $\mathfrak{G}$.

Proof. Let $\{\zeta_i\}$ be the set of nonprincipal irreducible characters of $\mathfrak{E}$. Let $\alpha_i = \zeta_i(1)1_{\mathfrak{E}} - \zeta_i$. By (23.1) $\|\alpha_i^*\|^2 = \zeta_i(1)^2 + 1$. By the Frobenius reciprocity theorem $(\alpha_i^*, 1_{\mathfrak{G}}) = \zeta_i(1)$. Since $\alpha_i^*(1) = 0$ this implies that $\alpha_i^* = \zeta_i(1)1_{\mathfrak{G}} - \chi_i$ for some irreducible character $\chi_i$ of $\mathfrak{G}$. If $G \in \mathfrak{G}$ and $G$ is not conjugate to an element of $\mathfrak{E}$ then $\chi_i(G) = \zeta_i(1) = \chi_i(1)$ and so $G \in \mathfrak{M}_i$ by (6.7) where $\mathfrak{M}_i$ is the kernel of $\chi_i$. Let $\theta = 1_{\mathfrak{G}} + \Sigma_i \chi_i(1)\chi_i$ and let $\mathfrak{M} = \bigcap_i \mathfrak{M}_i$. Then $\theta(G) = |\mathfrak{E}| = \theta(1)$ if $G \in \mathfrak{M}$, while $\theta(G) = 0$ if $G \notin \mathfrak{M}$. Thus $\mathfrak{M} \triangleleft \mathfrak{G}$ and $\theta = \rho_{\mathfrak{G}/\mathfrak{M}}$. Furthermore $\mathfrak{M} \cap \mathfrak{E} = \langle 1 \rangle$. Since $|\mathfrak{G} : \mathfrak{M}| = \theta(1) = |\mathfrak{E}|$ we get that $\mathfrak{G} = \mathfrak{M}\mathfrak{E}$ completing the proof.

The following elementary result also due to Brauer and Suzuki is very useful when used in conjunction with (23.1).

(23.3) Let $n \geq 2$. Let $\{\theta_{ij} \mid 1 \leq i, j \leq n\}$ be a collection of generalized characters of $\mathfrak{G}$ such that $\theta_{ij}(1) = 0$ for $1 \leq i, j \leq n$ and

$$(\theta_{ij}, \theta_{st}) = \delta_{is} - \delta_{js} - \delta_{it} + \delta_{jt}$$

for

$$1 \leq i, j, s, t \leq n$$

Then there exists a sign $\epsilon = \pm 1$ and irreducible characters $\chi_1, \ldots, \chi_n$ of $\mathfrak{G}$ such that $\theta_{ij} = \epsilon(\chi_i - \chi_j)$ for $1 \leq i, j \leq n$. If $n > 2$ then $\epsilon$ is uniquely determined.

Proof. Since $\|\theta_{ij}\|^2 = 2 - 2\delta_{ij}$ and $\theta_{ij}(1) = 0$ it follows that $\theta_{ii} = 0$ and $\theta_{ij}$ is the difference of two irreducible characters if $i \neq j$. Since $(\theta_{ij}, \theta_{ji}) = 2\delta_{ij} - 2$ it follows that $\theta_{ij} = -\theta_{ji}$. If $n = 2$ this implies the result.

Suppose that $n > 2$. Since $(\theta_{12}, \theta_{13}) = 1$ we see that $\theta_{12} = \epsilon(\chi_1 - \chi_2)$ and $\theta_{13} = \epsilon(\chi_1 - \chi_3)$, where $\chi_1, \chi_2, \chi_3$ are pairwise distinct irreducible characters and $\epsilon = \pm 1$ is uniquely determined. Let $j > 2$. If $(\chi_1, \theta_{1j}) = 0$ then $(\chi_2, \theta_{1j}) = -\epsilon(\theta_{12}, \theta_{1j}) = -\epsilon$. Similarly $(\chi_3, \theta_{1j}) = -\epsilon$. Thus $\theta_{1j} = -\epsilon(\chi_2 + \chi_3)$ contrary to $\theta_{1j}(1) = 0$. Thus $\theta_{1j} = \epsilon_1(\chi_1 - \chi_j)$ for some irreducible character $\chi_j \neq \chi_1$ and $\epsilon_1 = \pm 1$. Since $(\theta_{12}, \theta_{1j}) = 1$ we get that $\epsilon_1 = \epsilon$. Consequently $\theta_{1j} = \epsilon(\chi_1 - \chi_j)$ and $\chi_1 \neq \chi_j$ for $2 \leq j \leq n$. Since $(\theta_{1j}, \theta_{1t}) = 1 - \delta_{jt}$ it follows that $\chi_j \neq \chi_t$ for $j \neq t$. If $1 < j \neq t \leq n$ then $\|(\theta_{1j} - \theta_{1t})\|^2 = 2$ and $(\theta_{jt}, \theta_{1t} - \theta_{1j}) = 2$. Therefore $\theta_{jt} = \theta_{1t} - \theta_{1j} = \epsilon(\chi_j - \chi_t)$ as required.

## §24. CHARACTERS OF RELATIVELY SMALL DEGREE

In this section it will be shown that if $\mathfrak{G}$ has a faithful character whose degree is small relative to some prime p in $\pi(\mathfrak{G})$ then the $S_p$-subgroup of $\mathfrak{G}$ is normal in $\mathfrak{G}$. Groups satisfying the following assumptions will be studied. The next two results are from Feit [5]. They are implicit in Feit-Thompson [1].

(24.1) (i) $\mathfrak{H}$ is an abelian subgroup of $\mathfrak{G}$, $\mathfrak{N} = \mathbf{N}_{\mathfrak{G}}(\mathfrak{H})$, $\mathfrak{Z} = \mathbf{Z}(\mathfrak{G})$, $|\mathfrak{N} : \mathfrak{H}\mathfrak{Z}| = t$ and

$$\mathfrak{N}_0 = \left\{ \bigcup_{H \in \mathfrak{H}^\#} \mathbf{C}_{\mathfrak{G}}(H) \right\} - \mathfrak{Z}$$

(ii) $\mathfrak{H}$ and $\mathfrak{N}_0$ are T.I. sets in $\mathfrak{G}$ and $\mathbf{N}_{\mathfrak{G}}(\mathfrak{N}_0) = \mathfrak{N}$.
(iii) $\mathfrak{N} \neq \mathfrak{G}$.

(24.2) Assume that (24.1) is satisfied. Let $\mathfrak{X}$ be an irreducible character of $\mathfrak{G}$ which does not have $\mathfrak{H}$ in its kernel. Then

$$(\mathfrak{X}_{\mathfrak{H}}, 1_{\mathfrak{H}})_{\mathfrak{H}} < \frac{1}{|\mathfrak{H}|^{1/2}} \mathfrak{X}(1)$$

Proof: Let $\mathfrak{X}_{|\mathfrak{N}} = \alpha + \beta$, where $\beta$ has $\mathfrak{H}$ in its kernel and no irreducible constituent of $\alpha$ has $\mathfrak{H}$ in its kernel. Let $b = \beta(1)$. Then $b = (X_{|\mathfrak{H}}, 1_{\mathfrak{H}})_{\mathfrak{H}}$. By (6.7) $|\beta(G)| = b$ for $G \in \mathfrak{H}\mathfrak{Z}$. Hence (6.8) and (24.1) imply that

$$1 = ||\chi||^2 > \frac{1}{|\mathfrak{G}|} \frac{|\mathfrak{G}|}{|\mathfrak{N}|} \sum_{\mathfrak{N}_0} |\chi(G)|^2$$

$$\geq \frac{1}{|\mathfrak{N}|} \left\{ -\sum_{\mathfrak{Z}} |\chi(G)|^2 + \sum_{\mathfrak{N}_0 \cup \mathfrak{Z}} |\alpha(G) + \beta(G)|^2 \right\}$$

$$\geq -\frac{\chi(1)^2 |\mathfrak{Z}|}{|\mathfrak{N}|} + ||\alpha||^2_{\mathfrak{N}} + (\alpha, \beta)_{\mathfrak{N}} + \overline{(\alpha, \beta)_{\mathfrak{N}}}$$

$$+ \frac{1}{|\mathfrak{N}|} \sum_{\mathfrak{H}\mathfrak{Z}} |\beta(G)|^2$$

$$= -\frac{\chi(1)^2}{t|\mathfrak{H}|} + ||\alpha||^2_{\mathfrak{N}} + \frac{b^2}{t}$$

By assumption $\alpha \neq 0$ and so $||\alpha||^2_{\mathfrak{N}} \geq 1$. Thus

$$\frac{\chi(1)^2}{t|\mathfrak{H}|} > \frac{b^2}{t}$$

which implies the required result.

(24.3) Suppose that (24.1) is satisfied. Assume further that $\mathfrak{H}$ is not contained in any proper normal subgroup of $\mathfrak{G}$. Let $\chi$ be a nonlinear irreducible character of $\mathfrak{G}$. Then $\chi(1) + 1 > |\mathfrak{H}|^{1/2}$

Proof. Let $\chi_0 = 1_{\mathfrak{G}}, \chi_1, \ldots$ be all the irreducible characters of $\mathfrak{G}$. Define $a_i = (\chi_i, \chi\bar{\chi})$, $b_i = (\chi_i|_{\mathfrak{H}}, 1_{\mathfrak{H}})$ for all i. The Frobenius reciprocity theorem implies that $b_i = (\chi_i, 1_{\mathfrak{H}}^*)$. Thus by the Frobenius reciprocity theorem

$$\sum_i a_i b_i = (\chi\bar{\chi}, 1_{\mathfrak{H}}^*)_{\mathfrak{G}} = (\chi\bar{\chi}|_{\mathfrak{H}}, 1_{\mathfrak{H}})_{\mathfrak{H}} = ||\chi|_{\mathfrak{H}}||^2$$

Since $\mathfrak{H}$ is abelian $\chi(1) \leq ||\chi|_{\mathfrak{H}}||^2_{\mathfrak{H}}$. As $a_0 = b_0 = 1$ (24.2) implies that

$$\chi(1) - 1 \leq \sum_{i\neq 0} a_i b_i < \frac{1}{|\mathfrak{H}|^{1/2}} \sum_{i\neq 0} a_i \chi_i(1) = \frac{\chi(1)^2 - 1}{|\mathfrak{H}|^{1/2}}$$

Since $\chi(1) \neq 1$ this yields the required result.

(24.4) Suppose that for some prime p the Sp-group $\mathfrak{P}$ of $\mathfrak{G}$ is abelian and a T.I. set in $\mathfrak{G}$. Assume that $\mathfrak{G}$ has a faithful character $\chi$ with $\chi(1) \leq p^{1/2} - 1$. Then $\mathfrak{P} \lhd \mathfrak{G}$.

Proof. Induction on $|\mathfrak{G}|$. It may be assumed that $\mathfrak{P}$ is not contained in any proper normal subgroup of $\mathfrak{G}$. Let $\chi$ be a faithful character of minimum degree and let $\chi_1$ be a nonlinear irreducible constituent of $\chi$ with kernel $\mathfrak{K}$. If $\mathfrak{K} \neq \langle 1 \rangle$ then by induction $\mathfrak{P}\mathfrak{K} \lhd \mathfrak{G}$. Since $\chi_1(1) \neq 1$, $\mathfrak{P}\mathfrak{K} \neq \mathfrak{G}$ and so $\mathfrak{P} \lhd \mathfrak{P}\mathfrak{K}$ by induction. Thus $\mathfrak{P} \lhd \mathfrak{G}$. If $\mathfrak{K} = \langle 1 \rangle$ then the minimality of $\chi(1)$ implies that $\chi = \chi_1$ is irreducible.

By (24.3) it suffices to verify (24.1) with $\mathfrak{H} = \mathfrak{P}$. Clearly $\mathfrak{N} \subseteq \mathbf{N}_{\mathfrak{G}}(\mathfrak{N}_0)$ thus it suffices to show that $\mathfrak{N}_0 \cap \mathfrak{N}_0^G$ is empty for $G \in \mathfrak{G} - \mathfrak{N}$. Suppose not and let $H \in \mathfrak{N}_0 \cap \mathfrak{N}_0^G$. Let $\mathfrak{P}_1, \mathfrak{P}_2$ be $S_p$-subgroups of $\mathbf{C}_{\mathfrak{P}}(H)$, $\mathbf{C}_{\mathfrak{P}}G(H)$ respectively. By definition $\mathfrak{P}_i \neq \langle 1 \rangle$ for $i = 1, 2$ and $\mathbf{C}_{\mathfrak{G}}(H) \neq \mathfrak{G}$. Thus by induction the $S_p$-subgroup of $\mathbf{C}_{\mathfrak{G}}(H)$ is normal in $\mathbf{C}_{\mathfrak{G}}(H)$. Hence $\mathfrak{P}_2 \subseteq \mathbf{C}_{\mathfrak{G}}(\mathfrak{P}_1) \subseteq \mathfrak{N}$. Thus $\mathfrak{P}_2 \subseteq \mathfrak{P}$ and so $\mathfrak{P}_2 \subseteq \mathfrak{P} \cap \mathfrak{P}^G = \langle 1 \rangle$. This contradiction establishes the result.

(24.5) Let $q$ be a prime and let $\mathfrak{Q}$ be a $q$-group such that $\mathbf{Z}(\mathfrak{Q}) = \mathfrak{Q}'$ is cyclic and $\mathfrak{Q}/\mathfrak{Q}'$ has exponent $q$. Then $|\mathbf{Z}(\mathfrak{Q})| = q$, $|\mathfrak{Q}:\mathfrak{Q}'| = q^{2n}$ for some integer $n$ and every nonlinear irreducible character of $\mathfrak{Q}$ has degree $q^n$.

Proof. It is easily verified that in any group

$$[G, H][G, K]^H = [G, KH]$$

Since $\mathfrak{Q}' = \mathbf{Z}(\mathfrak{Q})$ this implies that $[G, H^i] = [G, H]^i$ for $G, H \in \mathfrak{Q}$. Since $H^q \in \mathfrak{Q}' = \mathbf{Z}(\mathfrak{Q})$ we see that $[G, H]^q = [G, H^q] = 1$ for $G, H \in \mathfrak{Q}$. Thus $|\mathbf{Z}(\mathfrak{Q})| = q$ as $\mathbf{Z}(\mathfrak{Q})$ is cyclic.

Let $|\mathfrak{Q}:\mathfrak{Q}'| = q^m$ and let $\{\mu_i\}$ be all the linear characters of $\mathfrak{Q}$. Then for $Q \in \mathfrak{Q}$, $\Sigma_i |\mu_i(Q)|^2 = q^m$. If $Q \in \mathfrak{Q} - \mathfrak{Q}'$ then $|\mathfrak{Q}: \mathbf{C}_{\mathfrak{Q}}(Q)| \geq q$ and so by the orthogonality relations $|\mathbf{C}_{\mathfrak{Q}}(Q)| = q^m = \Sigma_i |\mu_i(Q)|^2$. Thus if $\chi$ is a nonlinear irreducible character of $\mathfrak{Q}$ then $\chi(Q) = 0$. Thus

$$1 = \|\chi\|^2 = \frac{1}{q^{m+1}} \sum_{\mathfrak{Q}'} |\chi(Q)|^2 = \frac{1}{q^m} \chi(1)^2$$

Therefore $\chi(1)^2 = q^m$ completing the proof.

(24.6) (Ito [2]) Suppose that $\mathfrak{G}$ is solvable. Let $\mathfrak{P}$ be a $S_p$-subgroup of $\mathfrak{G}$ for some prime $p$. Assume that $\mathfrak{G}$ has a faithful character $\chi$ with $\chi(1) < p - 1$. Then $\mathfrak{P}$ is abelian and $\mathfrak{P} \lhd \mathfrak{G}$.

Proof. Induction on $|\mathfrak{G}|$. Since every irreducible constituent of $\chi_{|\mathfrak{P}}$ is linear $\mathfrak{P}$ is abelian. Assume that $\chi$ is a faithful character of minimum degree. Let $\chi_1$ be a nonlinear irreducible constituent of $\chi$ with kernel $\mathfrak{K}$. If $\mathfrak{K} \neq \langle 1 \rangle$ then $\mathfrak{P}\mathfrak{K} \lhd \mathfrak{G}$ and $\mathfrak{P}\mathfrak{K} \neq \mathfrak{G}$ since $\chi_1$ is nonlinear. Thus by induction $\mathfrak{P} \lhd \mathfrak{P}\mathfrak{K}$ and so $\mathfrak{P} \lhd \mathfrak{G}$. Hence the minimality of $\chi(1)$ implies that $\chi = \chi_1$ is irreducible.

Suppose that $\pi(\mathfrak{G}) = \{p, q_1, \ldots, q_n\}$ with $n > 1$. By (18.10) there exist $S_{p,q_i}$-subgroups $\mathfrak{G}_i$ of $\mathfrak{G}$ with $\mathfrak{P} \subseteq \mathfrak{G}_i$ for $i = 1, \ldots, n$. By induction $\mathfrak{G}_i \subseteq \mathbf{N}_{\mathfrak{G}}(\mathfrak{P})$ for each i. Hence $|\mathfrak{G}| \mid |\mathbf{N}_{\mathfrak{G}}(\mathfrak{P})|$ and so $\mathfrak{G} = \mathbf{N}_{\mathfrak{G}}(\mathfrak{P})$ as required. Thus it may be assumed that $\pi(\mathfrak{G}) = \{p, q\}$.

If $\mathfrak{P}$ is contained in a proper normal subgroup of $\mathfrak{G}$ the result follows by induction. Hence $|\mathfrak{G} : \mathfrak{G}'|$ is a power of p. Let $\mathfrak{G}_0 \triangleleft \mathfrak{G}$ with $|\mathfrak{G} : \mathfrak{G}_0| = p$ and let $\mathfrak{P}_0$ be a $S_p$-subgroup of $\mathfrak{G}_0$. Thus $\mathfrak{P}_0 \triangleleft \mathfrak{G}$ by induction. Hence $\mathfrak{P} \subseteq \mathbf{C}_{\mathfrak{G}}(\mathfrak{P}_0) \triangleleft \mathfrak{G}$. Thus $\mathbf{C}_{\mathfrak{G}}(\mathfrak{P}_0) = \mathfrak{G}$ otherwise the result follows by induction. By (20.13) $\mathfrak{G}_0$, and thus $\mathfrak{G}$, has a normal p-complement $\mathfrak{Q}$. Then $\mathfrak{Q}$ is a $S_q$-subgroup of $\mathfrak{G}$. There exists a linear character $\mu$ of $\mathfrak{G}/\mathfrak{Q}$ such that $\chi|_{\mathfrak{P}_0} = \chi(1)\mu|_{\mathfrak{P}_0}$ since $\mathfrak{P}_0 \subseteq \mathbf{Z}(\mathfrak{G})$. Hence $\mathfrak{P}_0$ is the kernel of $\bar{\mu}\chi$. Thus by induction $\mathfrak{P}_0 = \langle 1 \rangle$ and $|\mathfrak{P}| = p$.

If $\chi|_{\mathfrak{Q}}$ is reducible then $p \mid \chi(1)$ by (9.10) contrary to assumption. Hence $\chi|_{\mathfrak{Q}}$ is irreducible. Thus in particular $\mathfrak{Q}$ is nonabelian.

If $\mathfrak{Q}_0$ is a characteristic subgroup of $\mathfrak{Q}$ with $\mathfrak{Q} \neq \mathfrak{Q}_0$ then $\mathfrak{Q}_0 \triangleleft \mathfrak{Q}$ and so $\mathfrak{P}\mathfrak{Q}_0$ is a group. Hence by induction $\mathfrak{P} \triangleleft \mathfrak{P}\mathfrak{Q}_0$. Thus $\mathfrak{P}\mathfrak{Q}_0 = \mathfrak{P} \times \mathfrak{Q}_0$ and $\mathfrak{P} \subseteq \mathbf{C}_{\mathfrak{G}}(\mathfrak{Q}_0) \triangleleft \mathfrak{G}$. Hence $\mathbf{C}_{\mathfrak{G}}(\mathfrak{Q}_0) = \mathfrak{G}$ by induction and so $\mathfrak{Q}_0$ is cyclic since $\chi$ is irreducible. As $\mathfrak{G}$ has no normal subgroup of index q neither does $\mathfrak{G}/\mathfrak{Q}'$. Thus by (20.11) $\mathfrak{Q}/\mathfrak{Q}'$ is a minimal normal subgroup of $\mathfrak{G}/\mathfrak{Q}'$ and $\mathbf{C}_{\mathfrak{G}}(\mathfrak{P}) = \mathbf{N}_{\mathfrak{G}}(\mathfrak{P}) = \mathfrak{P}\mathfrak{Q}'$. Hence $\mathbf{Z}(\mathfrak{Q}) = \mathfrak{Q}'$ is cyclic and $\mathfrak{Q}/\mathfrak{Q}'$ has exponent q. By (24.5) $|\mathfrak{Q} : \mathfrak{Q}'| = q^{2n}$ and $\chi(1) = q^n$ for some integer n. The number of $S_p$-subgroups in $\mathfrak{G}$ is $|\mathfrak{G} : \mathbf{N}_{\mathfrak{G}}(\mathfrak{P})| = q^{2n}$. Thus by the Sylow theorems $q^{2n} \equiv 1 \pmod{p}$. Hence $q^n \equiv \pm 1 \pmod{p}$ and so $p \leq q^n + 1 = \chi(1) + 1$ contrary to hypothesis. The proof is complete.

(24.7) <u>Suppose that</u> $\mathfrak{G}$ <u>has a normal p-complement</u> $\mathfrak{M}$ <u>for some prime</u> p. <u>Assume that</u> $\mathfrak{G}$ <u>has a faithful irreducible character</u> $\chi$ <u>with</u> $\chi(1) < p - 1$. <u>Then</u> $\mathfrak{G} = \mathfrak{P} \times \mathfrak{M}$, <u>where</u> $\mathfrak{P}$ <u>is a</u> $S_p$-<u>subgroup of</u> $\mathfrak{G}$.

*Proof*. Let $q \in \pi(\mathfrak{M})$. By the Sylow theorems there exists a $S_q$-subgroup $\mathfrak{Q}$ such that $\mathfrak{P} \subseteq \mathbf{N}(\mathfrak{Q})$. Hence $\mathfrak{P}\mathfrak{Q}$ is a solvable group and by (24.6) $\mathfrak{Q} \subseteq \mathbf{N}_{\mathfrak{G}}(\mathfrak{P})$. Thus $|\mathfrak{M}| \mid |\mathbf{N}_{\mathfrak{G}}(\mathfrak{P})|$ and so $\mathfrak{P} \lhd \mathfrak{G}$. The result follows.

The hypothesis of solvability in (24.6) is essential since for any odd prime p the group $SL_2(p)$ has an irreducible character of degree $(p-1)/2$ whose kernel has order at most 2. By combining these methods with some deep results of R. Brauer based on his theory of modular characters it is possible to show that if $\chi(1) < (p-1)/2$ for some irreducible faithful character $\chi$ of $\mathfrak{G}$ then $\mathfrak{G}$ has a normal $S_p$-subgroup. See Feit-Thompson [1]. A related result may be found in Feit [5]. Here these methods will be used to prove some weaker results. The next result is essentially due to Blichfeldt.

(24.8) *Let $\mathfrak{P}$ be a $S_p$-subgroup of $\mathfrak{G}$. Assume that $\mathfrak{G}$ has a faithful character $\chi$ with $\chi(1) \leq p^{1/2} - 1$. Then $\mathfrak{P}$ is abelian and $\mathfrak{P} \lhd \mathfrak{G}$.*

*Proof*. Induction on $|\mathfrak{G}|$. $\mathfrak{P}$ is abelian since $\chi_{|\mathfrak{P}}$ is a sum of linear characters. By induction every proper subgroup of $\mathfrak{G}$ has a normal $S_p$-subgroup.

Let $\mathfrak{H}$ be a minimal normal subgroup of $\mathfrak{G}$ such that $|\mathfrak{G}:\mathfrak{H}|$ is a power of p. Suppose that $\mathfrak{H} \neq \mathfrak{G}$ and let $\mathfrak{P}_0$ be a $S_p$-subgroup of $\mathfrak{H}$. By induction $\mathfrak{P}_0 \lhd \mathfrak{H}$ and so $\mathfrak{P}_0 \lhd \mathfrak{G}$. Hence $\mathfrak{P} \subseteq \mathbf{C}_{\mathfrak{G}}(\mathfrak{P}_0) \lhd \mathfrak{G}$. If $\mathbf{C}_{\mathfrak{G}}(\mathfrak{P}_0) \neq \mathfrak{G}$ then by induction $\mathfrak{P} \lhd \mathbf{C}_{\mathfrak{G}}(\mathfrak{P}_0)$ and so $\mathfrak{P} \lhd \mathfrak{G}$ as required. If $\mathbf{C}_{\mathfrak{G}}(\mathfrak{P}_0) = \mathfrak{G}$ then by (20.13) $\mathfrak{H}$ has a normal p-complement which is necessarily normal in $\mathfrak{G}$. Thus $\mathfrak{P}_0 = \langle 1 \rangle$ by the minimality of $\mathfrak{H}$. The result follows from (24.7) in this case. Consequently $\mathfrak{G} = \mathfrak{H}$. By (20.12) this implies that $\mathfrak{P} \cap \mathbf{Z}(\mathfrak{G}) = \langle 1 \rangle$.

Assume that $\mathfrak{T} = \mathfrak{P} \cap \mathfrak{P}^G \neq \langle 1 \rangle$ for some $G \in \mathfrak{G}$. Since $\{\mathfrak{P}, \mathfrak{P}^G\} \subseteq \mathbf{C}_{\mathfrak{G}}(\mathfrak{T}) \neq \mathfrak{G}$ we get that $\mathfrak{P} = \mathfrak{P}^G$ by induction. Thus $\mathfrak{P}$ is a T.I. set in $\mathfrak{G}$ and the result follows from (24.4).

The next result is due to Isaacs and Passman.

(24.9) Suppose that $\chi(1) \leq p - 1$ for every irreducible character $\chi$ of $\mathfrak{G}$ where p is a prime. Let $\mathfrak{P}$ be a $S_p$-subgroup of $\mathfrak{G}$. Then $\mathfrak{P} \triangleleft \mathfrak{G}$.

Proof. Induction on $|\mathfrak{G}|$. Since $\chi_{|\mathfrak{P}}$ is a sum of linear characters of $\mathfrak{P}$ for every irreducible character $\chi$ of $\mathfrak{G}$ it follows that $\mathfrak{P}$ is abelian. If $\mathfrak{T} = \mathfrak{P} \cap \mathfrak{P}^G \neq \langle 1 \rangle$ for some $G \in \mathfrak{G}$ then $\langle \mathfrak{P}, \mathfrak{P}^G \rangle \subseteq \mathbf{C}_{\mathfrak{G}}(\mathfrak{T})$. If $\mathbf{C}_{\mathfrak{G}}(\mathfrak{T}) = \mathfrak{G}$ then induction applied to $\mathfrak{G}/\mathfrak{T}$ yields the result. If $\mathbf{C}_{\mathfrak{G}}(\mathfrak{T}) \neq \mathfrak{G}$ then $\mathfrak{P} \triangleleft \mathbf{C}_{\mathfrak{G}}(\mathfrak{T})$ by induction. Thus $\mathfrak{P} = \mathfrak{P}^G$ and so $\mathfrak{P}$ is a T.I. set in $\mathfrak{G}$.

If $\mathfrak{G}$ is simple let $\chi$ be any nonprincipal character of $\mathfrak{G}$. Then $\chi$ is faithful. If $\mathfrak{G}$ is not simple let $\mathfrak{H}$ be a minimal normal subgroup of $\mathfrak{G}$. By induction $\mathfrak{H}\mathfrak{P} \triangleleft \mathfrak{G}$. If $\mathfrak{H}\mathfrak{P} \neq \mathfrak{G}$ then $\mathfrak{P} \triangleleft \mathfrak{H}\mathfrak{P}$ by induction and the result follows. Thus $\mathfrak{G} = \mathfrak{H}\mathfrak{P}$. Let $\chi$ be an irreducible character of $\mathfrak{G}$ whose kernel $\mathfrak{K}$ does not contain $\mathfrak{H}$. Thus $\mathfrak{K} \cap \mathfrak{H} = \langle 1 \rangle$ by the minimality of $\mathfrak{H}$. Since $\mathfrak{P} \cap \mathfrak{K} \triangleleft \mathfrak{K}$ by induction it follows that $\mathfrak{P} \cap \mathfrak{K} \triangleleft \mathfrak{G}$. Thus $\mathfrak{P} \cap \mathfrak{K} = \langle 1 \rangle$ as $\mathfrak{P}$ is a T.I. set in $\mathfrak{G}$. Hence $\mathfrak{K} = \langle 1 \rangle$. Since $\mathfrak{P} \ntriangleleft \mathfrak{P}\mathfrak{H}$ and $\mathfrak{H}$ is minimal we also see that $\mathbf{Z}(\mathfrak{G}) = \langle 1 \rangle$ and nonlinear irreducible characters of $\mathfrak{G}$ are faithful.

Let $|\mathfrak{P}| = p^n$. Choose t such that $t \equiv 1 \pmod{|\mathfrak{G}|/p^n}$ and t is a primitive root mod p. Let $\epsilon$ be a primitive $|\mathfrak{G}|$-th root of unity and define $\sigma \in \mathcal{G}_{\mathbb{Q}_{|\mathfrak{G}|}/\mathbb{Q}}$ by $\epsilon^\sigma = \epsilon^t$. Let $\mathcal{S}$ be the set of all nonprincipal irreducible characters $\chi$ of $\mathfrak{G}$ with $\chi^\sigma = \chi$. By the previous paragraph each $\chi$ in $\mathcal{S}$ is faithful. Since $\mathfrak{G}^\#$ contains p'-elements $\mathcal{S}$ is nonempty by (12.3). If $\chi \in \mathcal{S}$ let $\chi_{|\mathfrak{P}} = \Sigma\lambda_i$. Since $\chi(G) \in \mathbb{Q}$ for $G \in \mathfrak{P}$ it follows that the $\lambda_i$ are all algebraically conjugate. Thus the kernel of $\chi_{|\mathfrak{P}}$ is equal to the kernel of each $\lambda_i$ and so each $\lambda_i$ is faithful. Hence $\mathfrak{P}$ is cyclic. Let $\mathfrak{P} = \langle P \rangle$ then $P^p = 1$ since $\chi(P) \in \mathbb{Q}$ and $\chi(1) \leq p - 1$. Thus $|\mathfrak{P}| = p$, $\chi(1) = p - 1$ and $\chi_{|\mathfrak{P}} = \Sigma_{i=1}^{p-1} \lambda^i$ for some irreducible character $\lambda$ of $\mathfrak{P}$.

Suppose that $\mathbf{C}_{\mathfrak{G}}(\mathfrak{P}) \neq \mathfrak{P}$. Let A be a p'-element in $\mathbf{C}_{\mathfrak{G}}(P)^\#$ and let $\mathfrak{A} = \langle P \rangle \times \langle A \rangle$. Then $\chi_{|\mathfrak{A}} = \Sigma_{i=1}^{p-1} \lambda^i \mu_i$

where each $\mu_i$ is a linear character of $\langle A \rangle$. Reading subscripts mod p we get that

$$\sum_{i=1}^{p-1} \lambda^i(P)\mu_i(G) = \chi(PG) = \chi(PG)^{\sigma^{-1}}$$
$$= \sum_{i=1}^{p-1} \lambda^i(P)\mu_{it}(G)$$

Therefore $\Sigma_{i=1}^{p-1}\{\mu_i(G) - \mu_{it}(G)\}\lambda^i(P) = 0$. Hence $\mu_i(G) = \mu_1(G)$ for all i and $G \in \langle A \rangle$. Hence $\mu_i = \mu$ for all i. Consequently $\chi(A) = \chi(1)\mu(A)$ contrary to the fact that $\mathbf{Z}(\mathfrak{G}) = \langle 1 \rangle$. Therefore $\mathbf{C}_{\mathfrak{G}}(\mathfrak{P}) = \mathfrak{P}$.

Hence every element of $\mathfrak{G}$ is either a p′-element or is conjugate to a power of P. Let k be the number of conjugate classes of $\mathfrak{G}$ which contain elements in $\mathfrak{P}^{\#}$. By (12.3) this implies that there is at most one orbit $\mathfrak{J}$ with $|\mathfrak{J}| > 1$ under the action of $\langle\sigma\rangle$ on the irreducible characters of $\mathfrak{G}$ and $|\mathfrak{J}| = k$. Let each character in $\mathfrak{J}$ have degree d. Then $k \mid (p-1)$ since $|\langle\sigma\rangle| = p-1$ and $|\mathfrak{G}| = 1 + kd^2 + |\mathcal{S}|(p-1)$. Reading mod k yields that $1 \equiv 0 \pmod{k}$. Thus $k = 1$. Hence $\mathfrak{J}$ is empty and $|\mathfrak{G}| = 1 + |\mathcal{S}|(p-1)$. Since $\chi(1) \mid |\mathfrak{G}|$ for $\chi \in \mathcal{S}$ and $\chi(1) = p-1$ this implies that $0 \equiv 1 \pmod{p-1}$. Thus $p = 2$. Hence by assumption every irreducible character of $\mathfrak{G}$ is linear and the result follows.

The next result is due to Blichfeldt and is of a slightly different type.

(24.10) Let $\chi$ be a faithful character of $\mathfrak{G}$. Let $\pi = \{p \mid \chi(1) < p - 1\}$. Then $\mathfrak{G}$ contains an abelian $S_\pi$-subgroup.

Proof. Induction on $|\mathfrak{G}|$. Any $\pi$-subgroup $\mathfrak{H}$ of $\mathfrak{G}$ is abelian since $\chi_{|\mathfrak{H}}$ is a sum of linear characters. It remains to show that $\mathfrak{G}$ has an $S_\pi$-subgroup.

Suppose first that there exists $\mathfrak{G}_0 \lhd \mathfrak{G}$ such that $\mathfrak{G}/\mathfrak{G}_0$ is an abelian $\pi$-group. Thus there exists $\mathfrak{H} \lhd \mathfrak{G}$ with

$|\mathfrak{G}: \mathfrak{H}| = p$ and $p \in \pi$. By induction $\mathfrak{H}$ contains an abelian $S_\pi$-subgroup $\mathfrak{A}$. Let $\mathfrak{P}_0$ be a $S_p$-subgroup of $\mathfrak{A}$ and let $\mathfrak{P}$ be a $S_p$-subgroup of $\mathfrak{G}$ with $\mathfrak{P}_0 \subseteq \mathfrak{P}$. Thus $\langle \mathfrak{A}, \mathfrak{P} \rangle \subseteq \mathbf{C}_{\mathfrak{G}}(\mathfrak{P}_0)$. Hence by induction it may be assumed that $\mathbf{C}_{\mathfrak{G}}(\mathfrak{P}_0) = \mathfrak{G}$ and so by (20.13) $\mathfrak{G}$ has a normal p-complement. The result now follows from (24.7). Therefore $\mathfrak{G}/\mathfrak{G}'$ is a $\pi'$-group. Hence by (20.13) $\mathbf{Z}(\mathfrak{G})$ is a $\pi'$-group.

It may be assumed that $\chi$ is a faithful character of minimum degree. Let $\chi_1$ be an irreducible constituent of $\chi$ and let $\mathfrak{K}$ be the kernel of $\chi_1$. The minimality of $\chi(1)$ implies that $\chi_1 \neq 1_{\mathfrak{G}}$ and so $\mathfrak{K} \neq \mathfrak{G}$. If $\mathfrak{K} \neq \langle 1 \rangle$ then by induction $\mathfrak{K} \subseteq \mathfrak{A}$ where $\mathfrak{A}/\mathfrak{K}$ is a $S_\pi$-subgroup of $\mathfrak{G}/\mathfrak{K}$. Since $\mathfrak{G}/\mathfrak{G}'$ is a $\pi'$-group $\mathfrak{A} \neq \mathfrak{G}$. Thus $\mathfrak{A}$ contains a $S_\pi$-subgroup as required. Hence $\mathfrak{K} = \langle 1 \rangle$ and the minimality of $\chi(1)$ implies that $\chi = \chi_1$ is irreducible.

Let $\mathfrak{B}$ be a $\pi$-subgroup of maximum order. If $p \in \pi$ and $p \,||\mathfrak{B}|$ let P be a p-element in $\mathfrak{B}^\#$ and let $\mathfrak{P}$ be a $S_p$-subgroup of $\mathfrak{G}$ with $P \in \mathfrak{P}$. Thus $\langle \mathfrak{P}, \mathfrak{B} \rangle \subseteq \mathbf{C}_{\mathfrak{G}}(P) \neq \mathfrak{G}$. By induction $\mathbf{C}_{\mathfrak{G}}(P)$ contains a $S_\pi$-subgroup. Thus the maximality of $|\mathfrak{B}|$ implies that $\mathfrak{B}$ is a S-subgroup of $\mathfrak{G}$. Therefore it suffices to show that if $q \in \pi$ then $q \,||\mathfrak{B}|$.

Let $q \in \pi$ and let $p \in \pi$ such that $p\,||\mathfrak{B}|$. Let P, Q be elements of order p, q respectively. Since $\chi(Q) < q - 1$ and $\chi(Q)$ is a sum of $\chi(1)$ q-th roots of unity not all 1 it follows that $\mathcal{Q}_q$ is the smallest cyclotomic field containing $\chi(Q)$. Similarly $\mathcal{Q}_p$ is the smallest cyclotomic field containing $\chi(P)$. Hence by (6.13) there exists $G \in \mathfrak{G}$ of order pq. Let $G = P_1 Q_1 = Q_1 P_1$ where $P_1$ is a p-element and $Q_1$ is a q-element. Replacing G by a conjugate it may be assumed that $P_1 \in \mathfrak{B}$. Thus $\langle Q_1, \mathfrak{B} \rangle \subseteq \mathbf{C}_{\mathfrak{G}}(P_1) \neq \mathfrak{G}$. By induction $\mathbf{C}_{\mathfrak{G}}(P_1)$ contains a $S_\pi$-subgroup. Thus the maximality of $|\mathfrak{B}|$ implies that $q\,||\mathfrak{B}|$. Since q was an arbitrary prime in $\pi$ the proof is complete.

## §25. FROBENIUS GROUPS

A group $\mathfrak{G}$ is a Frobenius group with Frobenius kernel $\mathfrak{H}$ if

(i) $\mathfrak{H} \lhd \mathfrak{G}$, $\langle 1 \rangle \neq \mathfrak{H} \neq \mathfrak{G}$.

(ii) $\mathbf{C}_{\mathfrak{G}}(H) \subseteq \mathfrak{H}$ for $H \in \mathfrak{H}^{\#}$.

Frobenius groups arise naturally in many contexts. This section is concerned with investigating some of their properties.

(25.1) Let $\mathfrak{G}$ be a Frobenius group with Frobenius kernel $\mathfrak{H}$. Then $\mathfrak{H}$ is a S-subgroup of $\mathfrak{G}$.

Proof. Let $\mathfrak{P}_0$ be a $S_p$-subgroup of $\mathfrak{H}$ for some prime p and let $\mathfrak{P}$ be a $S_p$-subgroup of $\mathfrak{G}$ with $\mathfrak{P}_0 \subseteq \mathfrak{P}$. Assume that $\mathfrak{P}_0 \neq \langle 1 \rangle$. Then $\mathbf{Z}(\mathfrak{P}) \subseteq \mathbf{C}_{\mathfrak{G}}(\mathfrak{P}_0) \subseteq \mathfrak{H} \cap \mathfrak{P}$. Hence $\mathbf{Z}(\mathfrak{P}) \subseteq \mathfrak{P}_0$. Thus $\mathfrak{P} \subseteq \mathbf{C}_{\mathfrak{G}}(\mathbf{Z}(\mathfrak{P})) \subseteq \mathfrak{H}$. Therefore $\mathfrak{P} = \mathfrak{P}_0$ and the result follows.

(25.2) The following statements are equivalent.

(i) $\mathfrak{G}$ is a Frobenius group with Frobenius kernel $\mathfrak{H}$, $|\mathfrak{H}| = h$ and $|\mathfrak{G}| = he$.

(ii) $|\mathfrak{G}| = he$ with $(h, e) = 1$. If $G \in \mathfrak{G}$ then either $G^h = 1$ or $G^e = 1$. $\mathfrak{H} \lhd \mathfrak{G}$ where $\mathfrak{H} = \{G \mid G^h = 1\}$.

(iii) $\mathfrak{E}$ is a T.I. set in $\mathfrak{G}$ with $\mathbf{N}_{\mathfrak{G}}(\mathfrak{E}) = \mathfrak{E} \neq \mathfrak{G}$ and $|\mathfrak{E}| = e$.

Proof. (i) $\Rightarrow$ (ii). This is immediate by (25.1). (ii) $\Rightarrow$ (iii). By the Schur-Zassenhaus theorem there exists a complement $\mathfrak{E}$ of $\mathfrak{H}$ in $\mathfrak{G}$. Suppose that $G^e = 1$ for some $G \in \mathfrak{G}$. Let $\{E\} = \mathfrak{E} \cap G\mathfrak{H}$. Then $\langle E \rangle \mathfrak{H} = \langle G \rangle \mathfrak{H}$ and by the Schur-Zassenhaus theorem G is conjugate to an element of $\langle E \rangle \subseteq \mathfrak{E}$. Hence every element G with $G \neq 1$ and $G^e = 1$ is conjugate to an element of $\mathfrak{E}$. The number of such elements is $|\mathfrak{G}| - |\mathfrak{H}| = (e-1)h$. Thus $|\bigcup_G \mathfrak{E}^{\#G}| = (e-1)h$. The number of distinct conjugates of $\mathfrak{E}^{\#}$ is $|\mathfrak{G}: \mathbf{N}_{\mathfrak{G}}(\mathfrak{E})| \leq h$ and each conjugate of $\mathfrak{E}^{\#}$ contains $e - 1$ elements. Thus $|\mathfrak{G}: \mathbf{N}_{\mathfrak{G}}(\mathfrak{E})| = h$ and no element is counted twice. This proves (iii).

(iii) $\Rightarrow$ (i). By (23.2) $\mathfrak{E}$ has a normal complement $\mathfrak{H}$ in $\mathfrak{G}$. Let $|\mathfrak{H}| = h \neq 1$. The assumptions imply that $|\bigcup_G \mathfrak{E}^{\#G}| = (e-1)h$. Hence every element in $\mathfrak{G}$ is conjugate to an element of $\mathfrak{H}$ or of $\mathfrak{E}^{\#}$. Let $H \in \mathfrak{H}^{\#}$ and assume that

$\mathbf{C}_{\mathfrak{G}}(H) \not\subseteq \mathfrak{H}$. Then replacing H by a conjugate it may be assumed that there exists $E \in \mathfrak{E}^{\#} \cap \mathbf{C}_{\mathfrak{G}}(H)$. Hence $H \in \mathfrak{E} \cap \mathfrak{E}^H$ and so $\mathfrak{E} = \mathfrak{E}^H$ contrary to assumption. Hence $\mathbf{C}_{\mathfrak{G}}(H) \subseteq \mathfrak{H}$ as required.

Let $\mathfrak{G}$ be a Frobenius group with Frobenius kernel $\mathfrak{H}$. Let $\mathfrak{E}$ be defined as in (25.2). Then $\mathfrak{G} = \mathfrak{H}\mathfrak{E}$ and $\mathfrak{H} \cap \mathfrak{E} = \langle 1 \rangle$. Furthermore $\mathfrak{E}$ acts as a group of automorphisms of $\mathfrak{H}$ under conjugation such that no element of $\mathfrak{E}^{\#}$ fixes any element of $\mathfrak{H}^{\#}$. Conversely if $\mathfrak{E}$ is a nonidentity group of automorphisms of $\mathfrak{H}$ such that no element of $\mathfrak{E}^{\#}$ fixes any element of $\mathfrak{H}^{\#}$ then the semidirect product $\mathfrak{E}\mathfrak{H}$ is a Frobenius group with Frobenius kernel $\mathfrak{H}$. The group $\mathfrak{E}$ is sometimes called a Frobenius complement.

(25.3) Let $\mathfrak{G}$ be a Frobenius group with Frobenius kernel $\mathfrak{H}$. Let $\mathfrak{A}$ be a subgroup of $\mathfrak{G}$. Then one of the follow-lowing must occur:

(i) $\mathfrak{A} \subseteq \mathfrak{H}$.

(ii) $\mathfrak{A} \cap \mathfrak{H} = \langle 1 \rangle$.

(iii) $\mathfrak{A}$ is a Frobenius group with Frobenius kernel $\mathfrak{A} \cap \mathfrak{H}$.

If furthermore $\mathfrak{A} \lhd \mathfrak{G}$ then either $\mathfrak{H} \subseteq \mathfrak{A}$ or $\mathfrak{A} \subset \mathfrak{H}$ and $\mathfrak{G}/\mathfrak{A}$ is a Frobenius group with Frobenius kernel $\mathfrak{H}/\mathfrak{A}$.

Proof. By definition $\mathbf{C}_{\mathfrak{A}}(A) \subseteq \mathfrak{A} \cap \mathfrak{H}$ for $A \in (\mathfrak{A} \cap \mathfrak{H})^{\#}$. The first statement follows.

Suppose that $\mathfrak{A} \lhd \mathfrak{G}$. Let $|\mathfrak{H}| = h$ and $|\mathfrak{G}| = he$. By (25.2) $G^e = 1$ or $G^h = 1$ for $G \in \mathfrak{G}$. This property is preserved under homomorphism. Since $\mathfrak{H}\mathfrak{A}/\mathfrak{H} \cap \mathfrak{A} = \mathfrak{H}/\mathfrak{H} \cap \mathfrak{A} \times \mathfrak{A}/\mathfrak{H} \cap \mathfrak{A}$ it follows that either $\mathfrak{H}/\mathfrak{H} \cap \mathfrak{A} = \langle 1 \rangle$ or $\mathfrak{A}/\mathfrak{H} \cap \mathfrak{A} = \langle 1 \rangle$. Thus either $\mathfrak{H} \subseteq \mathfrak{A}$ or $\mathfrak{A} \subseteq \mathfrak{H}$. If $\mathfrak{A} \subseteq \mathfrak{H}$ then $\mathfrak{H}/\mathfrak{A} \lhd \mathfrak{G}/\mathfrak{A}$ and the result follows from (25.2).

(25.4) Let $\mathfrak{G}$ be a Frobenius group with Frobenius kernel $\mathfrak{H}$. If $\zeta$ is a nonprincipal irreducible character of $\mathfrak{H}$ then $\zeta^*$ is an irreducible character of $\mathfrak{G}$. If $\chi$ is an irreducible character of $\mathfrak{G}$ whose kernel does not contain $\mathfrak{H}$ then $\chi = \zeta^*$ for some irreducible character $\zeta$ of $\mathfrak{H}$. Furthermore $\chi_{|\mathfrak{E}} = \zeta(1)\rho_{\mathfrak{E}}$ and $1_{\mathfrak{E}} \subseteq \chi_{|\mathfrak{E}}$ where $\mathfrak{E}$ is a complement of $\mathfrak{H}$ in $\mathfrak{G}$.

Proof. The last statement is an immediate consequence of the first two. To prove the first two statements it suffices by (9.11) to show that if $\zeta$ is a nonprincipal character of $\mathfrak{H}$ and $E \in \mathfrak{E}^{\#}$ then $\zeta^E \neq \zeta$.

Let $\mathfrak{K}$ be a conjugate class of $\mathfrak{H}$, $\mathfrak{K} \neq \{1\}$ and let $K \in \mathfrak{K}$. Then $\bigcup_{\mathfrak{E}} \mathfrak{K}^E$ is the conjugate class of $\mathfrak{G}$ containing K. Since $|\mathfrak{G} : \mathbf{C}_{\mathfrak{G}}(K)| = |\mathfrak{E}|\, |\mathfrak{H} ; \mathbf{C}_{\mathfrak{H}}(K)|$ it follows that $|\bigcup_{\mathfrak{E}} \mathfrak{K}^E| = |\mathfrak{E}|\, |\mathfrak{K}|$. Thus $\mathfrak{K}^E \neq \mathfrak{K}$ for $E \in \mathfrak{E}^{\#}$. Let $k + 1$ be the number of conjugate classes of $\mathfrak{H}$. The group $\mathfrak{E}$ permutes these conjugate classes and there are exactly $1 + k/|\mathfrak{E}|$ orbits under the action of $\mathfrak{E}$. The group $\mathfrak{E}$ permutes the $k + 1$ irreducible characters of $\mathfrak{H}$ and so by (12.1) there are exactly $1 + k/|\mathfrak{E}|$ orbits under the action of $\mathfrak{E}$. Thus $\zeta^E \neq \zeta$ for $E \in \mathfrak{E}^{\#}$ where $\zeta$ is any nonprincipal irreducible character of $\mathfrak{H}$ as required.

(25.5) Let $\mathfrak{E} \neq \langle 1 \rangle$ be a group. There exists a Frobenius group $\mathfrak{G}$ with Frobenius kernel $\mathfrak{H}$ and $\mathfrak{G}/\mathfrak{H}$ isomorphic to $\mathfrak{E}$ if and only if there exists an irreducible character $\chi$ of $\mathfrak{E}$ such that for every subgroup $\mathfrak{E}_0$ of $\mathfrak{E}$ with $\mathfrak{E}_0 \neq \langle 1 \rangle$, $(\chi_{|\mathfrak{E}_0}, 1_{\mathfrak{E}_0}) = 0$.

Proof. Suppose first that $\mathfrak{G}$ exists. Let $p \in \pi(\mathfrak{H})$ and let $\mathfrak{P}$ be a $S_p$-subgroup of $\mathfrak{H}$. By the Sylow theorems $|\mathfrak{G} : \mathfrak{H}| \mid |\mathbf{N}_{\mathfrak{G}}(\mathfrak{P})|$. Hence by (25.3) $\mathbf{N}_{\mathfrak{G}}(\mathfrak{P})$ contains a complement of $\mathfrak{H}$ in $\mathfrak{G}$ which is necessarily isomorphic to $\mathfrak{E}$. Thus it may be assumed that $\mathfrak{E} \subseteq \mathbf{N}_{\mathfrak{G}}(\mathfrak{P})$. Hence $\mathfrak{E}\mathfrak{P}$ is a group. Let $\mathfrak{A}$ be a minimal normal subgroup of $\mathfrak{E}\mathfrak{P}$. By (25.3) $\mathfrak{E}\mathfrak{A}$ is a Frobenius group. Furthermore $\mathfrak{A}$ has exponent p. Since $\mathfrak{A}$ is minimal the action of $\mathfrak{E}$ on $\mathfrak{A}$ gives rise to a faithful $\mathfrak{F}$-irreducible $\mathfrak{F}$-representation $\mathfrak{F}$ of $\mathfrak{E}$ where $\mathfrak{F}$ is the field of p elements. Since $\mathfrak{A}\mathfrak{E}$ is a Frobenius group the restriction of $\mathfrak{F}$ to any subgroup $\mathfrak{E}_0 \neq \langle 1 \rangle$ of $\mathfrak{E}$ does not contain the trivial representation of $\mathfrak{E}_0$ as a constituent. By (4.4) this implies the required result.

Conversely suppose $\mathfrak{E}$ has a character $\chi$ with $(\chi_{|\mathfrak{E}_0}, 1_{\mathfrak{E}_0}) = 0$ for every subgroup $\mathfrak{E}_0 \neq \langle 1 \rangle$ of $\mathfrak{E}$. Let p be a prime with $(p, |\mathfrak{E}|) = 1$ then by (4.4) there exists a representation $\mathfrak{F}$ of $\mathfrak{E}$ with underlying vector space $\mathfrak{V}$ over a finite field of characteristic p such that the restriction of $\mathfrak{F}$ to any subgroup $\mathfrak{E}_0 \neq \langle 1 \rangle$ of $\mathfrak{E}$ does not contain the trivial representation of $\mathfrak{E}_0$ as a constituent. Let $H = \{H_v \mid v \in \mathfrak{V}\}$, where $H_v H_w = H_{v+w}$. Let $\mathfrak{G}$ be the semidirect product of $\mathfrak{E}$ and $\mathfrak{H}$ where $H_v E = EH_{v\mathfrak{F}(E)}$. It is easily seen that $\mathfrak{G}$ is a Frobenius group with Frobenius kernel $\mathfrak{H}$ as required.

(25.6) (Burnside) Let $\mathfrak{G}$ be a Frobenius group with Frobenius kernel $\mathfrak{H}$. Let $\mathfrak{E}$ be a complement of $\mathfrak{H}$ in $\mathfrak{G}$ and let q, r $\in \pi(\mathfrak{E})$ (q, r not necessarily distinct). Then every subgroup of $\mathfrak{G}$ of order qr is cyclic.

Proof. It may be assumed that $|\mathfrak{E}| = qr$. If $q = r$ then $\mathfrak{E}$ is abelian. By (25.5) $\mathfrak{E}$ has a faithful irreducible character. Thus $\mathfrak{E}$ is cyclic by (1.8). If $q \neq r$ and $\mathfrak{E}$ is not cyclic then $\mathfrak{E}$ is a Frobenius group. This contradicts (25.4) and (25.5). Thus $\mathfrak{E}$ is cyclic in all cases.

(25.7) Let $\mathfrak{G}$ be a Frobenius group with Frobenius kernel $\mathfrak{H}$. Let $\mathfrak{E}$ be a complement of $\mathfrak{H}$ in $\mathfrak{G}$. Then a Sylow group of $\mathfrak{E}$ is either cyclic or a quaternion group. Every abelian subgroup of $\mathfrak{E}$ is cyclic.

Proof. By (25.6) a $S_p$-subgroup of $\mathfrak{E}$ has a unique subgroup of order p for $p \in \pi(\mathfrak{E})$. This is known to imply the first statement. The second statement is an immediate consequence of the first.

By using (25.5) it is possible to give a complete classification of groups $\mathfrak{E}$ which can occur as the complement of a Frobenius kernel $\mathfrak{H}$ in a Frobenius group $\mathfrak{G}$. The conditions in (25.6) are in general not sufficient. However by using (20.16) it is easily shown that they are necessary and sufficient in case all Sylow subgroups of $\mathfrak{E}$ are cyclic. Much less is known about which groups $\mathfrak{H}$ can be the Frobenius kernel of a Frobenius group. Before looking at this question we prove another consequence of (25.5).

(25.8) The Frobenius kernel of a Frobenius group is unique.

Proof. Let $\mathfrak{H}$ and $\mathfrak{H}_1$ be Frobenius kernels of the Frobenius group $\mathfrak{G}$. It may be assumed that $\mathfrak{H}_1 \not\subseteq \mathfrak{H}$. Thus there exists $p \in \pi(\mathfrak{H}_1)$, $p \notin \pi(\mathfrak{H})$. Let $\mathfrak{P}$ be a $S_p$-subgroup of $\mathfrak{H}_1$. By (25.3) $\mathfrak{H} \subseteq \mathfrak{H}_1$. By the Sylow theorems $|\mathfrak{G}: \mathfrak{H}_1| \mid |\mathbf{N}_{\mathfrak{G}}(\mathfrak{P})|$. Thus by (25.3) there exists a complement $\mathfrak{E}$ of $\mathfrak{H}_1$ with $\mathfrak{E} \subseteq \mathbf{N}_{\mathfrak{G}}(\mathfrak{P})$. Hence $\mathfrak{E}\mathfrak{P}$ is a Frobenius group with Frobenius kernel $\mathfrak{P}$. Thus if $\chi$ is an irreducible character of $\mathfrak{E}\mathfrak{P}$ then by (25.4) either $1_{\mathfrak{P}} \subseteq \chi_{|\mathfrak{P}}$ or $1_{\mathfrak{E}} \subseteq \chi_{\mathfrak{E}}$. This contradicts (25.5) since $\mathfrak{E}\mathfrak{P}\mathfrak{H}$ is a Frobenius group with Frobenius kernel $\mathfrak{H}$.

(25.9) (Burnside) Let $\mathfrak{G}$ be a Frobenius group with Frobenius kernel $\mathfrak{H}$. If $|\mathfrak{G}: \mathfrak{H}|$ is even then $\mathfrak{H}$ is abelian.

Proof. Let J be an involution in $\mathfrak{G}$. Suppose that $H_1^{-1} H_1^J = H_2^{-1} H_2^J$ for $H_1, H_2 \in \mathfrak{H}$. Then $H_2 H_1^{-1} = (H_2 H_1^{-1})^J$. Therefore $H_1 = H_2$. Thus there are $|\mathfrak{H}|$ distinct elements of the form $H^{-1} H^J$ in $\mathfrak{H}$. Consequently if $G \in \mathfrak{H}$ then $G = H^{-1} H^J$ for some $H \in \mathfrak{H}$. Thus $G^J = H^{-J} H = G^{-1}$. Therefore if $G_1, G_2 \in \mathfrak{H}$ then

$$G_1 G_2 = (G_2^{-1} G_1^{-1})^J = G_2^{-J} G_1^{-J} = G_2 G_1$$

as required.

It is possible to give an elementary proof of (23.2) and thus of (25.2) in case $|\mathfrak{E}|$ is even by elaborating on the above argument. See Burnside p. 172. The following result is deeper.

(25.10) (Thompson) The Frobenius kernel of a Frobenius group is nilpotent.

Proof. Let $\mathfrak{G}$ be a Frobenius group with Frobenius kernel $\mathfrak{H}$. Induction on $|\mathfrak{H}|$. If $\mathbf{Z}(\mathfrak{H}) \neq \langle 1 \rangle$ then $\mathbf{Z}(\mathfrak{H}) \lhd \mathfrak{G}$. Hence by (25.3) and induction $\mathfrak{H}/\mathbf{Z}(\mathfrak{H})$ is nilpotent and so $\mathfrak{H}$ is nilpotent. Assume that $\mathbf{Z}(\mathfrak{H}) = \langle 1 \rangle$. Let $p \in \pi(\mathfrak{H})$ such that $\mathfrak{H}$ does not have a normal p-complement. Choose $p \neq 2$ if possible. Let $\mathfrak{P}$ be a $S_p$-subgroup of $\mathfrak{G}$. If $p = 2$ then $\mathfrak{P} \lhd \mathfrak{H}$ and so $\mathbf{T}(\mathfrak{P}) \lhd \mathfrak{H}$. Suppose that $p \neq 2$. By the Sylow theorems $|\mathfrak{G}: \mathfrak{H}| \mid |\mathbf{N}_{\mathfrak{G}}(\mathfrak{P})|$. Hence there exists a complement $\mathfrak{E}$ of $\mathfrak{H}$ in $\mathfrak{G}$ with $\mathfrak{E} \subseteq \mathbf{N}_{\mathfrak{G}}(\mathfrak{P})$. $\mathfrak{C} = \mathbf{C}_{\mathfrak{H}}(\mathbf{Z}(\mathfrak{P})) \neq \mathfrak{H}$ since $\mathbf{Z}(\mathfrak{H}) = \langle 1 \rangle$. By (25.3) $\mathfrak{E}\mathfrak{C}$ is a Frobenius group and by induction $\mathfrak{C}$ has a normal p-complement. By (22.2) $\mathbf{N}_{\mathfrak{H}}(\mathbf{T}(\mathfrak{P}))$ does not have a normal p-complement. Hence $\mathbf{T}(\mathfrak{P}) \lhd \mathfrak{H}$ by induction. Thus in any case $\mathbf{T}(\mathfrak{P}) \lhd \mathfrak{G}$. Let $\mathfrak{A}$ be the subgroup of $\mathbf{Z}(\mathbf{T}(\mathfrak{P}))$ generated by elements of order p. Then $\mathfrak{A} \lhd \mathfrak{G}$. By (25.3) and induction $\mathfrak{H}/\mathfrak{A}$ is nilpotent. Let $\mathfrak{B}$ be the inverse image in $\mathfrak{H}$ of the normal p-complement in $\mathfrak{H}/\mathfrak{A}$. Thus $\mathfrak{A} \subseteq \mathfrak{B}$ and $\mathfrak{E}\mathfrak{B}$ is a Frobenius group. Since $\mathfrak{B}$ does not have a normal p-complement it follows that $\mathbf{C}_{\mathfrak{B}}(\mathfrak{A}) \neq \mathfrak{B}$. Hence $\mathfrak{E}\mathfrak{B}/\mathbf{C}_{\mathfrak{B}}(\mathfrak{A})$ is a Frobenius group which is faithfully represented on $\mathfrak{A}$. By (4.4) and (25.4) there exists $A \in \mathfrak{A}^{\#}$ with $\mathfrak{E} \subseteq \mathfrak{C}(A)$ which is impossible. This contradiction establishes the result.

## § 26. AN EXCURSION INTO NUMBER THEORY

Let $\mathfrak{F}$ be a finite field of characteristic p and let $|\mathfrak{F}| = q$. For any integer $n > 0$ define

$$\mathfrak{G}_n = \langle (a^n, b) \mid a \in \mathfrak{F}^*, b \in \mathfrak{F}, (a^n, b)(a_1{}^n, b_1) \rangle$$

$$= \langle (aa_1)^n, a_1{}^n b + b_1 \rangle \qquad (26.1)$$

$$\mathfrak{H}_n = \langle (1, b) \rangle \subseteq \mathfrak{G}_n \qquad \mathfrak{E}_n = \langle (a^n, 0) \rangle \subseteq \mathfrak{G}_n$$

It is easily seen that $\mathfrak{G}_n = \mathfrak{E}_n \mathfrak{H}_n$, $\mathfrak{E}_n \cap \mathfrak{H}_n = \langle (1, 0) \rangle = \langle 1 \rangle$, $|\mathfrak{H}_n| = q$ and $|\mathfrak{E}_n| = (q - 1)/(q - 1, n)$. Furthermore if $|\mathfrak{E}_n| \neq 1$ then $\mathfrak{G}_n$ is a Frobenius group with Frobenius kernel $\mathfrak{H}_n$. Clearly $\mathfrak{G}_n = \mathfrak{G}_{(n,q-1)}$, $\mathfrak{H}_n = \mathfrak{H}_{(n,q-1)}$ and $\mathfrak{E}_n = \mathfrak{E}_{(n,q-1)}$. A simple computation shows that $\mathfrak{G}_n$ is isomorphic to a group of permutations on the elements of $\mathfrak{F}$ where $x(a^n, b) = a^n x + b$ for all $x \in \mathfrak{F}$.

Questions concerning $\mathfrak{F}$ can often be translated into questions concerning groups related to the groups $\mathfrak{G}_n$ for various n. We will illustrate this by proving a result closely related to a theorem of Hua-Vandiver [1] and Weil [1]. The proof is in the spirit of the proof of Feit-Thompson [2] Lemma 38.9.

(26.2) Let $\mathfrak{F}$ be a finite field with $|\mathfrak{F}| = q$. Let $n_1, \ldots, n_s$ be integers and let $d_i = (|n_i|, q-1)$ for $i = 1, \ldots, s$. Let $c_1, \ldots, c_s \in \mathfrak{F}$ with $\Pi_{i=1}^s c_i \neq 0$ and let k be the number of solutions in $\mathfrak{F}$ of $\Sigma_{i=1}^s c_i x_i^{n_i} = 0$ with $\Pi_{i=1}^s x_i \neq 0$. Then $|k - (q-1)^s/q| < d_1 \ldots d_s q^{s/2}$.

Proof. It is clear that k is also the number of solutions of $\Sigma_{i=1}^s c_i x_i^{d_i} = 0$ with $\Pi_{i=1}^s x_i \neq 0$. Furthermore $k = d_1 \ldots d_s m$ where m is the number of solutions of $\Sigma_{i=1}^s c_i y_i = 0$ and $y_i = x_i^{d_i}$ for some $x_i \in \mathfrak{F}^*$, $i = 1, \ldots, s$.

For $i = 1, \ldots, s$ let $\mathfrak{G}_i = \mathfrak{G}_{n_i}$, $\mathfrak{H}_i = \mathfrak{H}_{n_i}$ and $\mathfrak{E}_i = \mathfrak{E}_{n_i}$, where $\mathfrak{G}_{n_i}$, $\mathfrak{H}_{n_i}$ and $\mathfrak{E}_{n_i}$ are defined by (26.1). Let $\mathfrak{G} = \mathfrak{G}_1 \times \cdots \times \mathfrak{G}_s$, $\mathfrak{H} = \mathfrak{H}_1 \times \cdots \times \mathfrak{H}_s$ and $\mathfrak{E} = \mathfrak{E}_1 \times \cdots \times \mathfrak{E}_s$. Define the subgroup $\mathfrak{A}$ of $\mathfrak{H}$ by

$$\mathfrak{A} = \{((1, b_1), \ldots, (1, b_s)) \mid \sum_{i=1}^{s} b_i = 0\}$$

Let $H = ((1, c_1), \ldots, (1, c_s)) \in \mathfrak{H}$. Let $\mathfrak{K}$ be the conjugate class of $\mathfrak{G}$ with $H \in \mathfrak{K}$. Since $\mathfrak{H} = \mathbf{C}_{\mathfrak{G}}(H)$ it follows that $|\mathfrak{K}| = |\mathfrak{E}|$ and

$$\mathfrak{K} = \{((1, c_1 y_1), \ldots, (1, c_s y_s)) \mid y_i = x_i^{d_i},$$

$$x_i \in \mathfrak{F}^*, i = 1, \ldots, s\}$$

Therefore $m = |\mathfrak{K} \cap \mathfrak{A}|$.

Let $\tilde{1}_{\mathfrak{A}}$ denote the character of $\mathfrak{H}$ induced by $1_{\mathfrak{A}}$. Then for $K \in \mathfrak{H}$, $\tilde{1}_{\mathfrak{A}}(K) = q$ or 0 according to whether $K \in \mathfrak{A}$ or $K \notin \mathfrak{A}$. Thus

$$1^*_{\mathfrak{A}}(H) = \tilde{1}^*_{\mathfrak{A}}(H) = q\,|\,\mathfrak{K} \cap \mathfrak{A}\,| = mq = \frac{kq}{d_1 \ldots d_s}$$

Let $1^*_{\mathfrak{A}} = \Sigma\, a_j \chi_j$, where $\chi_j$ ranges over the irreducible characters of $\mathfrak{G}$. $\mathfrak{G}/\mathfrak{H}$ has $|\mathfrak{C}| = (q-1)^s/d_1 \ldots d_s$ linear characters and for each of these $a_j \chi_j(H) = 1$. Thus if $\mathcal{S}$ is the set of all j such that $\chi_j$ does not have $\mathfrak{H}$ in its kernel and $a_j \neq 0$ then

$$\text{(26.3)} \qquad \frac{kq}{d_1 \ldots d_s} = \sum a_j \chi_j(H)$$

$$= \frac{(q-1)^s}{d_1 \ldots d_s} + \sum_{j \in \mathcal{S}} a_j \chi_j(H)$$

Suppose that $j \in \mathcal{S}$. By (6.3) $\chi_j = \Pi_{i=1}^{s} \chi_{ji}$ where $\chi_{ji}$ is an irreducible character of $\mathfrak{G}_i$. Suppose that $\mathfrak{H}_i$ is in the kernel of $\chi_{ji}$ for some i. Then $\chi_j$ is a character of $\mathfrak{G}/\mathfrak{H}_i$. Since $\mathfrak{H}_i \cap \mathfrak{A} = \langle 1 \rangle$ it follows that $\mathfrak{H} = \mathfrak{H}_i \mathfrak{A}$. As $(\chi_{j|\mathfrak{A}}, 1_{\mathfrak{A}}) = a_j \neq 0$ we get that $1_{\mathfrak{H}} \subseteq \chi_{j|\mathfrak{H}}$. Hence by (9.10) $\mathfrak{H}$ is in the kernel of $\chi_j$ contrary to the fact $j \in \mathcal{S}$. If $\mathfrak{C}_i = \langle 1 \rangle$ then $\chi_{ji}$ is linear. Thus by (25.4) $\chi_{ji}$ is monomial in any case. Hence by (8.2) $\chi_j$ is monomial and so $\chi_j = \lambda_j^*$ for some linear character $\lambda_j$ of $\mathfrak{H}$. By (9.11) this implies that $\Sigma_{j\in\mathcal{S}}\, \chi_{j|\mathfrak{H}}$ is a sum of pairwise distinct linear characters. Thus for any linear character $\lambda$ of $\mathfrak{H}$

$$\left(\lambda, \sum_{j \in \mathcal{S}} \chi_{j|\mathfrak{H}}\right)_{\mathfrak{H}} \leq (\lambda, \rho_{\mathfrak{H}})_{\mathfrak{H}} = 1$$

and so

$$\left(\tilde{1}_{\mathfrak{A}}, \sum_{j \in \mathcal{S}} \chi_{j|\mathfrak{H}}\right)_{\mathfrak{H}} \leq q$$

Consequently

$$\sum_{j \in \mathcal{S}} a_j = \sum_{j \in \mathcal{S}} (1_{\mathfrak{A}}, \chi_{j|\mathfrak{A}})_{\mathfrak{A}} \leq q$$

Hence (26.3) implies that if $|\chi(H)|$ is maximal among $|\chi_j(H)|$ with $j \in \mathcal{S}$ then

$$\left|k - \frac{(q-1)^s}{q}\right| \leq d_1 \ldots d_s |\chi(H)|$$

The result now follows from the fact that

$$|\chi(H)|^2 < \sum |\chi_j(H)|^2 = |\mathbf{C}_{\mathfrak{G}}(H)| = |\mathfrak{H}| = q^s$$

## §27. CN GROUPS

A group $\mathfrak{G}$ is a CN group if $\mathbf{C}_{\mathfrak{G}}(G)$ is nilpotent for every $G \in \mathfrak{G}^{\#}$.

Suzuki [2] first showed that if $\mathfrak{G}$ is a group of odd order such that $\mathbf{C}_{\mathfrak{G}}(G)$ is abelian for every $G \in \mathfrak{G}^{\#}$ then $\mathfrak{G}$ is solvable. The purpose of this section and the next is to prove the more general result that CN groups of odd order are solvable. The proof given here follows the original one in Feit, M. Hall, and Thompson [1] except insofar as (22.2) can be used to simplify parts of the argument. In the process of proving this result it is first necessary to give a description of solvable CN groups. In proving that groups of odd order are solvable the first part of the proof is subsumed in a much more general argument. The second part of the proof is however still an essential ingredient of the general proof.

(27.1) Let $\mathfrak{G}$ be a CN group and let $p, q \in \pi(\mathfrak{G})$, $p \neq q$. Let $\mathfrak{P}$ be a $S_p$-subgroup of $\mathfrak{G}$ and let $\mathfrak{Q}$ be a $S_q$-subgroup of $\mathfrak{G}$. If $PQ = QP$ for some $P \in \mathfrak{P}^{\#}$ and $Q \in \mathfrak{Q}^{\#}$ then $\mathfrak{P}\mathfrak{Q} = \mathfrak{P} \times \mathfrak{Q}$.

Proof. Since $\langle P, \mathbf{Z}(\mathfrak{Q})\rangle \subseteq \mathbf{C}_{\mathfrak{G}}(Q)$ it follows that $\langle P, Q\rangle \subseteq \mathbf{C}_{\mathfrak{G}}(\mathbf{Z}(\mathfrak{Q}))$. Thus $P \in \mathbf{C}_{\mathfrak{G}}(\mathfrak{Q})$ and so $\langle \mathbf{Z}(\mathfrak{P}), \mathfrak{Q}\rangle \subseteq \mathbf{C}_{\mathfrak{G}}(P)$. Hence $\langle \mathfrak{P}, \mathfrak{Q}\rangle \subseteq \mathbf{C}_{\mathfrak{G}}(\mathbf{Z}(\mathfrak{P}))$ which implies the result.

(27.2) Let $\mathfrak{G}$ be a nonnilpotent CN group which contains a normal Sylow subgroup $\mathfrak{p} \neq \langle 1 \rangle$. Then $\mathfrak{G}$ is a Frobenius group with Frobenius kernel $\mathfrak{H}$ and $\mathfrak{G}/\mathfrak{H}$ is nilpotent.

Proof. Let $\mathfrak{H}$ be a maximal normal nilpotent S-subgroup of $\mathfrak{G}$. Thus $\langle 1\rangle \neq \mathfrak{H} \neq \mathfrak{G}$. If $\mathfrak{G}$ is not a Frobenius group with Frobenius kernel $\mathfrak{H}$ then there exist $q \in \pi(\mathfrak{H})$, and $r \in \pi(\mathfrak{G}) - \pi(\mathfrak{H})$ such that $QR = RQ$ for some elements Q, R of order q, r respectively. Let $\mathfrak{Q}$ be a $S_q$-subgroup of $\mathfrak{H}$ and $\mathfrak{R}$ a $S_r$-subgroup of $\mathfrak{G}$ with $Q \in \mathfrak{Q}$ and $R \in \mathfrak{R}$. By (27.1) $\mathfrak{R} \subseteq \mathbf{C}_{\mathfrak{G}}(\mathfrak{Q})$. Thus $\mathfrak{R}\mathfrak{H}$ is a S-subgroup of $\mathfrak{G}$ and $\mathfrak{R}\mathfrak{H} \subseteq \mathfrak{Q}\mathbf{C}_{\mathfrak{G}}(\mathfrak{Q}) \lhd \mathfrak{G}$. Since $\mathfrak{Q}\mathbf{C}_{\mathfrak{G}}(\mathfrak{Q})$ is nilpotent this implies that $\mathfrak{R}\mathfrak{H} \lhd \mathfrak{G}$ contrary to the maximality of $\mathfrak{H}$. Thus $\mathfrak{G}$ is a Frobenius group with Frobenius kernel $\mathfrak{H}$. Let $\mathfrak{E}\mathfrak{H} = \mathfrak{G}$ and $\mathfrak{E} \cap \mathfrak{H} = \langle 1\rangle$. It remains to show that $\mathfrak{E}$ is nilpotent.

Let $p \in \pi(\mathfrak{E})$ and let $\mathfrak{P}$ be a $S_p$-subgroup of $\mathfrak{E}$. By (25.4) and (25.5) $\mathbf{N}_{\mathfrak{E}}(\mathfrak{P})$ is not a Frobenius group. Thus $\mathbf{N}_{\mathfrak{E}}(\mathfrak{P})$ is nilpotent by the first part of the proof. If $p \neq 2$ then by (25.7) $\mathfrak{P}$ is cyclic. Hence by (20.13) $\mathfrak{E}$ has a normal p-complement. Suppose that $2 \in \pi(\mathfrak{E})$. Since $\mathfrak{E}$ has a normal p-complement for every odd prime p it follows that a $S_2$-subgroup of $\mathfrak{E}$ is normal in $\mathfrak{E}$ and hence $\mathfrak{E}$ is nilpotent. This proves the result in all cases.

(27.3) If $\mathfrak{G}$ is a CN group, $\mathfrak{H} \lhd \mathfrak{G}$ and $\mathfrak{H}$ is solvable then $\mathfrak{G}/\mathfrak{H}$ is a CN group.

Proof. Induction on $|\mathfrak{G}|$. Let $G\mathfrak{H} \neq \mathfrak{H}$. Suppose that $\mathbf{C}_{\mathfrak{G}/\mathfrak{H}}(G\mathfrak{H})$ is not nilpotent. Let $\mathfrak{C}$ be the inverse image of $\mathbf{C}_{\mathfrak{G}/\mathfrak{H}}(G\mathfrak{H})$ in $\mathfrak{G}$. By induction it may be assumed that $\mathfrak{G} = \mathfrak{C}$. By taking a suitable power of G it may be assumed that $G\mathfrak{H}$ has prime order q.

Suppose first that $\mathfrak{H}$ is an elementary abelian p-group for some prime p.

If $q \neq p$ then it may be assumed that G has order q. Since $G\mathfrak{H} \subseteq \mathbf{Z}(\mathfrak{G}/\mathfrak{H})$ it follows that for $K \in \mathfrak{G}$, $G^{-1}K\mathfrak{H}G = K\mathfrak{H}$. Since $|K\mathfrak{H}|$ is a power of p it follows that $G^{-1}KHG = KH$ for some $H \in \mathfrak{H}$. Hence $\mathfrak{G} = \mathbf{C}_{\mathfrak{G}}(G)\mathfrak{H}$ and so $\mathfrak{G}/\mathfrak{H}$ is nilpotent as $\mathbf{C}_{\mathfrak{G}}(G)$ is nilpotent.

If $q = p$ let $\mathfrak{A} = \langle G, \mathfrak{H}\rangle$ so that $\mathfrak{A}$ is a p-group. Let L be an element of prime order distinct from p in $\mathfrak{G}$. Since $L^{-1} G \mathfrak{H} L = G\mathfrak{H}$ and $|G\mathfrak{H}|$ is a power of p it follows that L centralizes an element of $G\mathfrak{H}$ and thus of $\mathfrak{A}^{\#}$. By (27.1) $L \in \mathbf{C}_{\mathfrak{G}}(\mathfrak{A})$. Thus by (27.1) $\mathfrak{G} \subseteq \mathbf{C}_{\mathfrak{G}}(\mathfrak{A})\mathfrak{P}$, where $\mathfrak{P}$ is a $S_p$-subgroup of $\mathfrak{G}$. Let $\mathfrak{A}_1 = \mathfrak{A} \cap \mathbf{Z}(\mathfrak{P})$. Then $\mathfrak{A}_1 \neq \langle 1\rangle$ since $\mathfrak{A} \lhd \mathfrak{G}$ and so $\mathfrak{G} \subseteq \mathbf{C}_{\mathfrak{G}}(\mathfrak{A}_1)\mathfrak{P} = \mathbf{C}_{\mathfrak{G}}(\mathfrak{A}_1)$ is nilpotent. Hence $\mathfrak{G}/\mathfrak{H}$ is nilpotent.

Suppose next that $\mathfrak{H}$ is not elementary abelian. Since $\mathfrak{H}$ is solvable it has a normal p-subgroup distinct from $\langle 1\rangle$ for some prime p. Let $\mathfrak{P}_0$ be a maximal normal p-subgroup of $\mathfrak{H}$. Then $\mathfrak{P}_0$ is characteristic in $\mathfrak{H}$ and so $\mathfrak{P}_0 \lhd \mathfrak{G}$. Thus $\mathfrak{P}_1 \lhd \mathfrak{G}$ where $\mathfrak{P}_1$ consists of the elements of prime order in $\mathbf{Z}(\mathfrak{P}_0)$. By the first part of the theorem $\mathfrak{G}/\mathfrak{P}_1$ is a CN group. Hence by induction $\mathfrak{G}/\mathfrak{H} = (\mathfrak{G}/\mathfrak{P}_1)/(\mathfrak{H}/\mathfrak{P}_1)$ is a CN group as required.

(27.4) Let $\mathfrak{G}$ be a solvable CN group. Assume that $\mathfrak{G}$ is not nilpotent and $\mathfrak{G}$ is not a Frobenius group. Then there exists a normal series $\langle 1\rangle \subset \mathfrak{H} \subset \mathfrak{L} \subset \mathfrak{G}$ where $\mathfrak{H}$ and $\mathfrak{G}/\mathfrak{L}$ are p-groups for some prime p, $\mathfrak{L}/\mathfrak{H}$ is a cyclic $\{2, p\}'$-group and $\mathfrak{G}/\mathfrak{L}$ is either cyclic or a quaternion group. Furthermore $\mathfrak{L}$ and $\mathfrak{G}/\mathfrak{H}$ are Frobenius groups with Frobenius kernels $\mathfrak{H}$ and $\mathfrak{L}/\mathfrak{H}$ respectively.

Proof. Let $\mathfrak{H}$ be a maximal normal nilpotent subgroup of $\mathfrak{G}$. Let $p \in \pi(\mathfrak{H})$, let $\mathfrak{P}$ be a $S_p$-subgroup of $\mathfrak{H}$ and let $\mathfrak{H} = \mathfrak{P} \times \mathfrak{H}_0$. Since $\mathfrak{P}\mathbf{C}_{\mathfrak{G}}(\mathfrak{P})$ is nilpotent the maximality of $\mathfrak{H}$ implies that $\mathfrak{H} = \mathfrak{P}\mathbf{C}_{\mathfrak{G}}(\mathfrak{P})$. Thus $\mathfrak{H}_0$ is a S-subgroup of $\mathfrak{G}$ by (27.1). Hence $\mathfrak{H}_0 = \langle 1\rangle$ by (27.2). Consequently $\mathbf{C}_{\mathfrak{G}}(\mathfrak{H}) \subseteq \mathfrak{H} = \mathfrak{P}$. By (18.10) $\mathfrak{G}$ contains a $S_{p'}$-subgroup $\mathfrak{A}$. Hence by (27.2) $\mathfrak{H}\mathfrak{A} = \mathfrak{L}$ is a Frobenius group with Frobenius kernel $\mathfrak{H}$ and $\mathfrak{A}$ is nilpotent. By (27.3) $\mathfrak{G}/\mathfrak{H}$ is a CN group and by (25.7) every Sylow subgroup of $\mathfrak{A}$ is either cyclic or a quaternion group. Since $\mathfrak{H}$ is a maximal normal nilpotent subgroup of $\mathfrak{G}$ it follows that $\mathfrak{G}/\mathfrak{H}$ contains no normal p-subgroup. Thus $\mathfrak{G}/\mathfrak{H}$ is not nilpotent. Hence there exists a subgroup $\mathfrak{B}$ of $\mathfrak{A}$ with $\mathfrak{B}\mathfrak{H}/\mathfrak{H} \lhd \mathfrak{G}/\mathfrak{H}$. Since $\mathfrak{A} \subseteq \mathbf{C}_{\mathfrak{G}}(\mathfrak{B})$ and $\mathfrak{A}$ is a S-subgroup of $\mathfrak{G}$ it follows that $\mathfrak{A}\mathfrak{H}/\mathfrak{H} \lhd \mathfrak{G}/\mathfrak{H}$. Hence by (27.2) $\mathfrak{G}/\mathfrak{H}$ is a Frobenius group with Frobenius kernel $\mathfrak{L}/\mathfrak{H}$. If $2 \in \pi(\mathfrak{L}/\mathfrak{H})$ then $\mathfrak{L}/\mathfrak{H}$ contains a unique involution and thus $\mathbf{Z}(\mathfrak{G}/\mathfrak{H}) \neq \langle 1 \rangle$ which is impossible. Thus $\mathfrak{L}/\mathfrak{H}$ is a cyclic $\{2,p\}'$-group. By (25.7) $\mathfrak{G}/\mathfrak{L}$ is either cyclic or a quaternion group.

(27.5) Let $\mathfrak{G}$ be a solvable group in which every element has prime power order. Then $|\pi(\mathfrak{G})| \leq 2$.

Proof. Clearly $\mathfrak{G}$ is a CN group. If $\mathfrak{G}$ is nilpotent the result is clear. If $\mathfrak{G}$ is a Frobenius group with Frobenius kernel $\mathfrak{H}$ then $|\pi(\mathfrak{H})| = 1$ by (25.10) and $\pi(\mathfrak{G}/\mathfrak{H}) = 1$ by (27.2) If $\mathfrak{G}$ is neither nilpotent nor a Frobenius group than $|\pi(\mathfrak{L}/\mathfrak{H})| = 1$ where $\mathfrak{L}$ and $\mathfrak{H}$ are defined in (27.4) and the result follows from (27.4).

A group $\mathfrak{G}$ is a minimal simple group if $\mathfrak{G}$ is a noncyclic simple group and every proper subgroup of $\mathfrak{G}$ is solvable.

(27.6) Let $\mathfrak{G}$ be a CN group of odd order which is a minimal simple group. Then every Sylow subgroup of $\mathfrak{G}$ is a T.I. set in $\mathfrak{G}$.

Proof. Let $p \in \pi(\mathfrak{G})$ and suppose that a $S_p$-subgroup $\mathfrak{P}$ of $\mathfrak{G}$ is not a T.I. set in $\mathfrak{G}$. Choose $G \in \mathfrak{G}$ such that $\langle 1 \rangle \neq \mathfrak{P} \cap \mathfrak{P}^G \neq \mathfrak{P}$ Let $\mathfrak{M}$ be a maximal subgroup containing $\mathbf{N}_{\mathfrak{G}}(\mathfrak{P} \cap \mathfrak{P}^G)$. Then $\mathfrak{M}$ is a solvable CN group and a $S_p$-subgroup of $\mathfrak{M}$ is not a T.I. set in $\mathfrak{M}$. Thus $\mathfrak{M}$ is not nilpotent. By (27.2) $\mathfrak{M}$ is not a Frobenius group. Let $\mathfrak{T}$ be a maximal normal p-subgroup of $\mathfrak{M}$ and let $\mathfrak{P}_0$ be a $S_p$-subgroup of $\mathfrak{M}$. It may be assumed that $\mathfrak{P}_0 \subseteq \mathfrak{P}$. By (27.4) $\langle 1 \rangle \neq \mathfrak{T} \neq \mathfrak{P}_0$ and $\mathfrak{M} = \mathfrak{P}_0\mathfrak{A}$ where $\mathfrak{A}$ is cyclic, $\mathfrak{A} \cap \mathfrak{P}_0 = \langle 1 \rangle$, $\mathfrak{T}\mathfrak{A}$ is a Frobenius group with Frobenius kernel $\mathfrak{T}$ and $\mathfrak{M}/\mathfrak{T}$ is a Frobenius group with Frobenius kernel $\mathfrak{T}\mathfrak{A}/\mathfrak{T}$. Thus $\mathbf{C}_{\mathfrak{M}}(\mathbf{Z}(\mathfrak{P}_0)) \subseteq \mathfrak{P}_0$ and so $\mathbf{C}_{\mathfrak{M}}(\mathbf{Z}(\mathfrak{P}_0))$ has a normal p-complement. Since $\mathfrak{M}$ does not have a normal p-complement it follows by (22.2) that $\mathbf{N}_{\mathfrak{M}}(\mathbf{T}(\mathfrak{P}_0))$ does not have a normal p-complement. Suppose that

$\mathbf{T}(\mathfrak{P}_0) \nsubseteq \mathfrak{T}$. Since $\mathfrak{M}/\mathfrak{T}$ is a Frobenius group this implies that $\mathfrak{T}\mathbf{N}_{\mathfrak{M}}(\mathbf{T}(\mathfrak{P}_0)/\mathfrak{T} = \mathfrak{T}\mathfrak{P}_0/\mathfrak{T}$ and so $\mathbf{N}_{\mathfrak{M}}(\mathbf{T}(\mathfrak{P}_0)) = \mathfrak{P}_0$ contrary to the fact that $\mathbf{N}_{\mathfrak{M}}(\mathbf{T}(\mathfrak{P}_0))$ does not have a normal p-complement. Thus $\mathbf{T}(\mathfrak{P}_0) \subseteq \mathfrak{T}$. Hence $\mathfrak{M} \subseteq \mathbf{N}_{\mathfrak{G}}(\mathbf{T}(\mathfrak{P}_0))$. The maximality of $\mathfrak{M}$ implies that $\mathfrak{M} = \mathbf{N}_{\mathfrak{G}}(\mathbf{T}(\mathfrak{P}_0))$. Since $\mathbf{N}_{\mathfrak{P}}(\mathfrak{P}_0) \subseteq \mathbf{N}_{\mathfrak{G}}(\mathbf{T}(\mathfrak{P}_0))$ it follows that $\mathfrak{P}_0 = \mathfrak{P}$ is a $S_p$-subgroup of $\mathfrak{G}$. As $\mathbf{N}_{\mathfrak{G}}(\mathfrak{P}) \subseteq \mathbf{N}_{\mathfrak{G}}(\mathbf{T}(\mathfrak{P}))$ we also see that $\mathbf{N}_{\mathfrak{G}}(\mathfrak{P}) = \mathbf{N}_{\mathfrak{M}}(\mathfrak{P}) = \mathfrak{P}$. Thus we have shown that if $G \in \mathfrak{G} - \mathfrak{P}$ then $\mathfrak{P} \cap \mathfrak{P}^G \subseteq \mathbf{N}_{\mathfrak{G}}(\mathbf{T}(\mathfrak{P})) = \mathfrak{M}$ and so $\mathfrak{P} \cap \mathfrak{P}^G \subseteq \mathfrak{T}$ since the $S_p$-subgroups of $\mathfrak{M}/\mathfrak{T}$ are T.I. sets in $\mathfrak{M}/\mathfrak{T}$. By (20.1) $\mathfrak{G}$ has a normal complement of $\mathfrak{P}$ over $\mathfrak{T}$ contrary to the simplicity of $\mathfrak{G}$. The proof is complete.

It should be observed that (27.6) is false if the assumption that $|\mathfrak{G}|$ is odd is dropped. The proof breaks down because (22.2) is no longer valid if $p = 2$. It is easily checked that the simple group $PSL_2(7)$ of order 168 is a minimal simple CN group in which the $S_2$-subgroup is not a T.I. set.

(27.7)    <u>Let $\mathfrak{G}$ be a CN group of odd order which is a minimal simple group. Let $\mathfrak{M}_1, \ldots, \mathfrak{M}_k$ be a complete system of representatives of the conjugate classes of maximal subgroups of $\mathfrak{G}$. Then each $\mathfrak{M}_i$ is a Frobenius group. Furthermore if $\mathfrak{H}_i$ is the Frobenius kernel of $\mathfrak{M}_i$ then $\mathfrak{H}_i$ is a S-subgroup of $\mathfrak{G}$ which is a T.I. set in $\mathfrak{G}$, $(|\mathfrak{H}_i|, |\mathfrak{H}_j|) = 1$ for $i \neq j$, $\prod_{i=1}^k |\mathfrak{H}_i| = |\mathfrak{G}|$ and every element of $\mathfrak{G}$ is conjugate to an element of $\mathfrak{H}_i$ for some i.</u>

<u>Proof</u>. Let $\mathfrak{M}$ be a maximal subgroup of $\mathfrak{G}$. By (27.6) $\mathfrak{M}$ is a solvable CN group in which every Sylow group is a T.I. set. By (22.8) $\mathfrak{M}$ is not nilpotent. Hence by (27.4) $\mathfrak{M}$ is a Frobenius group.

Let $p \in \pi(\mathfrak{H}_i)$ and let $\mathfrak{P}$ be a $S_p$-subgroup of $\mathfrak{H}_i$. Since $\mathfrak{H}_i$ is nilpotent and $\mathfrak{M}$ is maximal it follows that $\mathfrak{M} = \mathbf{N}_{\mathfrak{G}}(\mathfrak{P})$. Thus $\mathfrak{H}_i$ is a S-subgroup of $\mathfrak{G}$. If $p \in \pi(\mathfrak{H}_j)$ then choosing a suitable conjugate it may be assumed that $\mathfrak{P} \subseteq \mathfrak{H}_j$ and so $\mathfrak{M}_i = \mathbf{N}_{\mathfrak{G}}(\mathfrak{P}) = \mathfrak{M}_j$. Hence $(|\mathfrak{H}_i|, |\mathfrak{H}_j|) = 1$ for $i \neq j$ since p was arbitrary in $\pi(\mathfrak{H})$. If $p \in \pi(\mathfrak{H}_i \cap \mathfrak{H}_i^G)$ let $\mathfrak{T}$ be a

$S_p$-subgroup of $\mathfrak{H}_i \cap \mathfrak{H}_i^G$. Thus $\langle \mathfrak{T}, \mathfrak{T}^G \rangle \subseteq \mathfrak{P}$ and so $G \in \mathbf{N}_{\mathfrak{G}}(\mathfrak{P}) = \mathfrak{M}_i = \mathbf{N}_{\mathfrak{G}}(\mathfrak{H}_i)$. Since p was arbitrary in $\pi(\mathfrak{H}_i)$ this implies that $\mathfrak{H}_i$ is a T.I. set in $\mathfrak{G}$.

Let $q \in \pi(\mathfrak{G})$ and let $\mathfrak{Q}$ be a $S_q$-subgroup of $\mathfrak{G}$. Let $\mathfrak{M}$ be a maximal subgroup of $\mathfrak{G}$ with $\mathbf{N}_{\mathfrak{G}}(\mathfrak{Q}) \subseteq \mathfrak{M}$. It may be assumed that $\mathfrak{M} = \mathfrak{M}_i$ for some i. If $\mathfrak{Q} \not\subseteq \mathfrak{H}_i$ then by (25.7) and (27.2) $\mathbf{N}_{\mathfrak{G}}(\mathfrak{Q})$ is cyclic contrary to the simplicity of $\mathfrak{G}$ by (20.13). Hence $\mathfrak{Q} \subseteq \mathfrak{H}_i$ and so $\Pi_{i=1}^k |\mathfrak{H}_i| = |\mathfrak{G}|$. If $G \in \mathfrak{G}$ then some power Q of G has prime order. Replacing G by a conjugate it may be assumed that $Q \in \mathfrak{H}_i^\#$ for some i. Thus $G \in \mathbf{C}_{\mathfrak{G}}(Q) \subseteq \mathfrak{H}_i$ as required.

## §28. NONSIMPLICITY OF CERTAIN GROUPS OF ODD ORDER

Let $\mathfrak{M}_1, \ldots, \mathfrak{M}_k$ be a complete set of representatives of the conjugate classes of maximal subgroups of $\mathfrak{G}$. Groups satisfying the following conditions will be studied in this section.

(28.1) (i) <u>For</u> $i = 1, \ldots, k$, $\mathfrak{M}_i$ <u>is a Frobenius group with Frobenius kernel</u> $\mathfrak{H}_i$. $|\mathfrak{H}_i| = h_i$ <u>and</u> $|\mathfrak{M}_i| = h_i e_i$.

(ii) <u>For</u> $i = 1, \ldots, k$, $\mathfrak{H}_i$ <u>is a</u> S-<u>subgroup of</u> $\mathfrak{G}$ <u>which is a T.I. set in</u> $\mathfrak{G}$.

(iii) $(h_i, h_j) = 1$ <u>for</u> $i \neq j$, $|\mathfrak{G}| = \Pi_{i=1}^k h_i$. <u>Every element of</u> $\mathfrak{G}$ <u>is conjugate to an element of</u> $\mathfrak{H}_i$ <u>for some</u> $i = 1, \ldots, k$.

(iv) $|\mathfrak{G}|$ <u>is odd</u>.

Observe that if $\mathfrak{G}$ satisfies (28.1) then each $\mathfrak{H}_i$ is nilpotent. If furthermore $\mathfrak{G}$ is simple then $\mathfrak{G}$ is a minimal simple group. The purpose of this section is to prove

(28.2) <u>If</u> $\mathfrak{G}$ <u>satisfies (28.1) then</u> $\mathfrak{G}$ <u>is not simple</u>.

Before proving (28.2) we will deduce the following consequence from it.

(28.3) <u>A CN group of odd order is solvable</u>.

Proof. Induction on $|\mathfrak{G}|$. By (27-3) and induction every subgroup and every quotient group of $\mathfrak{G}$ is solvable. Thus it may be assumed that $\mathfrak{G}$ is simple. Hence $\mathfrak{G}$ is a minimal simple group. By (27.7) $\mathfrak{G}$ satisfies (28.1). Thus the result follows from (28.2).

Throughout the rest of this section $\mathfrak{G}$ is a simple group which satisfies (28.1). A contradiction will be derived from the assumed existence of $\mathfrak{G}$ proving (28.2).

(28.4) $$1 = \frac{1}{|\mathfrak{G}|} + \sum_{i=1}^{k} \frac{h_i - 1}{h_i e_i}$$

Proof. Since each $\mathfrak{H}_i$ is a T.I. set in $\mathfrak{G}$ it follows that the number of elements in $\mathfrak{G}$ which are conjugate to an element of $\mathfrak{H}_i^{\#}$ is $|\mathfrak{G}|/e_i h_i (h_i - 1)$. By assumption every element in $\mathfrak{G}^{\#}$ is conjugate to an element of $\mathfrak{H}_i^{\#}$ for some unique i. Hence

$$|\mathfrak{G}^{\#}| = |\mathfrak{G}| - 1 = \sum_{i=1}^{k} \frac{(h_i - 1)}{h_i e_i} |\mathfrak{G}|$$

as required.

For each $i = 1, \ldots, k$ let $\mathcal{S}_i$ be the set of irreducible characters of $\mathfrak{M}_i$ which do not have $\mathfrak{H}_i$ in their kernel. If $\zeta \in \mathcal{S}_i$ then $e_i \mid \zeta(1)$ by (25.4). Let $\{e_i d_{is}\}$ be the set of integers which are degrees of characters in $\mathcal{S}_i$. Choose the notation so that $d_{i1} < d_{i2} < \ldots$. Let $\mathcal{S}_{is} = \{\zeta \mid \zeta \in \mathcal{S}_i, \zeta(1) = e_i d_{is}\}$. Let $w_{is} = |\mathcal{S}_{is}|$. By (12.4) $w_{is}$ is even since $|\mathfrak{G}|$ is odd. Thus $w_{is} \geq 2$ for all i, s. Since $\mathfrak{H}_i$ is nilpotent (25.4) implies that $d_{i1} = 1$ and $w_{i1} = (|\mathfrak{H}_i : \mathfrak{H}_i'| - 1)/e_i$ for $i = 1, \ldots, k$. Choose the notation so that

(28.5) $$e_1 \leq e_2 \leq \cdots \leq e_k \qquad w_{11} > w_{i1} \ \underline{\text{for}} \ e_i = e_1$$

Let $\mathcal{S}_{is} = \{\zeta_{ist} \mid t = 1, \ldots, w_{is}\}$. Let $\alpha_{istu} = (\zeta_{ist} - \zeta_{isu})$ and let $\theta_{istu} = \alpha_{istu}^*$. By (23.1)

$$(\theta_{istu}, \theta_{ist'u'})_{\mathfrak{G}} = (\alpha_{istu}, \alpha_{ist'u'})_{\mathfrak{M}_i}$$

$$= \delta_{tt'} - \delta_{tu'} - \delta_{t'u} + \delta_{uu'}$$

Since $w_{is} \geq 2$ (23.3) implies the existence of a sign $\epsilon_{is} = \pm 1$ and a set $\mathfrak{I}_{is} = \{\chi_{ist}\}$ of irreducible characters of $\mathfrak{G}$ such that $|\mathfrak{I}_{is}| = w_{is}$ and $\theta_{istu} = \epsilon_{is}(\chi_{ist} - \chi_{isu})$.

(28.6) <u>If</u> $\sigma \in \mathcal{G}_{\mathbb{Q}_{|\mathfrak{G}|}/\mathbb{Q}}$ <u>then</u> $\mathfrak{I}_{is}^{\sigma} = \mathfrak{I}_{is}$. <u>If</u> $i \neq j$ <u>then</u> $\chi_{ist} | \mathfrak{H}_j$ <u>is rational valued.</u>

<u>Proof</u>. Since $\mathcal{S}_{is}^{\sigma} = \mathcal{S}_{is}$ and

$$\chi_{ist}^{\sigma} - \chi_{ist} = \epsilon_{is}(\zeta_{ist}^{\sigma} - \zeta_{ist})^*$$

the first result follows. As $(\zeta_{ist}^{\sigma} - \zeta_{ist})^*$ vanishes on $\mathfrak{H}_j$ we also get that $\chi_{ist}^{\sigma}(H) = \chi_{ist}(H)$ for $H \in \mathfrak{H}_j$ which implies the second statement.

(28.7) $\chi_{ist} = \chi_{i's't'}$ <u>if and only if</u> $i = i'$, $s = s'$ <u>and</u> $t = t'$. <u>Furthermore</u> $\chi_{ist} \neq 1_{\mathfrak{G}}$ <u>for all</u> i, s, t <u>and</u> $\{1_{\mathfrak{G}}\} \cup_{i,s} \mathfrak{I}_{is}$ <u>is the set of all irreducible characters of</u> $\mathfrak{G}$.

<u>Proof</u>. Clearly $(1_{\mathfrak{G}}, \theta_{istu}) = 0$ and so $\chi_{ist} \neq 1_{\mathfrak{G}}$ for all i, s, t. Suppose that $\chi_{ist} = \chi_{i's't'}$. If $i \neq i'$ then $\chi_{ist}$ is rational valued by (28.6) contrary to (12.4). Thus $i = i'$ and

$$((\zeta_{ist} - \bar{\zeta}_{ist}), (\zeta_{is't'} - \bar{\zeta}_{is't'}))_{\mathfrak{M}_i}$$

$$= ((\chi_{ist} - \bar{\chi}_{ist}), (\chi_{is't'} - \bar{\chi}_{is't'}))_{\mathfrak{G}} = 2$$

Hence $s = s'$ and $t = t'$. Since $\Sigma_s |\mathfrak{I}_{is}| = \Sigma_s w_{is}$ is the number of conjugate classes of $\mathfrak{M}_i$ which lie in $\mathfrak{H}_i^{\#}$ it follows that $\Sigma_{i,s} |\mathfrak{I}_{is}|$ is the number of conjugate classes of

$\mathfrak{G}$ in $\mathfrak{G}^\#$. The last statement now follows from the first two.

Let $\mathfrak{H}_1 = \mathfrak{H}$, $h_1 = h$, $e_1 = e$ and $w_{11} = w$. Let $\zeta_t = \zeta_{11t}$ and $\chi_t = \chi_{11t}$ for $t = 1, \ldots, w$. Let $\Delta = \Sigma_{t=1}^{w} \chi_t$.

By (15.4) there exist nonprincipal linear characters $\varphi_1, \ldots, \varphi_w$ of $\mathfrak{H}$ such that $\zeta_s = \tilde{\varphi}_s$ is the character of $\mathfrak{M}_1$ induced by $\varphi_s$. Let $\beta = (1_{\mathfrak{H}} - \varphi_1)^*$. Then $(\beta, \chi_{ist} - \overline{\chi}_{ist}) = 0$ for $i \neq 1$ since $\beta$ vanishes outside $\cup_{\mathfrak{G}} \mathfrak{H}^{\#G}$ and $\chi_{ist} - \overline{\chi}_{ist}$ vanishes on $\cup_{\mathfrak{G}} \mathfrak{H}^{\#G}$. By (23.1) $\|\beta\|^2 = e + 1$ and

$$(\beta, \chi_{1st} - \chi_{1st'}) = \epsilon_{11} \delta_{s1} (\delta_{1t'} - \delta_{1t})$$

Therefore there exists an integer $a$ and a real valued character $\Gamma$ with $(\Gamma, 1_{\mathfrak{G}}) = 0 = (\Gamma, \chi_t)$ for $t = 1, \ldots, w$ such that

$$\text{(28.8)} \qquad \beta = 1_{\mathfrak{G}} - \epsilon_{11}\chi_1 + a\Delta + \Gamma \qquad \|\Gamma\|^2 \leq e - 1$$

Let $\mathfrak{A} = \{j \mid j > 1, (\chi_{jst}, \beta) = 0 \text{ for all } s, t\}$. Let $\mathfrak{B} = \{2, \ldots, k\} - \mathfrak{A}$.

$$\text{(28.9)} \qquad \sum_{j \in \mathfrak{B}} \frac{(h_j - 1)}{h_j e_j} \leq \frac{e - 1}{2e_2}$$

Proof. If $j \in \mathfrak{B}$ then $(\chi_{jst} + \overline{\chi}_{jst}, \Gamma) \geq 2$ for some s, t. Since $\|\Gamma\|^2 \leq e - 1$ by (28.8) this implies that $|\mathfrak{B}| \leq (e-1)/2$. By (28.5) $(h_j - 1)/h_j e_j \leq 1/e_2$ for all $j \in \mathfrak{B}$ and (28.9) follows.

$$\text{(28.10)} \qquad \sum_{j \in \mathfrak{A}} \frac{(h_j - 1)}{h_j e_j} \leq \frac{1}{w}$$

Proof. Suppose that $j \in \mathfrak{A}$. Let $H \in \mathfrak{H}_j$. If $(\chi, \beta) \neq 0$ for an irreducible character $\chi$ of $\mathfrak{G}$ then the definition of $\mathfrak{A}$ and (28.6) imply that $\chi(H)$ is rational and so $\chi(H) = \overline{\chi(H)}$. Thus $\Delta(H)$ and $\Gamma(H)$ are even. Since $\beta(H) = 0$ (28.8) implies that

$$0 \equiv \beta(H) \equiv 1 - \epsilon_{11}\chi_1(H) \pmod 2$$

Hence $\chi_1(H) \neq 0$. Thus $|\chi_1(H)| \geq 1$ since $\chi_1(H)$ is rational. As $\chi_1 - \chi_s$ vanishes on $\mathfrak{H}_j$ for all $s = 1, \ldots, w$ we see that $|\Delta(H)| = w|\chi_1(H)| \geq w$. Let $\mathfrak{G}_0$ be the set of all elements in $\mathfrak{G}$ which are conjugate to an element of $\mathfrak{H}_j$ for some $j \in \mathfrak{A}$. Then $|\mathfrak{G}_0| = |\mathfrak{G}| \sum_{j\in\mathfrak{A}}(h_j - 1)/h_j e_j$. Thus

$$w = ||\Delta||^2 \geq \frac{1}{|\mathfrak{G}|} \sum_{\mathfrak{G}_0} |\Delta(H)|^2 \geq \frac{w^2}{|\mathfrak{G}|} |\mathfrak{G}_0|$$

$$= w^2 \sum_{j\in\mathfrak{A}} \frac{h_j - 1}{h_j e_j}$$

This implies the result.

If we now combine (28.4), (28.9), and (28.10) we get that

(28.11) $$1 = \frac{1}{|\mathfrak{G}|} + \sum_{i=1}^{k} \frac{(h_i - 1)}{h_i e_i}$$

$$\leq \frac{1}{|\mathfrak{G}|} + \frac{h-1}{he} + \frac{1}{w} + \frac{e-1}{2e_2}$$

Suppose that $w > 2$ so that $w \geq 4$ since $w$ is even. Since $e_2 \geq e \geq 3$, (28.11) implies that

$$1 \leq \frac{1}{|\mathfrak{G}|} + \frac{1}{e} + \frac{1}{4} + \frac{1}{2} - \frac{1}{2e}$$

$$\leq \frac{1}{|\mathfrak{G}|} + \frac{3}{4} + \frac{1}{2e} \leq \frac{1}{|\mathfrak{G}|} + \frac{3}{4} + \frac{1}{6}$$

Therefore $1/12 \leq 1/|\mathfrak{G}|$ or $|\mathfrak{G}| \leq 12$ which is not the case. Thus $w = 2$. Hence by (28.5) $e_2 > e$ and so $e_2 \geq e + 2$ since $e$ and $e_2$ are odd. Now (28.11) becomes

$$\frac{1}{2} \leq \frac{1}{|\mathfrak{G}|} + \frac{h-1}{he} + \frac{e-1}{2(e+2)}$$

$$= \frac{1}{|\mathfrak{G}|} - \frac{1}{he} + \frac{1}{e} + \frac{1}{2} - \frac{3}{2(e+2)}$$

Thus

$$(28.12) \qquad 0 \leq \frac{1}{|\mathfrak{G}|} - \frac{1}{he} + \frac{(-e+4)}{2e(e+2)}$$

If $e \geq 5$ this yields that $0 < 1/|\mathfrak{G}| - 1/he$ or $|\mathfrak{G}| < he$ which is impossible. If $e < 5$ then $e = 3$ since e is odd and $e \neq 1$. Since $w = 2$ this implies that $|\mathfrak{H}: \mathfrak{H}'| = we + 1 = 7$. Consequently $\mathfrak{H}' = \langle 1 \rangle$ and $|\mathfrak{H}| = 7$. Now (28.12) becomes

$$0 \leq \frac{1}{|\mathfrak{G}|} - \frac{1}{21} + \frac{1}{30} = \frac{1}{|\mathfrak{G}|} - \frac{1}{70}$$

Therefore $|\mathfrak{G}| \leq 70$ which is not the case. The proof of (28.2) is complete.

## §29. PROPERTIES OF INVOLUTIONS

The results in this section are due to Brauer and Fowler [1]. While these results are quite elementary they are of fundamental importance for almost everything that is known concerning groups of even order.

(29.1) If I, J are involutions then $(IJ)^I = (IJ)^J = (IJ)^{-1}$. If furthermore $IJ \neq JI$ then $\langle I, J \rangle$ is a dihedral group.

Proof.

$$(IJ)^I = (IJ)^J = JI = (IJ)^{-1}$$

This implies the result.

(29.2) If I, J are involutions which are not conjugate in $\mathfrak{G}$ then there exists an involution $K \in \mathfrak{G}$ such that $\langle I, J\rangle \subseteq \mathbf{C}_{\mathfrak{G}}(K)$.

Proof. Let $|\langle I, J\rangle| = 2a$. If a is odd then any two involutions in $\langle I, J\rangle$ are conjugate by Sylow's theorem contrary to assumption. If a is even then by (29.1) $\langle I, J\rangle \subseteq \mathbf{C}_{\mathfrak{G}}(K)$ where $K = (IJ)^{a/2}$ and K is an involution.

(29.3) Let $\mathfrak{P}$ be a $S_2$-subgroup of $\mathfrak{G}$. Assume that $\mathfrak{P}$ is a T.I. set in $\mathfrak{G}$. Then either $\mathfrak{P} \lhd \mathfrak{G}$ or $\mathfrak{G}$ contains exactly one class of involutions.

Proof. Assume that $\mathfrak{P} \not\!\lhd \mathfrak{G}$. Let $\mathfrak{P}_1$ be a $S_2$-subgroup of $\mathfrak{G}$ with $\mathfrak{P} \neq \mathfrak{P}_1$. Let I, J be involutions with $I \in \mathfrak{P}$ and $J \in \mathfrak{P}_1$. If I is not conjugate to J then by (29.2) there exists an involution $K \in \mathbf{C}_{\mathfrak{G}}(\langle I, J\rangle)$. Let $K \in \mathfrak{P}^G$. Thus $\langle I, J\rangle \subseteq \mathbf{N}_{\mathfrak{G}}(\mathfrak{P}^G)$ and so $\langle I, J\rangle \subseteq \mathfrak{P}^G$. Hence $I \in \mathfrak{P} \cap \mathfrak{P}^G$ and $J \in \mathfrak{P}_1 \cap \mathfrak{P}^G$. Thus $\mathfrak{P} = \mathfrak{P}^G = \mathfrak{P}_1$ contrary to assumption. Therefore I is conjugate to J. Since I was arbitrary this implies that J is conjugate to every involution in $\mathfrak{P}$. Hence $\mathfrak{G}$ contains only one class of involutions.

For $G \in \mathfrak{G}$ let $\mathbf{C}^*_{\mathfrak{G}}(G) = \{H \mid H^{-1}GH = G \text{ or } G^{-1}\}$. It is easily seen that $\mathbf{C}^*_{\mathfrak{G}}(G)$ is a group and $|\mathbf{C}^*_{\mathfrak{G}}(G) : \mathbf{C}_{\mathfrak{G}}(G)| \leq 2$. Furthermore $\mathbf{C}^*_{\mathfrak{G}}(G) = \mathbf{C}_{\mathfrak{G}}(G)$ if and only if either $G^2 = 1$ or G is not a real element in $\mathfrak{G}$.

An element G is strongly real if it is the product of two involutions. By (29.1) strongly real elements are real.

Throughout the rest of this section $|\mathfrak{G}| = g$ is assumed to be even and the following notation is used:

$\mathfrak{K}_1, \ldots, \mathfrak{K}_s$ are the distinct conjugate classes of $\mathfrak{G}$ consisting of involutions, $\mathfrak{K}_{s+1}, \ldots, \mathfrak{K}_t$ are the conjugate classes consisting of strongly real elements which are not involutions and $\mathfrak{K}_t = \{1\}$, $\mathfrak{K}_{t+1}, \ldots, \mathfrak{K}_k$ are the remaining conjugate classes of $\mathfrak{G}$. For $G_i \in \mathfrak{K}_i$, $c_i = |\mathbf{C}_{\mathfrak{G}}(G_i)|$, $a_i$ is the number of ordered pairs of involutions (I, J) with $IJ = G_i$ and $b_i$ is the number of involutions in $\mathbf{C}_{\mathfrak{G}}(G_i)$. $\mathfrak{M} = \bigcup_{i=1}^{s} \mathfrak{K}_i$ and $|\mathfrak{M}| = m$. Furthermore c =

$\max_{s+1 \leq i \leq t-1} c_i$, $b = \max_{1 \leq i \leq s} b_i$.

(29.4) If $G_i^2 \neq 1$ then $a_i$ is the number of involutions I with $G_i^I = G_i^{-1}$. If $G_i \in \mathfrak{M}$ then $a_i = b_i - 1$. If $G_i = 1$ then $a_i = m$.

Proof. If $G_i^I = G_i^{-1}$ for $I \in \mathfrak{M}$ let $J = IG_i$. Then $IJ = G_i$ and $J^2 = G_i^I G_i = 1$. Conversely if $IJ = G_i$ with $I, J \in \mathfrak{M}$ then by (29.1) $G_i^I = G_i^{-1}$. If $G_i^2 \neq 1$ then $J \neq 1$ and the result follows in this case. If $G_i = 1$ the result is clear. If $G_i \in \mathfrak{M}$ then $J \in \mathfrak{M}$ unless $I = G_i$ and so $a_i = b_i - 1$ as required.

(29.5) If $G_i$ is not strongly real and $G_i^2 \neq 1$ then $a_i = 0$. If $G_i \in \mathfrak{M}$ then $a_i \leq c_i - 2$. In any case $a_i \leq c_i$.

Proof. The first statement follows by definition. If $G_i \in \mathfrak{M}$ then $b_i \leq c_i - 1$ and so $a_i \leq c_i - 2$ by (29.4). If $G_i = 1$ then $a_i \leq g = c_i$. If $G_i^2 \neq 1$ then $a_i \leq |\mathbf{C}^*_{\mathfrak{G}}(G_i)| - |\mathbf{C}_{\mathfrak{G}}(G_i)| \leq c_i$ proving the last statement.

(29.6)
$$m^2 \leq m + \sum_{i=1}^{s} (b_i - 1)\frac{g}{c_i} + (t - s - 1)g$$
$$\leq cg + (b - c)m - c$$

Proof. The number of ordered pairs of involutions in $\mathfrak{G}$ is $m^2$. Thus $m^2 = \Sigma\, a_i g/c_i$. The first inequality follows from (29.4) and (29.5). Since $m = \Sigma_{i=1}^{s} g/c_i$ we get that

$$m^2 \leq mb + (t - s - 1)g$$

However the number of strongly real elements is at most g. Thus

$$1 + m + \sum_{i=s+1}^{t-1} \frac{g}{c_i} \leq g$$

Consequently

$$(t - s - 1)g \leq c(g - m - 1)$$

which implies the second inequality.

(29.7) $\quad t - 1 \geq \dfrac{m(m + 1)}{g}$

Proof. Since $b_i \leq c_i - 1$, (29.6) yields that

$$m^2 \leq m + sg - 2\sum_{i=1}^{s} \frac{g}{c_i} + (t - s - 1)g$$

As $m = \Sigma_{i=1}^{s} g/c_i$ this implies that $m^2 \leq -m + (t - 1)g$ as required.

(29.8) If $g > 2$ there exists a subgroup $\mathfrak{H}$ of $\mathfrak{G}$ with $\mathfrak{H} \neq \mathfrak{G}$ and $|\mathfrak{H}|^3 > g$.

Proof. Induction on $|\mathfrak{G}|$. Let $n = |\mathfrak{G}|/m$. By the second inequality in (29.6)

$$g \leq cn^2 + (b - c)n = cn(n - 1) + bn$$

For some j with $1 \leq j \leq s$, $b_j = b \leq c_j - 1$. Since $1/n = \Sigma_{i=1}^{s} 1/c_i$ we get that $n \leq c_j$. Thus

$$g \leq cc_j(c_j - 1) + c_j(c_j - 1) = (c + 1)c_j(c_j - 1)$$

If $c_j \leq c$ then $g \leq c^3$. As $c = |\mathbf{C}_{\mathfrak{G}}(G_i)|$ for some strongly real element with $G_i^2 \neq 1$ it follows that $\mathbf{C}_{\mathfrak{G}}(G_i) \neq \mathfrak{G}$ as required. If $c < c_j$ then $|\mathfrak{G}| < c_j^3$ and we are done unless $c_j = g$. In that case $G = G_j$ is an involution in the center of $\mathfrak{G}$. If $g = 4$ the result is trivial. If $g \neq 4$ and $g/2$ is even then by induction there exists $\mathfrak{H}$ such that $\mathfrak{H}/\langle G \rangle \neq$

$\mathfrak{G}/\langle G\rangle$ and $|\mathfrak{H}/\langle G\rangle|^3 > |\mathfrak{G}/\langle G\rangle|^3$. This implies that $|\mathfrak{H}|^3 > |\mathfrak{G}|$ as required. If finally $g/2$ is odd then by (20.14) $\mathfrak{G}$ has a normal 2-complement $\mathfrak{H}$ and $|\mathfrak{H}| = g/2 > \sqrt[3]{g}$ as required.

## §30. GROUPS WITH QUATERNION $S_2$-SUBGROUPS

In this section the following result of Brauer and Suzuki [1] will be proved. The result is still true without the hypothesis that $|\mathfrak{P}| \geq 16$; however all known proofs for the case $|\mathfrak{P}| = 8$ depend on the theory of modular characters.

(30.1) Suppose that the $S_2$-subgroup $\mathfrak{P}$ of $\mathfrak{G}$ is a quaternion group and $|\mathfrak{P}| \geq 16$. Let $\mathfrak{M}$ be a maximal normal subgroup of $\mathfrak{G}$ of odd order. Then $\mathfrak{G}/\mathfrak{M}$ has a normal subgroup of order 2. Thus in particular $\mathfrak{G}$ is not simple.

Proof. It may clearly be assumed that $\mathfrak{G}$ has no normal subgroups of odd order. Let

$$\mathfrak{P} = \langle A, B \mid A^{2^n} = 1,\ B^2 = A^{2^{n-1}},\ B^{-1}AB = A^{-1}\rangle$$

Then $|\mathfrak{P}| = 2^{n+1}$ and $n \geq 3$. Let $\mathfrak{C} = \mathbf{C}_{\mathfrak{G}}(A^2)$ and $\mathfrak{N} = \mathbf{N}_{\mathfrak{G}}(\langle A^2\rangle)$. Then $\langle A\rangle$ is a $S_2$-subgroup of $\mathfrak{C}$ since $n \geq 3$ and the center of a quaternion group has order 2. Thus $|\mathfrak{N} : \mathfrak{C}| = 2$ since $\mathfrak{P} \subseteq \mathfrak{N}$ and $\mathfrak{N}/\mathfrak{C}$ is an automorphism group of the cyclic 2-group $\langle A^2\rangle$. By (20.14) $\mathfrak{C}$ has a normal 2-complement $\mathfrak{H}$. Thus $\mathfrak{H} \lhd \mathfrak{N}$. Define $\mathfrak{A} = \langle A\rangle\mathfrak{H} - \langle A^4\rangle\mathfrak{H}$.

(30.2) $\mathfrak{A}$ is a T.I. set in $\mathfrak{G}$ with $\mathbf{N}_{\mathfrak{G}}(\mathfrak{A}) = \mathfrak{N}$.

Since $\langle A\rangle\mathfrak{H} \lhd \mathfrak{N}$ and $\langle A^4\rangle\mathfrak{H} \lhd \mathfrak{N}$ it follows that $\mathfrak{N} \subseteq \mathbf{N}_{\mathfrak{C}}(\mathfrak{A})$. Suppose that $\mathfrak{A} \cap \mathfrak{A}^G$ is nonempty for some $G \in \mathfrak{G}$. Let $C \in \mathfrak{A} \cap \mathfrak{A}^G$. Then some power $C^m$ has order $2^{n-1}$ and $C^m \in \mathfrak{C} \cap \mathfrak{C}^G$. Since $\langle A^2\rangle$ contains all elements of order $2^{n-1}$ in $\mathfrak{C}$ it follows that $\langle A^2\rangle = \langle C^m\rangle = \langle A^2\rangle^G$. Therefore $G \in \mathfrak{N}$ as required.

Let $\lambda$ be a linear character of $\mathfrak{C}$ whose kernel is $\langle A^4\rangle\mathfrak{H}$. Let $\alpha = 1_{\mathfrak{C}} - \tilde{\lambda}$ where $\sim$ denotes induction to $\mathfrak{N}$. Then $\alpha$

vanishes on $\mathfrak{N} - \mathfrak{A}$. It is easily seen that $\tilde{\lambda}$ is an irreducible character of $\mathfrak{N}$. Thus $\|\alpha\|_{\mathfrak{N}}^2 = 3$. By (23.1) and (30.2) $\|\alpha^*\|_{\mathfrak{G}}^2 = 3$. Since $\alpha^*(1) = 0$ this imples that $\alpha^* = 1_{\mathfrak{G}} + \chi_1 - \chi_2$ where $\chi_1$ and $\chi_2$ are nonprincipal irreducible characters of $\mathfrak{G}$. As $\alpha^*$ vanishes on involutions we get that if J is an involution then

(30.3) $\quad 1 + \chi_1(1) - \chi_2(1) = 0$

(30.4) $\quad 1 + \chi_1(J) - \chi_2(J) = 0$

$\mathfrak{G}$ contains a unique class of involutions $\mathfrak{K}$ since a $S_2$-subgroup of $\mathfrak{G}$ contains only one involution. For $G \in \mathfrak{G}$ let a(G) be the number of ordered pairs of involutions $I_1, I_2$ with $I_1 I_2 = G$. Suppose that G has even order and $a(G) \neq 0$. G is not an involution since $\mathfrak{G}$ contains no two distinct involutions which commute. Thus by (29.1) a $S_2$-subgroup of $\langle I_1, I_2 \rangle$ has at least two distinct involutions where $G = I_1 I_2$. This is impossible as a $S_2$-subgroup of $\mathfrak{G}$ has only one involution. Hence if $a(G) \neq 0$ then G has odd order. Therefore $a(G)\alpha^*(G) = 0$ for all $G \in \mathfrak{G}$. Consequently $(a, \alpha^*)_{\mathfrak{G}} = 0$. Let $1_{\mathfrak{G}}, \chi_1, \chi_2, \ldots$ be all the irreducible characters of $\mathfrak{G}$. By (2.15)

$$a(G) = \frac{|\mathfrak{K}|^2}{|\mathfrak{G}|} \sum_t \frac{\chi_t(J)^2}{\chi_t(1)} \chi(G)$$

Hence

(30.5) $$1 + \frac{\chi_1(J)^2}{\chi_1(1)} - \frac{\chi_2(J)^2}{\chi_2(1)} = 0$$

Substituting (30.3) and (30.4) in (30.5) yields that if $\chi = \chi_1$ then

$$1 + \frac{\chi(J)^2}{\chi(1)} = \frac{\{1 + \chi(J)\}^2}{1 + \chi(1)}$$

or equivalently

$$\chi(1) + \chi(1)^2 + \chi(J)^2 + \chi(1)\chi(J)^2$$

$$= \chi(1) + 2\chi(1)\chi(J) + \chi(1)\chi(J)^2$$

Hence $\{\chi(1) - \chi(J)\}^2 = 0$ or $\chi(1) = \chi(J)$. Thus also $\chi_2(1) = \chi_2(J)$ and so J is the kernel of $\chi_1$ and $\chi_2$. By (30.3) either $\chi_1$ or $\chi_2$ is nonlinear. Hence J is in the kernel of some nonlinear irreducible character of $\mathfrak{G}$.

Let $\mathfrak{B}$ be the normal subgroup of $\mathfrak{G}$ generated by the involutions in $\mathfrak{G}$. Let $\mathfrak{P}_0$ be a $S_2$-subgroup of $\mathfrak{G}$ with $\mathfrak{P}_0 \subseteq \mathfrak{P}$. Thus $\mathfrak{P}_0 \triangleleft \mathfrak{P}$. Hence $\mathfrak{P}_0$ contains a unique involution and so $\mathfrak{P}_0$ is either cyclic or a quaternion group.

Suppose that $\mathfrak{P}_0$ is a quaternion group. Then $BA^i \in \mathfrak{P}_0$ for some i. Since $|\mathbf{C}_{\mathfrak{P}}(BA^i)| = 4$ it follows that $BA^i$ has $2^{n-1}$ conjugates in $\mathfrak{P}$ which must all lie in $\mathfrak{P}_0$. Thus $|\mathfrak{P}: \mathfrak{P}_0| \leq 2$. Apply the first part of the argument to the group $\mathfrak{P}\mathfrak{B}$. Thus there exists a nonlinear irreducible character $\zeta$ of $\mathfrak{P}\mathfrak{B}$ whose kernel $\mathfrak{T}$ contains all the involutions in $\mathfrak{P}\mathfrak{B}$. Hence $\mathfrak{B} \subseteq \mathfrak{T}$ and so $\mathfrak{P}\mathfrak{B}/\mathfrak{T}$ is abelian contrary to the fact that $\zeta$ is nonlinear.

Therefore $\mathfrak{P}_0$ is cyclic. By (20.14) $\mathfrak{B}$ has a normal 2-complement which is necessarily normal in $\mathfrak{G}$. By assumption $\mathfrak{G}$ contains no normal subgroup of odd order. Thus $\mathfrak{P}_0 = \mathfrak{B}$. Since $\mathfrak{P}_0$ is generated by involutions $|\mathfrak{P}_0| = 2$ as was to be shown.

## § 31. COHERENCE

For any set $\mathcal{S}$ of characters of a group let $\mathcal{I}(\mathcal{S})$ denote the set of all integral linear combinations of characters in $\mathcal{S}$. Let $\mathcal{I}_0(\mathcal{S})$ be the set of all $\alpha \in \mathcal{I}(\mathcal{S})$ with $\alpha(1) = 0$.

Observe that the character ring of a group has a natural metric which is defined by the inner product.

Suppose that $\mathfrak{N}$ is a subgroup of $\mathfrak{G}$. Let $\mathcal{S}$ be a set of characters of $\mathfrak{N}$ such that $\mathcal{I}_0(\mathcal{S}) \neq 0$. Assume further that there exists a linear isometry $\tau$ from $\mathcal{I}_0(\mathcal{S})$ into the character ring of $\mathfrak{G}$ such that $\alpha^\tau(1) = 0$ for $\alpha \in \mathcal{I}_0(\mathcal{S})$. The pair $(\mathcal{S}, \tau)$ is coherent if it is possible to extend $\tau$ to a linear isometry of $\mathcal{I}(\mathcal{S})$ into the character ring of $\mathfrak{G}$. In case $\tau$ is determined by the context we will also say that the set $\mathcal{S}$ is coherent. In case $\mathcal{S}$ is coherent an extension of $\tau$ to $\mathcal{I}(\mathcal{S})$ will also be denoted by $\tau$.

If $\mathcal{S}$ is a coherent set and $\zeta$ is an irreducible character of $\mathfrak{N}$ in $\mathcal{S}$ then $\|\zeta^\tau\|^2_{\mathfrak{G}} = \|\zeta\|^2_{\mathfrak{N}} = 1$. Thus $\pm\zeta^\tau$ is an irreducible character of $\mathfrak{G}$. In this way it is possible to construct irreducible characters of $\mathfrak{G}$.

This method proceeds in two stages. First it is necessary to construct a linear isometry $\tau$ on $\mathcal{I}_0(\mathcal{S})$ with $\alpha^\tau(1) = 0$ for $\alpha \in \mathcal{I}_0(\mathcal{S})$. Then it must be shown that $\mathcal{S}$ is coherent. In one case such a $\tau$ has already been constructed on $\mathcal{I}_0(\mathcal{S})$. Namely if $\mathfrak{A}$ is a T.I. set in $\mathfrak{G}$ with $\mathfrak{N} = \mathbf{N}_{\mathfrak{G}}(\mathfrak{A})$ and if $\mathcal{S}$ is the set of characters of $\mathfrak{N}$ which vanish on $\mathfrak{N}^\# - \mathfrak{A}$ then (23.1) asserts that $\tau$ is an isometry on $\mathcal{I}_0(\mathcal{S})$ where $\alpha^\tau = \alpha^*$ for $\alpha \in \mathcal{I}_0(\mathcal{S})$. Clearly $\tau$ is linear.

In this section it will generally be assumed that $\tau$ has been defined on $\mathcal{I}_0(\mathcal{S})$ and $\mathcal{I}_0(\mathcal{S}) \neq 0$. We will be concerned with finding criteria which ensure that $\mathcal{S}$ is coherent. Suppose that $\mathcal{S} = \{\zeta_i\}$ consists of irreducible characters with $\zeta_i(1) = \zeta(1)$ for all i and $|\mathcal{S}| \geq 2$. Let $\theta_{ij} = (\zeta_i - \zeta_j)^\tau$. Then (23.3) implies the coherence of $\mathcal{S}$ where $\zeta_i^\tau = \epsilon\chi_i$. It was precisely this fact which was exploited in Section 28. The first result in this section is a generalization of that situation. See Feit [3] and Feit-Thompson [2, Theorem 10.1]. The following situation will be studied.

(31.1) (i) <u>$\mathfrak{N}$ is a subgroup of $\mathfrak{G}$. $\mathcal{S}$ is a set of irreducible characters of $\mathfrak{N}$. There exists a linear isometry $\tau$ from $\mathcal{I}_0(\mathcal{S})$ into the character ring of $\mathfrak{G}$ with $\alpha^\tau(1) = 0$ for $\alpha \in \mathcal{I}_0(\mathcal{S})$.</u>

(ii) $\mathcal{S} = \bigcup_{i=1}^k \mathcal{S}_i$ <u>and</u> $\mathcal{S}_i = \{\zeta_{is} \mid s = 1, \ldots, n_i\}$. <u>For each</u> i <u>either</u> $\mathcal{S}_i$ <u>is coherent or all the characters in</u> $\mathcal{S}_i$ <u>have the same degree.</u>

(iii) <u>There exist integers</u> $\ell_{is}$ <u>such that</u> $\zeta_{is}(1) = \ell_{is}\zeta_{11}(1)$ <u>for</u> $1 \leq i \leq k$, $1 \leq s \leq n_i$ <u>and</u> $\ell_{i1} \mid \ell_{is}$.

(iv) $n_1 \geq 2$. <u>For any integer</u> m <u>with</u> $1 < m \leq k$

$$\sum_{i=1}^{m-1} \sum_{s=1}^{n_i} \ell_{is}^2 > 2\ell_{m1}$$

(31.2) Suppose that (31.1) is satisfied. Then $\mathcal{I}_0(\mathcal{S}) \neq 0$ and $\mathcal{S}$ is coherent. Furthermore $\tau$ is uniquely determined unless $k = 1$, $n_1 = 2$ and $\ell_{11} = \ell_{12}$.

Proof. Since $n_1 \geq 2$, $\mathcal{I}_0(\mathcal{S}) \neq 0$. Induction on k. If $k = 1$ then $\mathcal{S}$ is coherent either by assumption or by (23.3). If $\ell_{11} = \ell_{1s}$ for $s = 1, \ldots, n_1$ then the uniqueness of $\tau$ follows from (23.3) in case $n_1 \geq 3$. If $\ell_{1s} > \ell_{11}$ for some s then $\zeta_{11}^\tau$ is uniquely determined by $|(\zeta_{11}^\tau, \ell_{1s}\zeta_{11}^\tau - \zeta_{1s}^\tau)| > 1$. Thus $\zeta_{1s}^\tau = \ell_{1s}\zeta_{11}^\tau - (\ell_{1s}\zeta_{11} - \zeta_{1s})^\tau$ and so $\tau$ is uniquely determined in this case also.

Assume that $k > 1$. Let $\mathfrak{J} = \bigcup_{i=1}^{k-1} \mathcal{S}_i$. Then $\mathfrak{J}$ is coherent by induction. Thus there exist irreducible characters $\chi_{it}$ of $\mathfrak{G}$ such that $\zeta_{it}^\tau = \pm \chi_{it}$ defines a linear isometry $\tau$ on $\mathcal{I}(\mathfrak{J})$ which extends $\tau$ defined on $\mathcal{I}_0(\mathfrak{J})$. Since $\ell_{it}\zeta_{11}^\tau(1) - \zeta_{it}^\tau(1) = 0$ for $\zeta_{it} \in \mathfrak{J}$ it follows that $\zeta_{it}^\tau = \epsilon\chi_{it}$ for $\zeta_{it} \in \mathfrak{J}$ where $\epsilon = \pm 1$. Since $\Sigma_{s=1}^{n_1} \ell_{1s}^2 \geq 3$ the first part of the result implies that $\tau$ is uniquely determined on $\mathfrak{J}$.

For $\zeta_{it} \in \mathcal{S}$ let $\theta_{it} = (\ell_{it}\zeta_{11} - \zeta_{it})^\tau$. Thus $\theta_{it} = \epsilon(\ell_{it}\chi_{11} - \chi_{it})$ for $\zeta_{it} \in \mathfrak{J}$. Define the integer a by $(\chi_{11}, \theta_{k_1}) = \epsilon(\ell_{k_1} - a)$. If $\zeta_{it} \in \mathfrak{J}$, $\zeta_{it} \neq \zeta_{11}$ then

$$\begin{aligned}(\chi_{it}, \theta_{k_1}) &= (\ell_{it}\chi_{11}, \theta_{k_1}) - (\ell_{it}\chi_{11} - \chi_{it}, \theta_{k_1})\\ &= \ell_{it}(\chi_{11}, \theta_{k_1}) - \epsilon(\theta_{it}, \theta_{k_1})\\ &= \epsilon\ell_{it}(\ell_{k_1} - a) - \epsilon\ell_{it}\ell_{k_1}\\ &= -\epsilon a\ell_{it}\end{aligned}$$

Furthermore $\|\theta_{k_1}\|^2 = \ell_{k_1}^2 + 1$. As $\mathcal{I}(\mathfrak{J}^\tau) \cap \mathcal{I}_0(\mathcal{S}^\tau) = \mathcal{I}_0(\mathfrak{J}^\tau)$ it follows that $\theta_{k_1} \notin \mathcal{I}_0(\mathfrak{J}^\tau)$ since $\ell_{k_1}\zeta_{11} - \zeta_{k_1} \notin \mathcal{I}_0(\mathfrak{J})$. Hence there exists an irreducible character $\chi$ of $\mathfrak{G}$ such that $\chi \notin \mathfrak{J}^\tau$ and $(\theta_{k_1}, \chi) \neq 0$. Therefore

$$(\ell_{k_1} - a)^2 + a^2 \left\{\sum_{i=1}^{k-1} \sum_{t=1}^{n_i} \ell_{it}^2\right\} - a^2 \leq \|\theta_{k_1}\|^2 - 1 = \ell_{k_1}^2$$

or equivalently

$$-2\ell_{k1} a + a^2 \sum_{i=1}^{k-1} \sum_{t=1}^{n_i} \ell_{it}^2 \leq 0$$

If $a \neq 0$ then, (31.1) (iv) yields that

$$2a^2 \ell_{k1} < a^2 \sum_{i=1}^{k-1} \sum_{t=1}^{n_i} \ell_{it}^2 \leq 2a\ell_{k1}$$

Hence $a^2 < a$. This is not the case as $a$ is an integer. Thus $a = 0$.

Consequently $\theta_{k1} = \epsilon(\ell_{k1} \chi_{11} - \chi_{k1})$ where $\chi_{k1}$ is a generalized character of $\mathfrak{G}$ which is orthogonal to $\mathfrak{I}^\tau$. Hence $\|\chi_{k1}\|^2 = 1$. Since $\theta_{k1}(1) = 0$ this yields that $\chi_{k1}$ is an irreducible character of $\mathfrak{G}$. If $n_k = 1$ setting $\zeta_{k1}^\tau = \epsilon\chi_{k1}$ completes the proof.

Suppose that $n_k > 1$. Then in any case $\mathcal{S}_k$ is coherent by (23.3). Thus there exist irreducible characters $\chi'_{kt}$ of $\mathfrak{G}$ and $\epsilon_k = \pm 1$ such that $(\ell_{kt}\zeta_{k1} - \ell_{k1}\zeta_{kt})^\tau = \epsilon_k(\ell_{kt}\chi'_{k1}$ $\ell_{k1}\chi'_{kt})$. If $\chi_{11} = \chi'_{kt}$ for some $t$ then choosing $s \neq t$ we get that

$$\begin{aligned} 0 &= (\theta_{12}, (\ell_{kt}\zeta_{ks} - \ell_{ks}\zeta_{kt})^\tau) \\ &= -\epsilon\epsilon_k\{\ell_{12}\ell_{ks} + (\chi_{12}, \chi'_{ks})\ell_{kt}\} \end{aligned}$$

which is impossible as $(\chi_{12}, \chi'_{ks}) \geq 0$. If $n_k = 2$ and $\ell_{k1} = \ell_{k2}$ choose $\epsilon_k = \epsilon$. Thus $\chi_{k1} = \chi'_{k1}(\theta_{k1}, (\zeta_{k1} - \zeta_{kt})^\tau) = -1$. Hence also $\chi_{k2} = \chi'_{k2}$ and the proof is complete in this case. If $n_1 \geq 3$ or $\ell_{k2} > \ell_{k1}$ it follows that $\epsilon\chi_{k1} = \epsilon_k\chi'_{k1}$ since $(\theta_{k1}, (\ell_{kt}\zeta_{k1} - \ell_{k1}\zeta_{kt})^\tau) = -\ell_{kt}$ for all $t$. Thus $\epsilon = \epsilon_k$ and $\tau$ defined by $\zeta_{kt}^\tau = \epsilon\chi_{kt}$ is the required isometry.

In case $\mathcal{S}$ contains some reducible characters the situation is a good deal more complicated though there is a similar criterion available. See Feit-Thompson [2, Theorem 10.1]. The remaining results in this section are concerned with conditions under which (31.2) may be applied. See Feit-Thompson [2, Section 11] and Feit [2, Section 2].

If $\mathcal{S}$ is a set of characters of a group $\mathfrak{N}$ and $\mathfrak{A} \triangleleft \mathfrak{N}$ let $\mathcal{S}(\mathfrak{A})$ denote the set of those characters in $\mathcal{S}$ which have $\mathfrak{A}$ in their kernel.

(31.3) Let $\mathfrak{H}$ be a nilpotent subgroup of $\mathfrak{G}$, $\mathfrak{N} = \mathbf{N}_{\mathfrak{G}}(\mathfrak{H})$ and assume that $\hat{\mathfrak{N}} \subseteq \mathfrak{N}$ where $\hat{\mathfrak{N}} = \bigcup_{H \in \mathfrak{H}^\#} \mathbf{C}_{\mathfrak{G}}(H)$. Let $\mathcal{S}$ be the set of irreducible characters of $\mathfrak{N}$ which vanish on $\mathfrak{N} - \hat{\mathfrak{N}}$. Assume that there exists a linear isometry $\tau$ from $\mathcal{I}_0(\mathcal{S})$ into the character ring of $\mathfrak{G}$ such that $\alpha^\tau(1) = 0$ for $\alpha \in \mathcal{I}_0(\mathcal{S})$. Suppose there exists $\zeta_1 \in \mathcal{S}$ with $\zeta_1(1) = d$ and $d \mid \zeta(1)$ for all $\zeta \in \mathcal{S}$.

Let $\mathfrak{H}_1 \triangleleft \mathfrak{N}$, $\mathfrak{H}_1 \subseteq \mathfrak{H}$ and let a be the square free part of $|\mathfrak{H}: \mathfrak{H}_1|$. If $|\mathfrak{H}: \mathfrak{H}_1| > 4(d^2 - 1)/a + 2$ and if $\mathcal{S}(\mathfrak{H}_1)$ is coherent and contains a character of degree d then $\mathcal{S}$ is coherent.

Proof. Let $\mathfrak{H}_2 \triangleleft \mathfrak{N}$, $\mathfrak{H}_2 \subseteq \mathfrak{H}_1$ be minimal with the property that $\mathcal{S}(\mathfrak{H}_2)$ is coherent. Suppose that $\mathfrak{H}_2 \neq \langle 1 \rangle$. Choose $\mathfrak{H}_3$ so that $\mathfrak{H}_2/\mathfrak{H}_3$ is a chief factor of $\mathfrak{N}$. Let $\mathcal{S}_1 = \mathcal{S}(\mathfrak{H}_2) = \{\zeta_{1s} \mid 1 \leq s \leq n_1\}$ with $\zeta_{11}(1) = d$. Let $\ell_2 d, \ldots, \ell_k d$ be all the distinct degrees of characters in $\mathcal{S}(\mathfrak{H}_3) - \mathcal{S}_1$. For $2 \leq i \leq k$ let $\mathcal{S}_i$ be the set of all characters in $\mathcal{S}(\mathfrak{H}_3) - \mathcal{S}_1$ of degree $\ell_i d$. By (31.2) it suffices to verify (31.1). All parts of (31.1) are clearly satisfied except possibly (31.1 iv.). Suppose (31.1iv.) is false. Thus for some i with $2 \leq i \leq k$ $\Sigma_{s=1}^{n_1} \zeta_{1s}(1)^2 \leq 2\ell_i d^2$. By (6.8) $\mathcal{S}_1$ contains all irreducible characters of $\mathfrak{N}/\mathfrak{H}_2$ which do not have $\mathfrak{H}/\mathfrak{H}_2$ in their kernel. Thus

$$(31.4) \qquad 2\ell_i d^2 \geq \sum_{s=1}^{n_1} \zeta_{1s}(1)^2 \geq \rho_{\mathfrak{N}/\mathfrak{H}_2}(1) - \rho_{\mathfrak{N}/\mathfrak{H}}(1)$$

$$= |\mathfrak{N}: \mathfrak{H}_2| - |\mathfrak{N}: \mathfrak{H}|$$

Since $\mathfrak{H}/\mathfrak{H}_3$ is nilpotent it follows that $\mathfrak{H}_2/\mathfrak{H}_3 \cap \mathbf{Z}(\mathfrak{H}/\mathfrak{H}_3) \neq \langle 1 \rangle$. Since $\mathfrak{H}_2/\mathfrak{H}_3$ is a chief factor of $\mathfrak{N}$ it follows that $\mathfrak{H}_2/\mathfrak{H}_3 \subseteq \mathbf{Z}(\mathfrak{H}/\mathfrak{H}_3)$. Thus if $\varphi$ is an irreducible character of $\mathfrak{H}/\mathfrak{H}_3$ then $\varphi(1)^2 |\mathfrak{H}_2 : \mathfrak{H}_3| \leq |\mathfrak{H}:\mathfrak{H}_3|$. Since $\mathfrak{H}$ is nilpotent this implies that $\varphi(1)^2 \,|\, |\mathfrak{H}: \mathfrak{H}_2|$. Let b be the square free part of $|\mathfrak{H}_1 : \mathfrak{H}_2|$ and let $c = (a, b)$. Then the square free part of $|\mathfrak{H}: \mathfrak{H}_2|$ is $ab/c^2$. Thus $\varphi(1)^2 \,|\, |\mathfrak{H}: \mathfrak{H}_2| c^2/ab$. Every character in $\mathcal{S}_i$ is a constituent of some character of $\mathfrak{N}$ induced by an irreducible character of $\mathfrak{H}$. Hence if $\zeta \in \mathcal{S}_i$ $\zeta(1) \leq |\mathfrak{N}: \mathfrak{H}| \sqrt{|\mathfrak{H}: \mathfrak{H}_2| c^2/ab}$. Thus (31.4) implies that

$$|\mathfrak{N}: \mathfrak{H}_2| - |\mathfrak{N}: \mathfrak{H}| \leq 2\ell_i d^2 \leq 2d|\mathfrak{N}: \mathfrak{H}| \sqrt{\frac{|\mathfrak{H}: \mathfrak{H}_2| c^2}{ab}}$$

Therefore

$$|\mathfrak{H}: \mathfrak{H}_2|^2 - 2|\mathfrak{H}: \mathfrak{H}_2| + 1$$

$$= (|\mathfrak{H}: \mathfrak{H}_2| - 1)^2 \leq 4d^2 \frac{|\mathfrak{H}: \mathfrak{H}_2| c^2}{ab}$$

Since $ab/c^2$ is a common denominator this yields that

$$|\mathfrak{H}: \mathfrak{H}_1| b - 2 \leq |\mathfrak{H}: \mathfrak{H}_2| - 2 \leq \frac{(4d^2 - 1)c^2}{ab}$$

Thus

$$|\mathfrak{H}: \mathfrak{H}_1| - 2 \leq \frac{(4d^2 - 1)}{a} \frac{c^2}{b^2} \leq \frac{(4d^2 - 1)}{a}$$

contrary to assumption. Hence $\mathfrak{H}_2 = \langle 1 \rangle$ and $\mathcal{S} = \mathcal{S}(\mathfrak{H}_2)$ is coherent.

(31.5) Let $\mathfrak{H}$ be a subgroup of $\mathfrak{G}$ such that $\mathfrak{N} = \mathbf{N}_{\mathfrak{G}}(\mathfrak{H})$ is a Frobenius group with Frobenius kernel $\mathfrak{H}$. Let $\mathcal{S}$ be the set of irreducible characters of $\mathfrak{N}$ which do not have $\mathfrak{H}$ in their kernel. Suppose there exists a linear isometry $\tau$ from $\mathcal{I}_0(\mathcal{S})$ into the character ring of $\mathfrak{G}$ such that $\alpha^\tau(1) = 0$ for $\alpha \in \mathcal{I}_0(\mathcal{S})$. Let $e = |\mathfrak{N}: \mathfrak{H}|$. Then one of the following possibilities must occur.

(i) $e + 1 = |\mathfrak{H}|$ and $\mathcal{I}_0(\mathcal{S}) = 0$.

(ii) $\mathfrak{H}$ is a nonabelian p-group for some prime p and $|\mathfrak{H}: \mathfrak{H}'| \leq 4e^2 + 1$.

(iii) $\mathcal{S}$ is coherent.

Proof. If $\mathcal{I}_0(\mathcal{S}) = 0$ then $|\mathcal{S}| = 1$. Thus $|\mathfrak{H}| = e + 1$ as required. Assume that $\mathcal{I}_0(\mathcal{S}) \neq 0$. Let $\mathfrak{H} = \mathfrak{P}_1 \times \cdots \times \mathfrak{P}_n$ where $\mathfrak{P}_i$ is a $S_{p_i}$-group of $\mathfrak{H}$ for $p_i \in \pi(\mathfrak{H})$, $i = 1, \ldots, n$. Then $|\mathfrak{P}_i : \mathfrak{P}_i'| \equiv 1 \pmod e$ for each i. Thus

$$(31.6) \qquad |\mathcal{S}(\mathfrak{H}')| = \frac{|\mathfrak{H}: \mathfrak{H}'| - 1}{e} \geq \frac{1}{e} \prod_{i=1}^{n} (|\mathfrak{P}_i : \mathfrak{P}_i'| - 1)$$

Hence if $|\mathcal{S}(\mathfrak{H}')| = 1$ then $n = 1$ and (ii) holds. Assume now that $|\mathcal{S}(\mathfrak{H}')| \neq 1$. Thus $\mathcal{S}(\mathfrak{H}')$ is coherent by (31.2). If $\mathfrak{H}' = \langle 1 \rangle$ then $\mathcal{S} = \mathcal{S}(\mathfrak{H}')$ is coherent. Thus it may be assumed that $\mathfrak{H}$ is nonabelian. Hence by (25.9) e is odd. By (25.4) e divides the degree of every character in $\mathcal{S}$ and $\mathcal{S}(\mathfrak{H}')$ contains a character of degree e. If $|\mathfrak{H}: \mathfrak{H}'| > 4e^2 + 1$ then $\mathcal{S}$ is coherent by (31.3). Assume that $|\mathfrak{H}: \mathfrak{H}'| \leq 4e^2 + 1$. If $n = 1$ then (ii) holds. Suppose that $n \geq 2$. If $p_i$ is odd then $|\mathfrak{P}_i : \mathfrak{P}_i'| \equiv 1 \pmod{2e}$. Hence if $\pi(\mathfrak{H})$ contains at least two odd primes (31.6) implies that $|\mathfrak{H}: \mathfrak{H}'| \geq (2e + 1)^2 - 1 > 4e^2 + 1$ contrary to assumption.

Thus it may be assumed that $n = 2$, $p_1 = 2$ and $p_2 = p$ is an odd prime. Let $|\mathfrak{P}_1 : \mathfrak{P}_1'| = 2^s$ and $|\mathfrak{P}_2 : \mathfrak{P}_2'| = p^t$. Let $2^s - 1 = m_1 e$, $p^t - 1 = 2m_2 e$. Thus

$$4e^2 + 1 \geq |\mathfrak{H}: \mathfrak{H}'| > 2m_1 m_2 e^2 + 1$$

Hence $m_1 = m_2 = 1$. Consequently

$$p^t \equiv 2e + 1 \equiv 2^{s+1} - 1 \pmod 4$$

Thus t is odd. Hence $p \mid a$ where a square free part of $|\mathfrak{H}:\mathfrak{H}'|$. If $(p-2)e^2 < p$ then $e^2 < p/(p-2) \leq 3$ which is not the case. Thus $(p-2)e^2 \geq p$ and so $pe^2 \geq 2e^2 + p$. Thus

$$p\,|\mathfrak{H}:\mathfrak{H}'| > p(p^t - 1)(2^s - 1) > 2pe^2 \geq 4e^2 + 2p$$

Hence

$$|\mathfrak{H}:\mathfrak{H}'| > \frac{4e^2}{p} + 2 \geq \frac{4e^2}{a} + 2$$

and so $\mathcal{S}$ is coherent by (31.3) as required.

For the next result it is necessary to know more about the original mapping $\tau$ defined on $\mathcal{I}_0(\mathcal{S})$. Generalizations of this result may be found in Feit-Thompson [2] Section 10.

(31.7) Let $\mathfrak{H}$ be a T.I. set in $\mathfrak{G}$ with $\mathfrak{N} = \mathbf{N}_{\mathfrak{G}}(\mathfrak{H})$. Assume that $\mathfrak{N}$ is a Frobenius group with Frobenius kernel $\mathfrak{H}$ and $e = |\mathfrak{N}:\mathfrak{H}|$. Let $\mathcal{S}$ be the set of irreducible characters of $\mathfrak{N}$ which do not have $\mathfrak{H}$ in their kernel. For $\alpha \in \mathcal{I}_0(\mathcal{S})$ let $\alpha^\tau = \alpha^*$. Assume that $(\mathcal{S}, \tau)$ is coherent. Then there exists a rational integer c such that if $\zeta \in \mathcal{S}$ then

$$\zeta^\tau(H) = \zeta(H) + \frac{\zeta(1)}{e} c$$

for $H \in \mathfrak{H}^\#$. If furthermore $\chi$ is an irreducible character of $\mathfrak{G}$ such that $\pm\chi \notin \mathcal{S}^\tau$ then $\chi$ is constant on $\mathfrak{H}^\#$.

Proof. Let $\mathcal{S} = \{\zeta_i\}$ where $\zeta_1(1) = e$. Let $\zeta_s^\tau|_{\mathfrak{N}} = \Sigma_j a_{sj}\zeta_j + \lambda_s$ where $\lambda_s$ is a character of $\mathfrak{N}/\mathfrak{H}$. By the Frobenius reciprocity theorem, (23.1) and the coherence of $\mathcal{S}$ we get that

$$\frac{\zeta_j(1)}{e} a_{s1} - a_{sj} = \left(\zeta_s^{\tau}|_{\mathfrak{N}}, \frac{\zeta_j(1)}{e}\zeta_1 - \zeta_j\right)_{\mathfrak{N}}$$

$$= \left(\zeta_s^{\tau}, \frac{\zeta_j(1)}{e}\zeta_1^* - \zeta_j^*\right)_{\mathfrak{G}}$$

$$= \frac{\zeta_j(1)}{e}\delta_{s1} - \delta_{sj}$$

Thus

$$\zeta_s^{\tau}|_{\mathfrak{N}} = \zeta_s + \frac{a_{s1}}{e}\sum_j \zeta_j(1)\zeta_j - \frac{\delta_{s1}}{e}\sum_j \zeta_j(1)\zeta_j + \lambda_s$$

$$= \zeta_s + \frac{a_{s1} - \delta_{s1}}{e}(\rho_{\mathfrak{N}} - \rho_{\mathfrak{N}/\mathfrak{H}}) + \lambda_s$$

Since $\lambda_s(H) = \lambda_s(1)$ for $H \in \mathfrak{H}$ this implies that there exists an integer $c_s$ with

$$\zeta_s^{\tau}|_{\mathfrak{H}^{\#}} = \zeta_s|_{\mathfrak{H}^{\#}} + c_s$$

By (23.1)

$$\frac{\zeta_s(1)}{e}\zeta_1^{\tau}|_{\mathfrak{H}} - \zeta_s^{\tau}|_{\mathfrak{H}} = \frac{\zeta_s(1)}{e}\zeta_1|_{\mathfrak{H}} - \zeta_s|_{\mathfrak{H}}$$

and so $c_s = (\zeta_s(1)/e)\, c_1$ proving the first statement.

Let $\chi|_{\mathfrak{N}} = \Sigma b_j \zeta_j + \lambda$ where $\lambda$ is a character of $\mathfrak{N}/\mathfrak{H}$. The Frobenius reciprocity theorem, (23.1) and the coherence of $\mathcal{S}$ yield that

$$\frac{\zeta_j(1)}{e} b_1 - b_j = \left(\chi|_{\mathfrak{N}}, \frac{\zeta_j(1)}{e}\zeta_1 - \zeta_j\right)_{\mathfrak{N}}$$

$$= \left(\chi, \frac{\zeta_j(1)}{e}\zeta_1^* - \zeta_j^*\right)_{\mathfrak{G}} = 0$$

Therefore

$$\chi_{|\mathfrak{N}} = \frac{b_1}{e} \sum_j \zeta_j(1)\zeta_j + \lambda = \frac{b_1}{e}(\rho_{\mathfrak{N}} - \rho_{\mathfrak{N}/\mathfrak{H}}) + \lambda$$

Hence if $H \in \mathfrak{H}^{\#}$, $\chi(H) = \lambda(1) - b_1$ completing the proof.

## §32. A CLASS OF DOUBLY TRANSITIVE GROUPS

A group $\mathfrak{G}$ is a <u>Zassenhaus group</u> if it has a faithful permutation representation which is doubly transitive and in which no nonidentity permutation leaves 3 or more letters fixed.

If $\mathfrak{G}$ is a Zassenhaus group the following notation will be used:

$h + 1$ is the degree of the defining permutation representation.

$\mathfrak{N}$ is the subgroup of $\mathfrak{G}$ consisting of all elements leaving a given letter fixed in the defining permutation representation.

$\mathfrak{E}$ is the subgroup of $\mathfrak{N}$ consisting of all elements leaving a second given letter fixed in the defining permutation representation.

$$|\mathfrak{E}| = e \qquad |\mathfrak{N}| = eh \qquad |\mathfrak{G}| = eh(h+1)$$

If $e = 1$ it is easily seen that $\mathfrak{G}$ is a Frobenius group whose Frobenius kernel has order $h + 1$. If $e \neq 1$ then $\mathfrak{N}$ is a Frobenius group whose Frobenius kernel has order $h$. In this case $\mathfrak{H}$ will denote the Frobenius kernel of $\mathfrak{N}$. Thus $e \mid (h-1)$. It follows directly from the definition that $\mathfrak{H}$ is a T.I. set in $\mathfrak{G}$ and $\mathfrak{N} = \mathbf{N}_{\mathfrak{G}}(\mathfrak{H})$.

Zassenhaus groups have been completely classified. See Zassenhaus [1], [2], Feit [2], Ito [3] and Suzuki [4]. In this section we will only give an intermediate step in this classification to illustrate how the results of Section 31 can be applied. The following will be proved.

(32.1) <u>Let $\mathfrak{G}$ be a simple Zassenhaus group. Assume</u>

that e is odd. Then either $\mathfrak{H}$ is a nonabelian p-group for some prime p with $|\mathfrak{H}:\mathfrak{H}'| \leq 4e^2 + 1$ or $e \geq (h-1)/2$. Thus in any case $\mathfrak{H}$ is a p-group for some prime p.

The proof will be given in a series of short steps. Until further notice it is assumed that $\mathfrak{G}$ satisfies the hypotheses of (32.1) and $e < (h-1)/2$. Observe that the simplicity of $\mathfrak{G}$ implies that $e > 1$.

(32.2) $\mathfrak{E}$ is cyclic and a T.I. set in $\mathfrak{G}$. $\mathbf{N}_{\mathfrak{G}}(\mathfrak{E})$ is a Frobenius group with Frobenius kernel $\mathfrak{E}$ and $|\mathbf{N}_{\mathfrak{G}}(\mathfrak{E}):\mathfrak{E}| = 2$.

Proof. If $E \in \mathfrak{E}^{\#}$ then E leaves exactly two letters fixed in the defining permutation representation. Thus if $\mathfrak{E} \neq \mathfrak{E}^G$ for some $G \in \mathfrak{G}$ and $E \in \mathfrak{E}^{\#} \cap \mathfrak{E}^G$ then E leaves more than two letters fixed and $E \neq 1$ contrary to the definition. Thus $\mathfrak{E}$ is a T.I. set in $\mathfrak{G}$. Hence $\mathbf{N}_{\mathfrak{G}}(\mathfrak{E})/\mathfrak{E}$ is a permutation group on the two letters fixed by all the elements in $\mathfrak{E}^{\#}$ and so $|\mathbf{N}_{\mathfrak{G}}(\mathfrak{E})| \leq 2e$. By (25.7) every Sylow group of $\mathbf{N}_{\mathfrak{G}}(\mathfrak{E})$ is cyclic. By (20.15) $\mathbf{N}_{\mathfrak{G}}(\mathfrak{E})'$ is cyclic and $\mathbf{N}_{\mathfrak{G}}(\mathfrak{E})/\mathbf{N}_{\mathfrak{G}}(\mathfrak{E})'$ is cyclic. Suppose q is an odd prime and $q \,\|\, |\mathbf{N}_{\mathfrak{G}}(\mathfrak{E}):\mathbf{N}_{\mathfrak{G}}(\mathfrak{E})'|$. Let $\mathfrak{Q}$ be a $S_q$-subgroup of $\mathbf{N}_{\mathfrak{G}}(\mathfrak{E})$. Then $\mathfrak{Q}$ is a $S_q$-subgroup of $\mathfrak{G}$ and $\mathbf{N}_{\mathfrak{G}}(\mathfrak{Q}) \subseteq \mathbf{N}_{\mathfrak{G}}(\mathfrak{E})$ since $\mathfrak{E}$ is a T.I. set in $\mathfrak{G}$. Thus by (20.10) $\mathfrak{G}$ is not simple contrary to assumption. Hence $|\mathbf{N}_{\mathfrak{G}}(\mathfrak{E}):\mathbf{N}_{\mathfrak{G}}(\mathfrak{E})'| = 2$ and so $\mathfrak{E} = \mathbf{N}_{\mathfrak{G}}(\mathfrak{E})'$ is cyclic. If $E \in \mathfrak{E}^{\#}$ and $\mathbf{C}_{\mathfrak{G}}(E) \nsubseteq \mathfrak{E}$ then replacing E by a suitable power it may be assumed that E has prime order. Since $\mathfrak{E}$ is cyclic $E \in \mathbf{Z}(\mathbf{N}_{\mathfrak{G}}(\mathfrak{E}))$ and by (20.12) $\mathfrak{G}$ is not simple contrary to assumption. Thus $\mathbf{C}_{\mathfrak{G}}(E) \subseteq \mathfrak{E}$ for $E \in \mathfrak{E}^{\#}$ and so $\mathbf{N}_{\mathfrak{G}}(\mathfrak{E})$ is a Frobenius group with Frobenius kernel $\mathfrak{E}$. The proof is complete.

(32.3) $\mathfrak{G}$ contains only one class of involutions and the only strongly real elements in $\mathfrak{H}^{\#}$ are involutions. If h is even then $\mathfrak{G}$ contains $e(h+1)$ involutions. If h is odd then $\mathfrak{G}$ contains eh involutions.

Proof. Assume first that h is even. By (25.10) $\mathfrak{H}$ is nilpotent. Thus a $S_2$-subgroup of $\mathfrak{G}$ is a T.I. set in $\mathfrak{G}$ and so by (29.3) $\mathfrak{G}$ contains exactly one class of involutions. There exists an involution $J \in \mathbf{Z}(\mathfrak{H})$ and so $|\mathfrak{G}: \mathbf{C}_{\mathfrak{G}}(J)| = |\mathfrak{G}: \mathfrak{H}| = e(h + 1)$. Thus $\mathfrak{G}$ contains exactly $e(h+1)$ involutions. Thus every involution in $\mathfrak{H}$ is in $\mathbf{Z}(\mathfrak{H})$. Suppose that H is strongly real and $H \in \mathfrak{H}^{\#}$. Then $H = IJ$ where I, J are involutions and $\langle I, J\rangle \subseteq \mathbf{N}_{\mathfrak{G}}(\langle H\rangle) \subseteq \mathfrak{N}$. Thus $\langle I, J\rangle \subseteq \mathfrak{H}$ as $|\mathfrak{N}: \mathfrak{H}|$ is odd and so $\langle I, J\rangle \subseteq \mathbf{Z}(\mathfrak{H})$. Thus $IJ = JI$ and $H^2 = 1$ as required.

Suppose next that h is odd. If $H \in \mathfrak{H}^{\#}$ and H is strongly real then $H = IJ$ where I, J are involutions. Thus $\langle I, J\rangle \subseteq \mathbf{N}_{\mathfrak{G}}(\langle H\rangle) \subseteq \mathfrak{N}$ contrary to the fact that $|\mathfrak{N}|$ is odd. Thus $\mathfrak{H}^{\#}$ contains no strongly real elements and $\mathfrak{H}I = \mathfrak{H}J$ for I, J involutions implies that $I = J$. Thus no right coset of $\mathfrak{H}$ contains more than one involution and $\mathfrak{N}$ contains no involutions. Therefore the number of involutions in $\mathfrak{G}$ is at most $e(h + 1) - e = eh$. Let J be an involution in $\mathfrak{G}$. By (32.2) $(eh, \mathbf{C}_{\mathfrak{G}}(J)) = 1$. Thus $|\mathbf{C}_{\mathfrak{G}}(J)| \mid (h + 1)$. Hence the conjugate class of $\mathfrak{G}$ containing J contains $|\mathfrak{G}: \mathbf{C}_{\mathfrak{G}}(J)| \geq eh$ involutions. Thus $\mathfrak{G}$ contains exactly eh involutions and they are all conjugate.

(32.4) $\mathfrak{G}$ contains at least e conjugate classes which have no elements in common with $\mathfrak{H}$.

Proof. Let $t - 1$ be the number of strongly real conjugate classes of $\mathfrak{G}$ which do not contain involutions. By (32.3) $\mathfrak{G}$ contains at least $t - 2$ conjugate classes which have no elements in common with $\mathfrak{H}$ and are not involutions. Suppose that h is even then (29.7) and (32.3) imply that

$$t - 2 \geq \frac{e(h + 1)\{e(h + 1) + 1\}}{|\mathfrak{G}|} - 1$$

$$= \frac{eh + e + 1}{h} - 1$$

$$= e + \frac{e + 1}{h} - 1 > e - 1$$

Thus $t - 2 \geq e$ as required. If h is odd then (29.7) and (32.3) imply that

$$t - 2 \geq \frac{eh(eh + 1)}{|\mathfrak{G}|} - 1$$

$$= \frac{eh + 1}{h + 1} - 1$$

$$= e - \frac{(e - 1)}{h + 1} - 1 > e - 2$$

Thus $t - 2 \geq e - 1$. Since $\mathfrak{H}$ contains no involutions the result follows in this case also.

Let $\mathcal{S}$ be the set of irreducible characters of $\mathfrak{N}$ which do not have $\mathfrak{H}$ in their kernel. For $\alpha \in \mathcal{I}_0(\mathcal{S})$ let $\alpha^\tau = \alpha^*$. By (23.1) $\tau$ is a linear isometry. If $\mathcal{S}$ is not coherent the result follows from (31.5). Thus it may be assumed that $\mathcal{S}$ is coherent. Let $\mathcal{S} = \{\zeta_i\}$ and choose the notation so that $\zeta_1(1) = e$. Let $\zeta = \zeta_1$.

(32.5) $\quad ||\zeta^*||_{\mathfrak{G}}^2 = e + 1$ <u>and</u> $\zeta^*(H) = \zeta(H)$ <u>for</u> $H \in \mathfrak{H}^\#$.

<u>Proof</u>. If $H \in \mathfrak{H}^\#$ then $\zeta^*(H) = \zeta(H)$ by (23.1). Since $\zeta^*(1) = (h + 1)e$ and $\zeta^*(G) = 0$ if G is not conjugate to an element of $\mathfrak{H}$ this implies that

$$||\zeta^*||^2 = \frac{1}{|\mathfrak{G}|}\left\{e^2(h + 1)^2 + \frac{|\mathfrak{G}|}{he}\sum_{\mathfrak{H}^\#}|\zeta(H)|^2\right\}$$

$$= \frac{1}{|\mathfrak{G}|}\left\{e^2(h + 1)^2 - \frac{e^2|\mathfrak{G}|}{he} + \frac{|\mathfrak{G}|}{he}\sum_{\mathfrak{H}}|\zeta(H)|^2\right\}$$

$$= \frac{e(h + 1)}{h} - \frac{e}{h} + ||\zeta||_{\mathfrak{N}}^2 = e + 1$$

(32.6) $\zeta_i^* = \zeta_i^\tau + \zeta_i(1)/e\ \Gamma$ where $\Gamma$ is a sum of irreducible characters none of which are in $\pm \mathcal{S}^\tau$.

Proof. If $\chi$ is a nonprincipal irreducible character of $\mathfrak{G}$ which is not in $\pm \mathcal{S}^\tau$ then $\mathfrak{H}$ is not in the kernel of $\chi$ and so by (31.7) $(\zeta^*, \chi) \neq 0$. By (32.4) there exist at least e such characters. By (31.7) and (32.5) there exists $\theta \in \pm \mathcal{S}^\tau$ such that $(\zeta^*, \theta) \neq 0$. Thus by (32.5) $\zeta^* = \theta + \Gamma$ where $\Gamma$ is a sum of irreducible characters of $\mathfrak{G}$ which are not in $\pm \mathcal{S}^\tau$. If $|\mathcal{S}| = 2$ then $e + 1 = |\mathfrak{H}: \mathfrak{H}'|$ and $\mathfrak{H}$ is a p-group for some prime p since $(h-1)/e > 2$. Thus it may be assumed that $|\mathcal{S}| \geq 3$. There exists $\epsilon = \pm 1$ such that

$$(32.7) \qquad \zeta_i^* - \frac{\zeta_i(1)}{e}\zeta^* = \epsilon\left(\zeta_i^\tau - \frac{\zeta_i(1)}{e}\zeta^\tau\right)$$

If $\epsilon = -1$ then $(\zeta_i^\tau, \zeta^*) \neq 0$ for $i > 1$. Hence $\theta = \zeta_2^\tau = \zeta_3^\tau$ which is impossible. Thus $\epsilon = 1$ and so $\theta = \zeta^\tau$. Now (32.6) follows from (32.7).

Let $\eta_1, \ldots, \eta_{e-1}$ be all the irreducible nonprincipal characters of $\mathfrak{N}/\mathfrak{E}$ where $\eta_j = \eta_{j + (e-1)/2}$ for $j = 1, \ldots, (e-1)/2$. Then $\eta_j(1) = 1$ for all j. It follows easily from (32.2) that

$$(32.8) \qquad \begin{aligned} \eta_j^*(E) &= \eta_j(E) + \eta_j(E) && \text{for } E \in \mathfrak{E}^\# \\ \eta_j^*(H) &= 1 && \text{for } H \in \mathfrak{H}^\# \end{aligned}$$

By (32.8) $|\eta_j^*(G)| \leq |1_{\mathfrak{N}}^*(G)|$ for all $G \in \mathfrak{G}$ and $|\eta_{\mathfrak{N}}^*(E)| < 2 = |1_{\mathfrak{N}}^*(E)|$ for some $E \in \mathfrak{E}$. Hence $\|\eta_j^*\|^2 < \|1_{\mathfrak{N}}^*\|^2$. As $\mathfrak{G}$ is doubly transitive on the cosets of $\mathfrak{N}$, $\|1_{\mathfrak{N}}^*\|^2 = 2$ by (9.9). Thus $\|\eta_j^*\|^2 = 1$. Hence (32.8) implies that $\{\eta_j^* \mid j = 1, \ldots, (e-1)/2\}$ is a set of pairwise distinct irreducible characters of $\mathfrak{G}$. Furthermore $1_{\mathfrak{N}}^* = 1_{\mathfrak{G}} + \xi$ where $\xi$ is an irreducible character of $\mathfrak{G}$ with $\xi(H) = 0$ for $H \in \mathfrak{H}^\#$. Thus $\xi \notin \pm \mathcal{S}^\tau$ and $\eta_j \notin \pm \mathcal{S}^\tau$ by (31.7) and (32.8). Since $1_{\mathfrak{H}}^* = 1_{\mathfrak{G}} + \xi + \Sigma^{(e-1)/2}\, 2\eta_j^*$ it follows that $(\zeta^\tau_{|\mathfrak{H}}, 1_{\mathfrak{H}}) =$

$(\zeta^\tau, 1^*_{\mathfrak{H}}) = 0$. The Frobenius reciprocity theorem and (32.6) imply that $(\zeta^\tau_{|\mathfrak{N}}, \zeta_i) = 0$ for $i > 1$. Thus $\zeta^\tau_{|\mathfrak{N}} = \zeta$. Hence in particular

$$(32.9) \qquad \zeta^\tau(1) = e$$

The proof of (32.1) can now be given by applying an argument due to Brauer. By (32.8)

$$\left(\frac{\zeta_2(1)}{e}\zeta^\tau - \zeta_2^\tau\right)(\eta_j^* - 1_{\mathfrak{G}}) = 0 \quad \text{for} \quad j = 1, \ldots, \frac{e-1}{2}$$

Thus

$$\frac{\zeta_2(1)}{e}\zeta^\tau \eta_j^* + \zeta_2^\tau = \zeta_2^\tau \eta_j^* + \frac{\zeta_2(1)}{e}\zeta^\tau$$

Hence $\zeta^\tau \subseteq \zeta^\tau \eta_j^*$ and so $\eta_j^* \subseteq \zeta^\tau \zeta^\tau$ by (6.6). Since $\eta_j^*(1) = h + 1$ and $1_{\mathfrak{G}} \subseteq \zeta^\tau \overline{\zeta^\tau}$ (32.9) implies that

$$e^2 = \zeta^\tau(1)\overline{\zeta^\tau}(1) \geq 1 + \frac{e-1}{2}(h+1)$$

Thus $e + 1 \geq (h+1)/2$ or $e \geq (h-1)/2$ completing the proof of (32.1).

## §33. ISOMETRIES

Let $\mathfrak{A}$ be a subset of $\mathfrak{G}$ with $\mathfrak{A} \subseteq \mathbf{N}_{\mathfrak{G}}(\mathfrak{A}) = \mathfrak{N}$. Let $\mathcal{I}(\mathfrak{A})$ be the set of all generalized characters of $\mathfrak{N}$ which vanish on $\mathfrak{N} - \mathfrak{A}$. If $\mathfrak{A}$ is a T.I. set in $\mathfrak{G}$ with $\mathfrak{A} = \mathfrak{A}^\#$ then by (23.1) the map $\tau$ defined by $\alpha^\tau = \alpha^*$ is a linear isometry from $\mathcal{I}(\mathfrak{A})$ into the character ring of $\mathfrak{G}$ with $\alpha^\tau(1) = 0$ for $\alpha \in \mathcal{I}(\mathfrak{A})$. For some purposes the assumption that $\mathfrak{A}$ is a T.I. set in $\mathfrak{G}$ is too restrictive. In Feit-Thompson [2] Section 9 such a map $\tau$ was constructed under weaker hypotheses. Dade [2] has simplified and generalized that construction and his method will be presented in this section.

The following notation will be used:

$\pi$ is a fixed set of primes. For $G \in \mathfrak{G}$, $G_\pi$ is defined by $G = G_\pi G_{\pi'} = G_{\pi'} G_\pi$ where $G_\pi$, $G_{\pi'}$ is a $\pi$-element, $\pi'$-element respectively.

$\mathfrak{A}$ is a subset of $\mathfrak{G}$ consisting of $\pi$-elements.

$\mathfrak{N}$ is a subgroup of $\mathfrak{G}$ such that $\mathfrak{A} \subseteq \mathfrak{N} \subseteq \mathbf{N}_{\mathfrak{G}}(\mathfrak{A})$.

$\mathscr{G}(\mathfrak{A})$, $\mathcal{C}(\mathfrak{A})$ is the set of generalized characters, complex valued class functions respectively, of $\mathfrak{N}$ which vanish on $\mathfrak{N} - \mathfrak{A}$.

The following assumptions are relevant.

(33.1) (i) If two elements in $\mathfrak{A}$ are conjugate in $\mathfrak{G}$ then they are conjugate in $\mathfrak{N}$.

(ii) If $A \in \mathfrak{A}$ then $\mathbf{C}_{\mathfrak{G}}(A) = \mathbf{C}_{\mathfrak{N}}(A)\mathfrak{H}(A)$ where $\mathbf{C}_{\mathfrak{N}}(A) \cap \mathfrak{H}(A) = \langle 1 \rangle$, $\mathfrak{H}(A) \lhd \mathbf{C}_{\mathfrak{G}}(A)$ and $\mathfrak{H}(A)$ is a $S_{\pi'}$-subgroup of $\mathbf{C}_{\mathfrak{G}}(A)$.

Assume that (33.1) holds. If $\alpha \in \mathcal{C}(\mathfrak{A})$ define $\alpha^\tau$ by

$$\alpha^\tau(G) = \alpha(A) \text{ if } G_\pi \text{ is conjugate to } A \in \mathfrak{A}.$$
$$= 0 \text{ otherwise}$$

By (33.1) (i) $\alpha^\tau$ is well defined.

Observe that if $\mathfrak{A}$ is a T.I. set in $\mathfrak{G}$ with $\mathfrak{A} = \mathfrak{A}^\#$ and $\mathfrak{N} = \mathbf{N}_{\mathfrak{G}}(\mathfrak{A})$ then (33.1) is satisfied with $\pi = \pi(\mathfrak{G})$. By (23.1) $\alpha^\tau = \alpha^*$ for $\alpha \in \mathcal{C}(\mathfrak{A})$. The main purpose of this section is to prove

(33.2) Assume that (33.1) is satisfied. If $\alpha, \beta \in \mathcal{C}(\mathfrak{A})$ then $(\alpha^\tau, \beta^\tau)_{\mathfrak{G}} = (\alpha, \beta)_{\mathfrak{N}}$. If furthermore $\alpha \in \mathscr{G}(\mathfrak{A})$ then $\alpha^\tau$ is a generalized character of $\mathfrak{G}$.

Since $\alpha^*(1) = \alpha(1)$, (33.2) implies that the mapping $\tau$ satisfies the assumptions needed in Section 31 provided that $\mathfrak{A} = \mathfrak{A}^\#$.

In case (33.1) holds let $\mathfrak{K}_1, \mathfrak{K}_2, \ldots$ be all the conjugate classes of $\mathfrak{N}$ which lie in $\mathfrak{A}$. Let

$\mathfrak{G}_i = \{G \mid G \in \mathfrak{G},\ G_\pi \text{ is conjugate to an element of } \mathfrak{K}_i\}$.

As an immediate consequence of (33.2) one gets the following analogue of the Frobenius reciprocity theorem for $\tau$. See Feit-Thompson [2, Lemma 9.4].

(33.3) Assume that (33.1) is satisfied. Let $\alpha \in \mathcal{C}(\mathfrak{A})$. If $\theta$ is a class function on $\mathfrak{G}$ such that for all $A \in \mathfrak{A}$, $\theta$ is constant on the coset $A\mathfrak{H}(A)$ then

$$(\alpha^\tau, \theta)_{\mathfrak{G}} = (\alpha, \theta_{|\mathfrak{N}})_{\mathfrak{N}}$$

Proof. Let $K_i \in \mathfrak{K}_i$. Then $\theta(G) = \theta(K_i)$ for $G \in \mathfrak{G}_i$. Thus if $\theta_0$ is the class function on $\mathfrak{N}$ defined by $\theta_0(A) = \theta(A)$ for $A \in \mathfrak{A}$ and $\theta_0(N) = 0$ for $N \in \mathfrak{N} - \mathfrak{A}$ then $\theta(G) = \theta_0^\tau(G)$ for $G \in \cup\mathfrak{G}_i$. Hence

$$(\alpha^\tau, \theta)_{\mathfrak{G}} = \frac{1}{|\mathfrak{G}|}\sum_{\mathfrak{G}} \alpha^\tau(G)\overline{\theta(G)}$$

$$= \frac{1}{|\mathfrak{G}|}\sum_{\cup\mathfrak{G}_i} \alpha^\tau(G)\overline{\theta_0^\tau(G)}$$

$$= (\alpha^\tau, \theta_0^\tau)_{\mathfrak{G}}$$

since $\alpha^\tau$ vanishes outside $\cup\mathfrak{G}_i$. Similarly

$$(\alpha, \theta_{|\mathfrak{N}})_{\mathfrak{N}} = \frac{1}{|\mathfrak{N}|}\sum_{\mathfrak{N}} \alpha(G)\overline{\theta(G)}$$

$$= \frac{1}{|\mathfrak{N}|}\sum_{\mathfrak{A}} \alpha(G)\overline{\theta_0(G)}$$

$$= (\alpha, \theta_0)_{\mathfrak{N}}$$

The result follows from (33.2).

Suppose that $\mathcal{S}$ is a set of irreducible characters of $\mathfrak{N}$ with $\mathcal{I}_0(\mathcal{S}) \subseteq \mathcal{C}(\mathfrak{A})$. Assume further that $(\mathcal{S}, \tau)$ is coherent. Let $\mathcal{S} = \{\zeta_i\}$. It is useful for many applications to have an analogue of (31.7) available for the mapping $\tau$ defined in this section. By using the theory of modular characters it can be shown that $\zeta_i^\tau$ is constant on $A\mathfrak{H}(A)$ for all $A \in \mathfrak{A}$ then (33.3) can be used to prove such an analogue of (31.7).

The proof of (33.2) will be given in a series of steps. Assume that (33.1) holds.

(33.4) <u>If</u> $\alpha, \beta \in \mathfrak{C}(\mathfrak{A})$ <u>then</u> $(\alpha^\tau, \beta^\tau)_{\mathfrak{G}} = (\alpha, \beta)_{\mathfrak{N}}$.

<u>Proof</u>. Let $K_i \in \mathfrak{K}_i$. Then by (33.1)

$$|\mathfrak{G}_i| = |\mathfrak{G}: \mathbf{C}_{\mathfrak{G}}(K_i)|\,|\{G \mid G \in \mathfrak{G},\ G_\pi = K_i\}|$$

$$= |\mathfrak{G}: \mathbf{C}_{\mathfrak{G}}(K_i)|\,|\{G \mid G \in \mathfrak{H}(K_i)\}|$$

$$= |\mathfrak{G}: \mathbf{C}_{\mathfrak{G}}(K_i)|\,|\mathfrak{H}(K_i)|$$

$$= \frac{|\mathfrak{G}|}{|\mathbf{C}_{\mathfrak{G}}(K_i): \mathfrak{H}(K_i)|}$$

$$= \frac{|\mathfrak{G}|}{|\mathbf{C}_{\mathfrak{N}}(K_i)|}$$

Therefore

$$\frac{1}{|\mathfrak{G}|} \sum_{\mathfrak{G}_i} \alpha^\tau(G)\overline{\beta^\tau(G)} = \alpha(K_i)\overline{\beta(K_i)}\,\frac{|\mathfrak{G}_i|}{|\mathfrak{G}|}$$

$$= \frac{1}{|\mathbf{C}_{\mathfrak{N}}(K_i)|}\,\alpha(K_i)\overline{\beta(K_i)}$$

$$= \frac{|\mathfrak{K}_i|}{|\mathfrak{N}|}\,\alpha(K_i)\overline{\beta(K_i)}$$

Hence

$$(\alpha^\tau, \beta^\tau)_{\mathfrak{G}} = \sum_i \frac{1}{|\mathfrak{G}|} \sum_{\mathfrak{G}_i} \alpha^\tau(G)\overline{\beta^\tau(G)}$$

$$= \frac{1}{|\mathfrak{N}|} \sum_i |\mathfrak{K}_i| \alpha(K_i) \overline{\beta(K_i)}$$

$$= (\alpha, \beta)_{\mathfrak{N}}$$

(33.5) If $\mathfrak{H}$ is a $\pi'$-group and G is a $\pi$-element with $G \in \mathbf{N}_{\mathfrak{G}}(\mathfrak{H})$ then

$$G\mathfrak{H} = \bigcup_{\mathfrak{H}} \{G\mathbf{C}_{\mathfrak{H}}(G)\}^H$$

Proof. Since $\mathfrak{H} \lhd \langle G\rangle \mathfrak{H}$ it follows that $(G\mathfrak{H})^H = G\mathfrak{H}$ for $H \in \mathfrak{H}$. Thus $\bigcup_{\mathfrak{H}} \{G\mathbf{C}_{\mathfrak{H}}(G)\}^H \subseteq G\mathfrak{H}$. Suppose that $L \in G\mathfrak{H}$ then $L_\pi$ is conjugate to G in $\langle G\rangle \mathfrak{H}$ by the Schur-Zassenhaus theorem. Thus $L_\pi = G^H$ for some $H \in \mathfrak{H}$. Hence $L \in L_\pi \mathbf{C}_{\mathfrak{H}}(L_\pi) = \{G\mathbf{C}_{\mathfrak{H}}(G)\}^H$ as required.

If $\mathfrak{B}$ is a nonempty subset of $\mathfrak{A}$ let $\mathfrak{H}(\mathfrak{B}) = \bigcap_{\mathfrak{B}} \mathfrak{H}(B)$.

(33.6) For any nonempty subset $\mathfrak{B}$ of $\mathfrak{A}$ $\mathbf{N}_{\mathfrak{N}}(\mathfrak{B}) \subseteq \mathbf{N}_{\mathfrak{G}}(\mathfrak{H}(\mathfrak{B}))$ and $\mathbf{N}_{\mathfrak{N}}(\mathfrak{B}) \cap \mathfrak{H}(\mathfrak{B}) = \langle 1\rangle$.

Proof. By (33.1) $\mathfrak{H}(\mathfrak{B}) \lhd \mathbf{C}_{\mathfrak{G}}(\mathfrak{B})$ and $\mathfrak{H}(\mathfrak{B})$ is a $S_{\pi'}$-subgroup of $\mathbf{C}_{\mathfrak{G}}(\mathfrak{B})$. Thus $\mathfrak{H}(\mathfrak{B})$ is characteristic in $\mathbf{C}_{\mathfrak{G}}(\mathfrak{B})$ and so $\mathfrak{H}(\mathfrak{B}) \lhd \mathbf{N}_{\mathfrak{G}}(\mathfrak{B})$. Hence $\mathbf{N}_{\mathfrak{N}}(\mathfrak{B}) \subseteq \mathbf{N}_{\mathfrak{G}}(\mathfrak{H}(\mathfrak{B}))$. For $B \in \mathfrak{B}$

$$\mathbf{N}_{\mathfrak{N}}(\mathfrak{B}) \cap \mathfrak{H}(\mathfrak{B}) \subseteq \mathfrak{N} \cap \mathfrak{H}(B) \subseteq \mathbf{C}_{\mathfrak{N}}(B) \cap \mathfrak{H}(B) = \langle 1\rangle$$

For any class function $\alpha$ of $\mathbf{N}_{\mathfrak{N}}(\mathfrak{B})$ define

(33.7) $\alpha_{\mathfrak{B}}(NH) = \alpha(N)$ for $N \in \mathbf{N}_{\mathfrak{N}}(\mathfrak{B})$, $H \in \mathfrak{H}(\mathfrak{B})$.

By (33.6) $\alpha_{\bar{\mathfrak{B}}}$ is a class function of $\mathbf{N}_{\mathfrak{N}}(\mathfrak{B})\mathfrak{H}(\mathfrak{B})$. Furthermore $\alpha_{\mathfrak{B}}$ is a generalized character of $\mathbf{N}_{\mathfrak{N}}(\mathfrak{B})\mathfrak{H}(\mathfrak{B})$ in case $\alpha$ is a generalized character of $\mathbf{N}_{\mathfrak{N}}(\mathfrak{B})$.

(33.8) If $\alpha \in \mathfrak{C}(\mathfrak{A})$ then

$$\alpha^\tau = -\sum_{\mathfrak{B}} \frac{(-1)^{|\mathfrak{B}|}}{|\mathfrak{N}: \mathbf{N}_{\mathfrak{N}}(\mathfrak{B})|} \alpha^*_{\mathfrak{B}}$$

where $\mathfrak{B}$ ranges over the nonempty subsets of $\mathfrak{A}$.

Proof. Define

$$\gamma = -\sum_{\mathfrak{B}} \frac{(-1)^{|\mathfrak{B}|}}{|\mathfrak{N} : \mathbf{N}_{\mathfrak{N}}(\mathfrak{B})|} \alpha^*_{\mathfrak{B}}$$

where $\mathfrak{B}$ ranges over all the nonempty subsets of $\mathfrak{A}$. Thus $\gamma$ is a class function and for $G \in \mathfrak{G}$

$$\gamma(G) = -\sum_{\mathfrak{B}} \sum_{M} \frac{(-1)^{|\mathfrak{B}|} \alpha_{\mathfrak{B}}(G^M)}{|\mathfrak{N} : \mathbf{N}_{\mathfrak{N}}(\mathfrak{B})| \, |\mathbf{N}_{\mathfrak{N}}(\mathfrak{B})\mathfrak{H}(\mathfrak{B})|}$$

where for each $\mathfrak{B}$, M ranges over all elements of $\mathfrak{G}$ with $G^M \in \mathbf{N}_{\mathfrak{N}}(\mathfrak{B})\mathfrak{H}(\mathfrak{B})$.

By (33.6) $|\mathbf{N}_{\mathfrak{N}}(\mathfrak{B})\mathfrak{H}(\mathfrak{B})| = |\mathbf{N}_{\mathfrak{N}}(\mathfrak{B})| \, |\mathfrak{H}(\mathfrak{B})|$.

If $N \in \mathbf{N}_{\mathfrak{N}}(\mathfrak{B})$ is the unique element such that $G^M \in N\mathfrak{H}(\mathfrak{B})$ then $\alpha_{\mathfrak{B}}(G^M) = \alpha(N)$ by (33.7). Thus $\alpha_{\mathfrak{B}}(G^M) = \alpha(N) = 0$ unless $N \in \mathfrak{A}$. Hence

$$(33.9) \qquad \gamma(G) = -\frac{1}{|\mathfrak{N}|} \sum_{\mathfrak{B},M,N} \frac{(-1)^{|\mathfrak{B}|} \alpha(N)}{|\mathfrak{H}(\mathfrak{B})|}$$

where for each $\mathfrak{B}$, (M, N) range over all ordered pairs such that $N \in \mathbf{N}_{\mathfrak{N}}(\mathfrak{B}) \cap \mathfrak{A}$ and $G^M \in N\mathfrak{H}(\mathfrak{B})$. Thus by (33.5) N is conjugate to $G_\pi$ if it occurs in the above summation. Thus $\gamma(G) = 0 = \alpha^\tau(G)$ if $G \notin \cup \mathfrak{G}_i$. Hence it may be assumed that $G \in \cup \mathfrak{G}_i$ and by changing notation that $G \in \mathfrak{G}_1$. Since $\gamma$ is a class function it may further be assumed that $G_\pi \in \mathfrak{K}_1$. If $G^M \in N\mathfrak{H}(\mathfrak{B})$ then by (33.5) $G_\pi$ is conjugate to N in $\langle N \rangle \mathfrak{H}$. Thus $\alpha(N) = \alpha(G_\pi)$ and $N \in \mathfrak{K}_1$. Interchanging the order of summation in (33.9) implies that

$$\gamma(G) = -\frac{\alpha(G_\pi)}{|\mathfrak{N}|} \sum_{N \in \mathfrak{K}_1} \sum_{M,\mathfrak{B}} \frac{(-1)^{|\mathfrak{B}|}}{|\mathfrak{H}(\mathfrak{B})|}$$

where for each N in $\mathfrak{K}_1$, $(\mathfrak{B}, M)$ ranges over all pairs such that $N \in \mathbf{N}_{\mathfrak{N}}(\mathfrak{B})$ and $G^M \in N\mathfrak{H}(\mathfrak{B})$. The inner sum is independent of N and $|\mathfrak{K}_1| = |\mathfrak{N} : \mathbf{C}_{\mathfrak{N}}(G_\pi)|$. The number of conjugates of $G_\pi$ in $G_\pi\mathfrak{H}(\mathfrak{B})$ is $|\mathfrak{H}(\mathfrak{B}) : \mathbf{C}_{\mathfrak{H}(\mathfrak{B})}(G_\pi)|$ by (33.5). Thus

$$(33.10) \qquad \gamma(G) = -\frac{\alpha(G_\pi)}{|\mathbf{C}_{\mathfrak{N}}(G_\pi)|} \sum_{M,\mathfrak{B}} \frac{(-1)^{|\mathfrak{B}|}}{|\mathbf{C}_{\mathfrak{H}(\mathfrak{B})}(G_\pi)|}$$

where $(\mathfrak{B}, M)$ ranges over all pairs such that $G_\pi \in \mathbf{N}_{\mathfrak{N}}(\mathfrak{B})$, $G^M \in G_\pi \mathfrak{H}(\mathfrak{B})$ and $M \in \mathbf{C}_{\mathfrak{G}}(G_\pi)$. $G_\pi \in \mathbf{N}_{\mathfrak{N}}(\mathfrak{B})$ if and only if $G_\pi \in \mathbf{N}_{\mathfrak{N}}(\mathfrak{B} \cup \{G_\pi\})$ and $G^M \in G_\pi \mathfrak{H}(\mathfrak{B})$ if and only if $G^M \in G_\pi \mathfrak{H}(\mathfrak{B} \cup \{G_\pi\})$. Thus (33.10) implies that

$$(33.11) \quad \gamma(G) = -\frac{\alpha(G_\pi)}{|\mathbf{C}_{\mathfrak{N}}(G_\pi)|} \sum_{M} \left( \frac{-1}{|\mathfrak{H}(G_\pi)|} + \sum_{\mathfrak{T}} \left\{ \frac{(-1)^{|\mathfrak{T}|}}{|\mathbf{C}_{\mathfrak{H}(\mathfrak{T})}(G_\pi)|} + \frac{(-1)^{|\mathfrak{T} \cup \{G_\pi\}|}}{|\mathbf{C}_{\mathfrak{H}(\mathfrak{T} \cup \{G_\pi\})}(G_\pi)|} \right\} \right)$$

where M ranges over $\mathbf{C}_{\mathfrak{G}}(G_\pi)$ and $\mathfrak{T}$ ranges over all non-empty subsets of $\mathfrak{A} - \{G_\pi\}$ with $G^M \in G_\pi \mathfrak{H}(\mathfrak{T})$, $G_\pi \in \mathbf{N}_{\mathfrak{N}}(\mathfrak{T})$. Since $\mathfrak{H}(\mathfrak{T})$ is a $\pi'$-group it follows that

$$\begin{aligned} \mathbf{C}_{\mathfrak{H}(\mathfrak{T})}(G_\pi) &= \mathbf{C}_{\mathfrak{G}}(G_\pi) \cap \mathfrak{H}(\mathfrak{T}) \\ &= \mathfrak{H}(G_\pi) \cap \mathfrak{H}(\mathfrak{T}) \\ &= \mathfrak{H}(\mathfrak{T} \cup \{G_\pi\}) \\ &= \mathbf{C}_{\mathfrak{H}(\mathfrak{T} \cup \{G_\pi\})}(G_\pi) \end{aligned}$$

Thus (33.11) implies that

$$\gamma(G) = \frac{\alpha(G_\pi)}{|\mathbf{C}_{\mathfrak{G}}(G_\pi)|} \sum_{M} 1$$

where M ranges over $\mathbf{C}_{\mathfrak{G}}(G_\pi)$. Thus

$$\gamma(G) = \alpha(G_\pi) = \alpha^\tau(G)$$

completing the proof of (33.8).

(33.12) <u>If</u> $\alpha \in \mathcal{C}(\mathfrak{A})$ <u>then</u>

$$\alpha^\tau = -\sum_{\mathfrak{B}} (-1)^{|\mathfrak{B}|} \alpha^*_{\mathfrak{B}}$$

<u>where $\mathfrak{B}$ ranges over a complete system of representations of equivalence classes of nonempty subsets of $\mathfrak{A}$ under the action of $\mathfrak{N}$ by conjugation.</u>

<u>Proof</u>. The number of distinct subsets of $\mathfrak{A}$ of the form $\mathfrak{B}^N$ with $N \in \mathfrak{N}$ is $|\mathfrak{N} : \mathbf{N}_{\mathfrak{N}}(\mathfrak{B})|$ for any nonempty subset $\mathfrak{B}$ of $\mathfrak{A}$. Since $\alpha^*_{\mathfrak{B}} = \alpha^*_{\mathfrak{B}} N$ the result follows from (33.8).

Now (33.2) is an immediate consequence of (33.4) and (33.12).

# NOTATION

All groups are assumed to be finite unless explicitly stated otherwise.

$|\mathfrak{A}|$ is the cardinality of $\mathfrak{A}$.

$\mathfrak{A}^{\#} = \mathfrak{A} - \{1\}$

$A^B = B^{-1}AB$

$[A,B] = A^{-1}A^B = A^{-1}B^{-1}AB$

$\mathfrak{A}^{\mathfrak{B}} = \{A^B \mid A \in \mathfrak{A},\ B \in \mathfrak{B}\}$

$\langle A,B\ldots\rangle$ is the group generated by $A, B, \ldots$

$[\mathfrak{A},\mathfrak{B}] = \langle [A,B] \mid A \in \mathfrak{A},\ B \in \mathfrak{B}\rangle$.

$\mathfrak{G}' = [\mathfrak{G},\mathfrak{G}]$

$\mathbf{N}_{\mathfrak{G}}(\mathfrak{A})$ is the normalizer of $\mathfrak{A}$ in $\mathfrak{G}$.

$\mathbf{C}_{\mathfrak{G}}(\mathfrak{A})$ is the centralizer of $\mathfrak{A}$ in $\mathfrak{G}$.

$\mathbf{Z}(\mathfrak{G})$ is the center of the group $\mathfrak{G}$.

$\mathfrak{H} \triangleright \mathfrak{G}$ means that $\mathfrak{H}$ is a normal subgroup of $\mathfrak{G}$:

If $\mathfrak{A} \triangleright \mathfrak{G}$, $\mathfrak{A} \subseteq \mathfrak{B} \triangleright \mathfrak{G}$, then $\mathfrak{B}/\mathfrak{A}$ is a factor of $\mathfrak{G}$.

If $\mathfrak{B}/\mathfrak{A}$ is a minimal normal subgroup of $\mathfrak{G}/\mathfrak{A}$, then it is a chief factor of $\mathfrak{G}$

If $\mathfrak{B}/\mathfrak{A}$ is a factor $\mathfrak{G}$, then $\mathbf{C}_{\mathfrak{G}}(\mathfrak{B}/\mathfrak{A}) = \{G \mid [G,B] \in \mathfrak{A}$ for all $B \in \mathfrak{B}\}$.

If $\pi$ is a set of primes, then $\pi'$ denotes the complementary set.

Generally $\{p\}$ will be identified with p for p any prime.

$n_\pi$ is the largest integer dividing the integer n all of whose prime factors are in $\pi$.

$\mathfrak{G}$ is a $\pi$-group if $|\mathfrak{G}|_\pi = |\mathfrak{G}|$.

G is a $\pi$-element if $\langle G \rangle$ is a $\pi$-group

$\mathfrak{H}$ is a Hall $\pi$-subgroup or a $S_\pi$-subgroup of $\mathfrak{G}$ if $|\mathfrak{H}| = |\mathfrak{G}|_\pi$

$\mathfrak{H}$ is a Hall-subgroup or a S-subgroup if $\mathfrak{H}$ is a $S_\pi$-subgroup for some set of primes $\pi$.

$\pi(\mathfrak{G})$ is the set of primes dividing $|\mathfrak{G}|$.

An involution is an element of order 2.

$SL(2,q) = SL_2(q)$, $PSL(2,q) = PSL_2(q)$ is the unimodular, projective unimodular group respectively of degree 2 over the field of q elements

$\mathfrak{Q}$ is the field of rational numbers.

$\mathfrak{Q}_n$ is the field of $n^{th}$ roots of unity over $\mathfrak{Q}$.

char $\mathfrak{F}$ is the characteristic of the field $\mathfrak{F}$.

If $\mathfrak{K}$ is an extension field of $\mathfrak{F}$ then $Tr_{\mathfrak{K}/\mathfrak{F}}$ is the trace of $\mathfrak{K}$ over $\mathfrak{F}$. If $\mathfrak{K}$ is a Galois extension of $\mathfrak{F}$ then $\mathcal{G}_{\mathfrak{K}/\mathfrak{F}}$ is the Galois group of $\mathfrak{K}$ over $\mathfrak{F}$.

# REFERENCES


R. Baer [1] *Math. Z.* **71**, 454-457 (1959).

R. Brauer [1] *Ann. of Math.* **42**, 926-935 (1941).

R. Brauer [2] *J. Math. Soc. Japan* **3**, 237-251 (1951).

R. Brauer [3] *Ann. of Math.* **57**, 357-377 (1953).

R. Brauer [4] "Proc. International Congress 1954," Vol. 1., pp. 1-9.

R. Brauer [5] *Proc. A.M.S.* **15**, 31-34 (1964).

R. Brauer [6] "Lectures on Modern Mathematics," Saaty, Vol. 1., pp. 133-175, New York (1963).

R. Brauer [7] *Math. Z.* **83**, 72-84 (1964).

R. Brauer and K. A. Fowler [1] *Ann. of Math.* **62**, 565-583 (1955).

R. Brauer and M. Suzuki [1] *P.N.A.S.* **45**, 1757-1759 (1959).

R. Brauer and J. Tate [1] *Ann. of Math.* **62**, 1-7 (1955).

E. C. Dade [1] *J. of Algebra* **1**, 1-4 (1964).

E. C. Dade [2] *Ann. of Math.* **79**, 590-596 (1964).

W. Feit [1] *Proc. A.M.S.* **7**, 177-187 (1956).

W. Feit [2] *Ill. J. of Math.* **4**, 170-186 (1960).

W. Feit [3] "Symposia in Pure Mathematics," Vol. 6 pp. 67-70, (1962).

W. Feit [4] *Trans. A.M.S.* **112**, 287-303 (1964).

W. Feit, M. Hall, Jr., and J. G. Thompson [1] *Math. Z.* **74**, 1-17 (1960).

W. Feit and J. G. Thompson [1] *Pac. J. Math.* **11**, 1257-1262 (1961).

W. Feit and J. G. Thompson [2] *Pac. J. Math.* **13**, 775-1029 (1963).

P. Fong [1] *Ill. J. Math.* **7**, 515-520 (1963).

P. Fong and W. Gaschütz [1] *J. Reine Agnew. Math.* **208**, 73-78 (1961).
P. X. Gallagher [1] *J. London Math. Soc.* **39**, 720-722 (1964).
L. K. Hua and H. S. Vandiver [1] *P.N.A.S.* **35**, 94-99 (1949).
N. Ito [1] *Nagoya Math.* J. **3**, 5-6 (1951).
N. Ito [2] *Nagoya Math.* J. **5**, 75-78 (1963).
N. Ito [3] *Ill. J. Math.* **6**, 341-352.(1962).
P. Roquette [1] *J. Reine Agnew. Math.* **190**, 148-168 (1952).
P. Roquette [2] *Arch. Math.* **9**, 241-250 (1958).
L. Solomon [1] *J. Math. Soc. Japan* **13**, 144-164 (1961).
L. Solomon [2] *Proc. A.M.S.* **12**, 962-3 (1961).
L. Solomon [3] *Math. Z.* **78**, 122-125 (1962).
M. Suzuki [1] *Amer. J. Math.* **77**, 657-691 (1955).
M. Suzuki [2] *Proc. A.M.S.* **8**, 686-695 (1957).
M. Suzuki [3] *J. Math. Soc. Japan* **15**, 387-391 (1963).
M. Suzuki [4] *Ann. of Math.* **75**, 105-145 (1962).
J. G. Thompson [1] *P.N.A.S.* **45**, 578-581 (1959).
J. G. Thompson [2] *Math. Z.* **72**, 332-354 (1960).
J. G. Thompson [3] *J. of Algebra* **1**, 43-46 (1964).
A. Weil [1] *Bull. A.M.S.* **55**, 497-508 (1949).
H. Wielandt [1] *Math. Nachrichten* **18**, 274-280 (1958).
H. Zassénhaus [1] *Abh. Math. Sem. Hamburg* **11**, 17-40 (1936).
H. Zassénhaus [2] *Abh. Math. Sem. Hamburg* **11**, 187-220 (1936).

## Books

W. Burnside, "Theory of Groups of Finite Order," Cambridge University Press, England, 1911.
C. W. Curtis and I. Reiner, "Representation Theory of Finite Groups and Associative Algebras," Interscience, New York, 1962.
M. Hall, Jr., "The Theory of Groups," Macmillan, New York, 1959.
W. R. Scott, "Group Theory," Prentice Hall, New York, 1964.
H. Zassénhaus, "The Theory of Groups," 2nd ed., Chelsea, New York, 1949.

# INDEX